D1134785

*Fundamentals of*
*Optical Engineering*

# Fundamentals of
# Optical Engineering

DONALD H. JACOBS

*Senior Physicist, U. S. Naval Observatory; Lecturer in Applied Optics,*
*The George Washington University; Formerly Associate*
*Physicist, National Bureau of Standards*

McGRAW-HILL BOOK COMPANY, Inc.

NEW YORK AND LONDON

1943

# Preface

It has always been the author's belief that, in the design of any optical instrument, optical and mechanical considerations are not separate entities to be dealt with by different individuals but are merely two phases of a single problem. It has been standard practice to have the optical design performed by one man and the mechanical design by another. This has probably been due in large measure to the fact that optical designers are generally uninterested in mechanical design and mechanical designers are equally uninterested in optical design. This is a most unfortunate situation and is responsible to some extent for the serious retardation of optical instrument development in this country. A primary purpose of the author in writing this book is to show how mechanical design and optical design are interrelated. Both these subjects are based on rather simple principles, a basic knowledge of which is usually sufficient to carry one through the most difficult problems.

This text had its beginnings when the author was invited to give a course in applied optics under the Engineering, Science, and Management War Training program at The George Washington University. The course was intended to give the student some knowledge of the fundamentals of optics, a description of various optical instruments, and finally an outline of the fundamentals of mechanical and optical design. The optical instruments considered were only those of a military nature because the course was intended primarily to train men for war work. As no single suitable text was found for the course, a series of notes to accompany each lecture was prepared by the author. The course was conducted under the supervision of Dr. Raymond J. Seeger of the university staff, and his whole-hearted cooperation in all phases of the work was responsible to a considerable extent for the success of the course. It was at Dr. Seeger's suggestion that the notes prepared for this course were expanded into the present work.

In selecting appropriate nomenclature and sign conventions for use in the sections on optical design the author, for the most part, adopted those suggested by A. E. Conrady in his definitive work "Applied Optics and Optical Design." This nomenclature is simple and consistent. It is used widely in optical plants in this country. It is sufficiently close to those used in foreign texts to enable one to read those texts with little difficulty. The author has made some slight changes for the purpose of further simplification, and to keep in accord with standard American practice when it differs from British procedure. Conrady's text has been consulted freely in the preparation of this work.

The author is indebted to Dr. Rudolph Kingslake of the Eastman Kodak Company for instruction (at the University of Rochester) in lens design. Some of the techniques outlined in this volume are based on methods suggested by him; some of the problems were propounded by him. To Fordyce Tuttle of the Eastman Kodak Company the author is indebted for some material on mechanical design. The author wishes to express his thanks to Dr. Seeger of The George Washington University and to Drs. Deane B. Judd and Robert E. Stephens of the National Bureau of Standards for reading and commenting upon sections of this work and offering valuable suggestions. The entire manuscript was read by Dr. I. C. Gardner of the National Bureau of Standards. Certain photographs used here were obtained through the efforts of R. C. Darnell and Major Van Ness of the Office of the Chief of Ordnance, U.S. War Department. Suggestions as to the inclusion of several topics of interest were made by Lieutenant Commander O. S. Reading of the U.S. Coast and Geodetic Survey. To these men and the others who made contributions to this work the author expresses his gratitude.

It is not possible to make drawings that clearly show the functioning of optical instruments without tremendous exaggeration of some details. In some cases these exaggerations lead to technical absurdities. The author feels that in a work of this sort the primary purpose of any drawing is to instruct rather than to be an exact representation of an original, and he has not hesitated to exaggerate details whenever necessary for the sake of clarity.

It will be noted that when data on representative military instruments are given in this work the instruments mentioned are usually foreign. The reason for this is that the author is too closely associated with the development of instruments in this country to feel free to reveal their details. By dealing almost exclusively with foreign instruments he has been able to discuss them without the fear of inadvertently revealing some confidential detail of construction.

DONALD H. JACOBS.

WASHINGTON, D.C.,
  *July*, 1943.

# Contents

ix

## PART IV
### OPTICAL DESIGN

# PART I

*Fundamental Considerations*

# CHAPTER I

## PROPERTIES OF LENSES

**General Properties.**—In certain cases light acts as though it were a wave motion. Since the concept of wave motion gives a good picture of the functioning of lenses, we shall begin our study of optics from this point of view. A point source of light may be regarded as the center of expanding spheres of waves emanating from it, the waves traveling away from the source in the same fashion as waves in water travel away from the point of impact of a dropped stone. As the spherical waves recede from the point source, their radii increase and their curvatures (*curvature* is the reciprocal of the radius of curvature) decrease. When the waves have advanced a great distance from the source, their radii will be very large and their curvatures will be essentially zero. These waves, or *wave fronts* as they are sometimes called, will then be essentially parallel planes. If we were to place in the path of an advancing wave front of essentially zero curvature an opaque object containing a large hole, the portions of the wave front that struck the object would be absorbed or reflected by it. Only those portions passing through the hole would continue on their way. These portions would constitute what is called a *beam* of light. If an opaque object containing a small hole were placed near the point source, the cone-shaped formation of light waves that would pass through this hole would be called a *pencil* of light. Any extended luminous object consists of an infinite number of point sources, each of which emanates pencils of light. If we reduce the size of the hole in the opaque screen until the conical pencil is reduced to a very narrow line, we have a *ray* of light.

Throughout this text, wherever drawings of optical systems are used, it will be assumed that light is incident *from the left*. This is the case in Fig. 1. The light was emitted from a *point source* (*i.e.*, an infinitely small source) on the axis *ab* but far off to the left of the page. The wave fronts shown are segments of spheres of such great radii that they are essentially planes.

3

The wave fronts referred to above are propagated through empty space with a large ($2.99776 \times 10^{10}$ cm per sec) but finite velocity. Their velocity in air is only slightly less than this. In glass or any other transparent material they travel with a considerably reduced velocity. For a given transparent material,

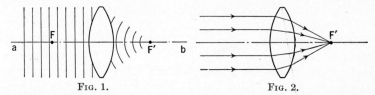

Fig. 1.              Fig. 2.

the ratio of the velocity of light in free space to its velocity in the material is called its *index of refraction*. Thus this term is a measure of the velocity of light in a given medium. For practical purposes we usually define index of refraction (or *index*, as it is sometimes called) as the ratio of the velocity of light in *air* to that

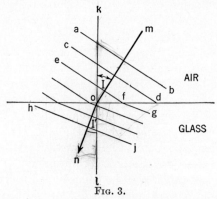

Fig. 3.

in the medium under consideration. In Fig. 3 are shown the successive positions of a wave front incident from air onto a plate of glass. We shall refer to each successive position as a separate wave for the sake of convenience. Wave *cd* is parallel to *ab* because the motion involved is in air. Note, however, that while *ef* remains parallel to *ab*, *fg* is changed in direction because this segment of the wave has traveled *at a reduced velocity* in glass. Note how successive portions of the wave front are bent purely because of this change of velocity. When the wave front has entirely entered the glass (*hj*), it is no longer parallel to *ab*. The change in the direction of travel of a wave front when crossing a boundary (called an *interface*) between two media in which light travels with different velocities is known as *refraction*. This phenomenon is responsible for the behavior of lenses.

Again referring to Fig. 3, let *mo* be the normal to the approaching wave front. This may also be regarded as a ray of light, as defined above. *on* is the normal to the wave front in the glass. The line *kol* is the normal to the interface erected at the point of incidence of ray *mo*. The angle *I* is measured between the incident ray *mo* and the normal, and the angle *I'* is measured between the refracted ray *on* and the normal. Using these rays and the data given above concerning velocity changes, one may show mathematically that

$$n_a \sin I = n_g \sin I' \tag{1}$$

where $n_a$ is the index of refraction of air and $n_g$ that of the glass. $n_a$ is very nearly one and is generally considered as being unity in optical calculations. The law expressed in this equation is *Snell's law*, which is the basis of all lens design computations. It applies to all cases of refraction where light passes from a medium of one index to a medium with a different index (*i.e.*, water to glass, one type of glass to another type of glass, etc.), the indices for the media in question being substituted in Eq. 1. It is the fundamental law of geometrical optics.

Now let us refer again to the lens shown in Fig. 1. Since this lens is thicker in the center than it is at the edge, the incident parallel light waves from the infinitely distant point object spend a longer time passing through the thick central portion of the lens than they do in traveling through the thin periphery. Thus the central portions of the waves are retarded more than the peripheral portions, and the wave front is bent into an approximately spherical form as shown. The waves then converge toward their new center of curvature *F'*, and the concentration of light at this point results in the formation of an *image* of the original source. If a screen were placed at *F'*, an image would be formed upon it. The type of lens shown, which is thicker at the center than at the margin, is known as a *converging* or *positive* lens because of its converging action on light waves or rays.

Lenses of the types shown in this book, and nearly all lenses encountered in practice (with a few special exceptions), have spherical surfaces because such surfaces are relatively easy to manufacture, because they are susceptible of comparatively easy mathematical treatment in lens design, as well as because they are generally capable of producing satisfactory optical results when properly designed. The centers of curvature of the two surfaces of any lens are generally not coincident and define a line called the *axis* of the lens. When several lenses are combined to produce an optical system, it is normally highly desirable to have the axes of the individual components colinear. When this is done, the line defined by these axes is designated the *optical axis* of the system. With most lens systems it is necessary to take special precautions thus to align the axes of the individual components. Some optical manufacturers are distressingly lax in this respect.

We shall call the *vertex* of a lens surface the point at which this surface crosses the axis of an optical system. If the center of curvature of the surface is to the right of its vertex, we shall consider the radius of curvature positive; if the center of curvature lies to the left of the vertex, we shall consider the radius negative.

The point $F'$ in Fig. 1 at which parallel light incident from the left was brought to a focus will be called the *second principal focus*, or more generally, the *focal point*. If light had been incident on the lens from the right, it would have converged to a focus at $F$, which is known as the *first principal focus*. In this preliminary discussion we shall consider all lenses as thin, and we shall define a *thin lens* as one whose thickness is sufficiently small as to make it of negligible importance in measuring distances to images and objects. We shall define the *focal length* of such a thin lens as the distance from the lens to the second principal focus $F'$, and we shall designate this by the symbol $f'$. This lens also has a focal length measured in the reverse direction, *i.e.*, from the lens to the first principal focus $F$. This we shall designate $f$.[1] For a lens in air these focal lengths are equal in magnitude but opposite in sign. If the lens is at an interface of two media of different refractive indices, its two focal lengths will differ in magnitude. This case is encountered infrequently. A positive or converging lens has a positive value of $f'$, while a negative lens has a negative $f'$. The reciprocal of the focal length of a lens is a measure of the

[1] In general throughout this text all values associated with the image side of a system will be primed; those associated with the object side will be unprimed.

converging power of that lens and is known as *power*. The power of a lens is usually designated by the symbol $\phi$. If $f'$ is expressed in meters, $\phi$ is given in *diopters*.

For a single thin lens in air the power and focal length may be computed from

$$\phi = \frac{1}{f'} = (n - 1)\left(\frac{1}{r_1} - \frac{1}{r_2}\right) \tag{2}$$

where $n$ is the index of refraction of the material, such as glass, of which the lens is constructed, $r_1$ is the radius of its first (left-hand) surface, and $r_2$ is the radius of its second (right-hand) surface. The signs for the values of $r$ must be chosen in accordance with the convention given previously. Thus, in Fig. 1 the first radius would be positive; the second, negative. In Fig. 6 the first radius would be negative; the second, positive. Equation (2) is of the greatest importance and should be memorized.

Curvature was defined above as the reciprocal of the radius of curvature. Thus, Eq. (2) may be written in the form

$$\phi = \frac{1}{f'} = (n - 1)(c_1 - c_2) \tag{3}$$

where $c_1$ is the curvature of the first surface and $c_2$ is the curvature of the second surface. The curvature $C$ of the whole lens may be defined by

$$C = c_1 - c_2 \tag{4}$$

Thus, Eq. (3) may be written

$$\phi = \frac{1}{f'} = (n - 1)(C) \tag{5}$$

It is easily seen that any increment of curvature $dc$ may be added to or subtracted from the curvatures of both surfaces without changing the value of $C$, and thus without changing $f'$, because $(c_1 + dc) - (c_2 + dc)$ equals $c_1 - c_2$. This process of altering the shape of a lens without changing its power is known as *bending*. Inasmuch as the aberration characteristics of a lens vary with a change in shape, the bending of a lens is a useful tool for the designer in the control of such aberrations.

In Fig. 4 is illustrated the general case of a point object located at a greater distance from a positive lens than its focal point. The object is at $A$, the first and second focal points are at

$F$ and $F'$, respectively. Here again, as was the case in Fig. 1, the fact that the lens is thicker in the middle than at the margin causes the central portions of the ray to be retarded with respect to the outer portions. As the incident waves are convex toward the lens, the emerging waves will of course not be as concave as was the case in Fig. 1. Thus the emerging waves have a larger radius of curvature than in the case of Fig. 1, and the image $A'$ is formed to the right of the focal point. If the object is closer to the lens than the first focal point, as is shown in Fig. 5, the change in curvature produced by the lens is not sufficiently great to reverse the direction of curvature of the emerging waves, but

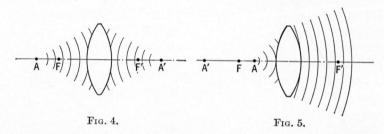

FIG. 4.                    FIG. 5.

it does definitely weaken the wave curvature because the outer portions of the waves are again bent forward with respect to the central sections. This moves the center of curvature of the emerging waves back to $A'$. Thus, to an observer at the right of the lens, the waves will appear to emanate from $A'$ instead of from $A$. Even though the waves themselves do not pass through $A'$, we can consider that an image of some sort is located there. We call this type of image, through which the waves themselves do not actually pass but only appear to do so because the image is at their center of curvature, a *virtual image*. As it is evident that no image would be formed on a screen placed at $A'$, we see that a property of virtual images is that they cannot be observed on a screen. The type of image formed at $A'$ in Fig. 4, in which the waves actually pass through the image point, is known as a *real image*. If a screen were placed at $A'$, the image would be seen upon it. This is a general property of real images.

It is important to know where the eye should be placed to see these various images. To understand this, the reader is again referred to Fig. 4. Where should the eye be placed to see the image at $A'$? If the eye were placed at $A'$, the image would not be seen for the same reason that any other object cannot be seen when placed in contact with the eye: it is too close. The nearest to the eye that an object can be clearly seen is at a distance of about 10 in. Consequently, the eye should be placed at least 10 in. to the right of $A'$ to see the image clearly. Obviously, too, the eye should be kept inside the cone of light having its vertex at $A'$.[1] In the case of virtual images, it is evident that an image

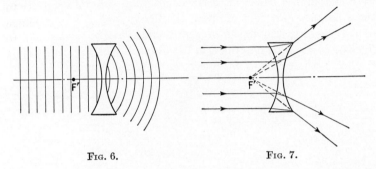

FIG. 6.                    FIG. 7.

such as $A'$ in Fig. 5 could be seen clearly by an eye placed anywhere to intercept a portion of the emerging wave front, provided that the distance from $A'$ to the eye was at least 10 in.

The lenses considered above have all been positive. Now let us consider a *negative lens:* one that is thinner at its center than at its margin. In Fig. 6 is shown, incident upon such a lens, a set of waves from an infinitely distant axial object point. Inasmuch as the lens is thicker at the margin than at its center, the marginal sections of each wave are retarded with respect to the central portions, and a diverging spherical wave results. The center of curvature of this wave is at the focal point $F'$ and the image is obviously virtual. In fact with any real object, regardless of its location, a negative lens forms a virtual image because the wave from such an object must be diverging or parallel (never converging), and such waves are obviously rendered more divergent by a negative lens. Only when converging wave fronts

[1] If the image $A'$ were to be seen by an eye outside the cone of light, a diffusing screen, such as ground glass, could be placed in the plane of $A'$. This would scatter the light, making $A'$ visible through a wide angle. What would happen if this screen were placed between the lens and the image, or between the image and the eye? What would be the effect of a screen placed in the plane of a virtual image?

leave a lens can a real image be formed.  The foregoing illustrations show why this is true.

The illustrations used above have all used light waves to illustrate the formation of images.  In practice, these light waves are not used to any great extent in optical diagrams.  Instead, the normals to the wave fronts are drawn, and these normals are called light *rays*.  If a few typical small portions of a wave front were chosen and their paths traced through the optical system, these paths would coincide with the light rays.  The procedure of determining the paths of representative rays is called *ray tracing*.  It will be described in detail later.  In Fig. 2 is shown the same situation as that illustrated in Fig. 1, but rays are used

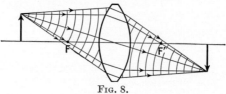

Fig. 8.

to show the path of the light instead of waves.  The two illustrations should be carefully compared to understand the significance of the rays.  These rays will be used extensively in further sections of this work, and their properties should be fully comprehended.  In Fig. 7 will be found the same situation as that shown in Fig. 6.  Again, rays are used instead of waves.

So far we have considered only the formation of images of point-objects.  Larger, extended objects are generally encountered in practice.  In the case of such an object, each point on it may be considered a point object, and the location of its image may be determined by application of the foregoing rules.  This general case is shown in Fig. 8.  Each point on the object emits waves that are brought to a focus in the usual fashion.  Note that light reaching each point in the image passes through all parts of the single lens.  Thus, if some one section of the lens is obscured, no part of the image will be missing, but there will be just a decrease in the amount of light in the image, *i.e.*, it will appear less bright.  Also note that each point in the image can be joined to the corresponding object point by a straight line passing through the center of the lens, which we shall consider to be very thin.  This is of great significance in establishing the law of magnification, as will be seen below. *The ray passing through the center of a lens is not deviated by it.* The reason for this will be appreciated when the properties of nodal points are studied.

**Location of Images.**—We have considered how images are formed. Now we are interested in determining where they are located. The general nature of this problem is illustrated in Fig. 9, in which is shown a thin lens with an extended object

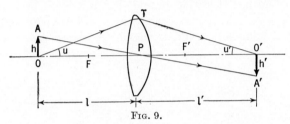

FIG. 9.

located a distance $l$ from it. Where is the image? If the focal length of the lens is known, the location of the image is determined by the application of the equation

$$\frac{1}{l'} = \frac{1}{l} + \frac{1}{f'} \tag{6}$$

where the distance from the lens to the image is $l'$. This equation is fundamental in character and should be committed to memory. In it, focal lengths are used with the sign convention stated previously, and the distance $l$ is considered positive if the object is to the right of the lens; negative, if the object is to the left. A similar rule is used to determine the sign of $l'$. Thus in Fig. 9 $l$ is negative and $l'$ is positive. When Eq. (6) is used with this particular sign convention, the correct result is always given without there being any need to make any exceptions to the general rules to fit specific cases. When a series of lenses is being considered, we locate, by means of Eq. (6), the image formed by the first lens through which passes light from the object. This image is used as the object for the second lens, its image is determined, and so on through the entire system. Note should be taken of the fact that if, for example, $l'$ for the first lens was +6 cm and if the second lens was 5 cm to the right of the first, the value of $l$ for the second lens would be +1 cm because of the distance between the lenses. It is suggested that the reader sketch this situation roughly to scale in order to understand fully the principle involved.

When an object located at one point is imaged at another point by an optical system, the two points are called *conjugate*. In Fig. 9, $O$ and $O'$ are conjugate points.

**Magnification.**—Now that we have learned how to locate the image formed by a single thin lens, let us consider how the size of such an image may be calculated. Reference should again be made to Fig. 9. It should be noted that the ray $AA'$ through the center of the lens is a straight line. Thus $APO$ and $A'PO'$ are similar triangles. Now we define the *linear lateral magnification* $M_{lat}$ by

$$M_{lat} = \frac{h'}{h} \tag{7}$$

and from the proportionality of corresponding sides we have

$$M_{lat} = \frac{l'}{l} \tag{8}$$

Of course, after Eq. (6) has been applied, both $l$ and $l'$ are known, so $M_{lat}$ can be calculated. Then, if the object height $h$ has been specified, the image height $h'$ may be obtained from

$$h' = M_{lat}h \tag{9}$$

The concept of linear lateral magnification applies only to objects and images located in planes perpendicular to the optical axis. This is why the term "lateral" is included in the description of the type of magnification being considered.

Although the significance of the following theorem may not be appreciated now, it is worth noting here that if any ray $OTO'$ is traced through the lens, where the initial slope angle (see Fig. 9) is $u$ and the final slope angle is $u'$

$$h \sin u = h' \sin u' \tag{10}$$

This holds only when the lens is in air. It is a restricted form of what is known as the *sine theorem*. When the student has learned to trace rays such as $OTO'$ through the lens, its value will be appreciated. A sign convention for the slope angles ($u$ and $u'$) has not yet been given, so the equation should not be applied for the present.

Equation (8) is very useful for determining the magnification produced by a single thin lens, but it cannot be used for a series of coaxial lenses. Instead, the magnification produced by each lens must be determined by taking the ratio $l'/l$ for that lens and then multiplying all these magnifications together to give the over-all magnification.

When magnification, as computed by any of the foregoing methods, is greater than unity, the image is larger than the object; if it is less than unity, the image is smaller than the object and reduction has been effected. If the magnification comes out positive, the image is *erect, i.e.*, a given image point is on the

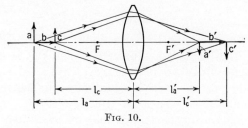

Fig. 10.

same side of the axis as the corresponding object point. If magnification comes out negative, the image is *inverted, i.e.*, the image point is on the opposite side of the axis from the corresponding object point.

Now consider for a moment Fig. 10, in which is shown a single lens forming images of three objects. These objects are of lengths $a$, $b$, and $c$, respectively, and their images have lengths $a'$, $b'$, and $c'$. The lengths $a'$ and $c'$ can easily be determined by applying the laws of lateral magnification, given above. The problem of calculating $b'$ is distinctly different, for this is not covered by the foregoing laws. When an object lies along the axis, the ratio of the length of its image to its own length is defined as the *linear longitudinal magnification*. For very short objects the longitudinal magnification is equal to the square of the lateral magnification; thus, if $h$ is the dimension of an object perpendicular to the axis and $x$ is its dimension parallel to the axis and if $h'$ and $x'$ give similar dimensions of the image,

$$M_{long} = \frac{x'}{x} = \frac{h'^2}{h^2} = M_{lat}^2 \tag{11}$$

The reason why this does not hold for objects with a long dimension parallel to the optical axis is that different lateral magnifications exist at the two ends of the object. Thus, in Fig. 10 the lateral magnification for $a$ $(l'_a/l_a)$ is certainly different from that for $c$ $(l'_c/l_c)$, and there would be some doubt as to which to use in computing the longitudinal magnification. In practice, the value of the lateral magnification at some intermediate point would give the best results, but this would still be only an approximation. The only correct way of getting longitudinal magnification is by actually computing the length $b'$ and taking the ratio of this to $b$. Thus, in the case shown,

$$M_{long} = \frac{l'_a - l'_c}{l_a - l_c} \tag{12}$$

Inasmuch as the longitudinal magnification is proportional to the square of the lateral magnification (and this is strictly true at any pair of conjugate *points*), it is evident that the longitudinal magnification must be positive regardless of the sign of the lateral magnification. This means in practice that, longitudinally, object and image always extend in the same direction. It further means that, *whenever an object moves toward or away from a lens, the image will always move in the same direction as the object.* If the object moves toward the right, the image does likewise, and conversely. It is important to keep this general rule in mind.

Equation (12) is not particularly accurate for computing purposes because both numerator and denominator contain quantities that are differences, and these are notoriously inaccurate because they bear the full uncertainty of the quantities entering into them. If, for example, $l'_a$ were 8,560 and $l'_c$ were 8,520, and both of these values were accurate to one part in the fourth place, the difference would be $l'_a - l'_c = 8,560 - 8,520 = 40$. The difference, 40, would be accurate to only 2 parts in the last place. Therefore, where the original data were known to be correct to 1 part in 8,500, the difference is correct to only 2 parts in 40, or 1 part in 20. Thus, in optics one must always view with suspicion a formula containing the difference of two large quantities. In computing longitudinal magnification, it is possible to use, instead of Eq. (12), the form

$$M_{long} = \frac{l'_a l'_c}{l_a l_c} \tag{13}$$

This is much more accurate than Eq. (12), particularly when the object is small and the intercept distances ($l$, $l'$) large.

The fact that the longitudinal magnification is the square of the lateral magnification of course means that the two magnifications can be equal only when they are both unity and the object and image are infinitely thin. At all other times they are different. This means that an image essentially never has the same *proportions* as the object. This property in microscopes, where a large image is formed of a small object, causes the depth of focus to be extremely small and makes it difficult for the user to get any sense of depth from the image, for he can bring only a single plane into focus at a time. In photography, where a small image is formed of a large object, the reverse effect occurs. Here a field of relatively great depth can be brought to focus on or near a single image plane.

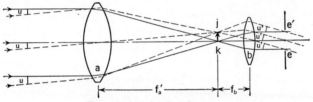

FIG. 11.—A simple telescope.

The types of magnification that we have considered thus far are useful in instruments in which real images are formed (cameras, projectors, etc.), but they are of little value in instruments intended for visual use. Thus consider Fig. 11. Here are shown two lenses so located that the second focal point of the first coincides with the first focal point of the second. The bundle of rays from a point of a distant object that is on the axis is shown by the solid lines; this comes to a focus at $k$ in the focal plane of the first lens. As this is also the focal plane (*i.e.*, a plane through the focal point perpendicular to the optical axis) of the second lens, these rays thus leave the second lens again parallel to the axis. A parallel bundle of rays entered this system and a parallel bundle left it; so little appears to have been accomplished. However, we do not get a complete picture of the functioning of this device until we consider the bundle of rays from a point on the distant object removed from the axis (dotted lines). This bundle that enters the lens at an angle $u$ to the axis comes to a focus at $j$, in the common focal plane of the two lenses, and emerges from the second lens as a parallel bundle (*i.e.*, a bundle of rays parallel to each other) making an angle $u'$ with the axis.   Note that, if a distant object were viewed without this device, it would subtend an angle $u$ at the eye; if the eye is placed at $ee'$ (to be identified later), the image would subtend an angle $u'$.   As $u'$ is greater than $u$, the object will appear to be magnified.   Such a device is a telescope; lens $a$ is called the *objective* and lens $b$ the *eyepiece*.

The two types of linear magnification that we defined previously are of no value here, for no final real image has been formed; but it is evident that the instrument has introduced magnification.   Inasmuch as we generally interpret the size of an object in terms of the angle that the object subtends at the eye, it is seen that a valid measure of the magnification produced by this telescope would be the ratio $u'/u$.   However, if linear objects were being considered, one could build up an equally valid case in favor of the ratio $\tan u'/\tan u$ as a useful measure of magnification.   In practice, it is easier to use the ratio of tangents than the ratio of angles because the tangents can be easily computed from the linear dimensions of the instrument, and their use thus eliminates the need for any trigonometric tables. Thus we shall define

$$M = \text{angular magnification} = \frac{\tan u'}{\tan u} \qquad (14)$$

We shall use this magnification exclusively in describing the performance of visual instruments.   The term *power* will be understood as referring to angular magnification.

The closer an object is held to the eye for examination, the larger will be the image that is formed on the retina, and the greater will be the amount of detail that can be discerned. Since the average human eye cannot conveniently accommodate to objects located closer than about 10 in., this ordinarily places a finite limit on the distance to which an object can be brought for examination.   However, with a simple magnifier, the object can be brought very close to the eye and a virtual image formed some distance from the eye.   This device permits the object to be brought sufficiently close to the eye to subtend at it a large angle; yet the image can be formed sufficiently far from the eye to be seen. The angular magnification produced by such a magnifier when the image is formed at infinity is given by

$$M = \frac{10}{f'} \tag{15}$$

where $f'$ is the focal length of the magnifier in inches. If the image is formed 10 in. from the eye, the magnification is

$$M = \frac{10}{f'} + 1 \tag{16}$$

**Thick Lenses.**—Thus far we have considered only thin lenses, which we defined as lenses sufficiently thin so that their thicknesses were not of significance in measuring distances. All other lenses we shall term *thick*. When dealing with thin lenses, we contented ourselves with measuring distances, such as object

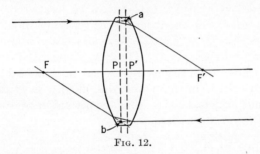

Fig. 12.

and image distances and focal lengths, from the lens—an ambiguous location for an actual lens. In dealing with thick lenses, we shall find it necessary to select specific points related to the lens to which to measure these various quantities.

We shall find that with any lens there are associated two points so located that an object placed at either is imaged at the other with positive, unit, linear lateral magnification. These two points, known as *principal points*, may be located by the construction shown in Fig. 12. A ray, parallel to the axis, is traced into the system from the left, and this cuts the axis at the second principal focus $F'$. If the emerging and entering rays are extended toward one another as shown, the extensions (or rays) will intersect at some point $a$. A line may be passed through $a$ perpendicular to the axis. This line intersects the axis at $P'$, the *second principal point*. By similarly tracing a ray in from the right through the first principal focus $F$, getting the intersection $b$ of the emerging and entering rays, and projecting a perpendicular through this point to the axis, the *first principal point* $P$ is located. These points will act as the reference points for our optical measurements. We shall define the *equivalent focal length* (sometimes called the *second focal length* or *focal length*) of a thick lens as the distance from the second principal point to the second principal focus. In Fig. 12 this is the distance $P'F'$, and will be designated $f'$. The reverse focal length $f$ is the distance $PF$. For a lens in air $f' = -f$.

The focal length of a lens of axial thickness $t$ may be calculated from

$$\frac{1}{f'} = (n-1)\left[\frac{1}{r_1} - \frac{1}{r_2} + \frac{t}{n}\frac{(n-1)}{r_1 r_2}\right] \tag{17}$$

Images formed by thick lenses may be located by applying Eq. (6) provided that object distances $l$ are measured from the first principal point, and image distances $l'$ are measured from the second principal point. Thus, by using the concept of principal points, calculations involving thick lenses are little more complicated than those with thin elements. The distance of the second principal focus from the second vertex of a lens is called the *back focal length*.

Generally speaking, the principal points are not located symmetrically within a lens, *i.e.*, the distance from the first vertex to the first principal point does not usually equal the distance of the second vertex from the second principal point. As a lens is bent (see page 7), the principal points shift in position; in a lens of strong meniscus form (both centers of curvature on the same side of the lens), the two principal points may be found outside the lens. The variation of the locations of the principal points with the shape of a lens is illustrated in Fig. 13. Here is shown a series of lenses, all of equal power but differing in shape. The lines perpendicular to the axis represent principal surfaces (see below), and their intersections with the axis locate the principal points.

It is well to keep in mind that with an equi-convex lens (a convex lens with its radii equal in magnitude and opposite in sign) the principal points are located symmetrically in the lens about one-third of the way in from the vertices. In the plano-convex form, one principal point is always at the vertex of the convex surface and the other is about one-third of the way inside the lens from the convex surface. Both of these cases are illustrated in Fig. 13.

Occasionally, one encounters a case in which the principal points are reversed, *i.e.*, $P'$ is to the left of $P$. In this case the principal points are said to be *crossed*. This happens quite frequently with both positive and negative meniscus lenses.

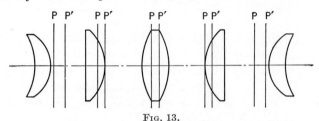

Fig. 13.

It will be noted that in the various illustrations considered thus far the location of each principal point has been shown by a line perpendicular to the axis. This line represents the surface formed by the locus of the principal points as located by rays taken through zones of the lens at different distances from the axis. The fact that it has been drawn straight implies that this locus is a plane. This is the case only for rays that pass through the lens very near to the axis (called *paraxial rays*)· However, the various equations given in this chapter will apply only to rays of this character and are used only for rough work; so, as far as calculations of this sort are concerned, we can visualize the surfaces as planes. For this reason these surfaces are often called *principal planes*. The surfaces are actually far from planes and are more correctly termed *principal surfaces* (see Chap. XXVII).

The locations of the principal points are readily calculated from the fundamental constants of each lens. In applying these equations, remember that we know the location of the vertices of the lens at the start and that we are determining the distances *from* these vertices *to* the principal points. Also keep in mind the sign convention: distances measured to the right (from the vertices to the principal points) are positive; those measured to the left are negative. The distance $K$ from the first vertex of any lens to its first principal point is given by

$$K = -\frac{tf'}{r_2}\frac{(n-1)}{n} \tag{18}$$

The distance $K'$ from the second vertex to the second principal point is given by

$$K' = -\frac{tf'}{r_1}\frac{(n-1)}{n} \tag{19,}$$

The spacing $S$ between the two principal points is given by

$$S = t - tf'\frac{n-1}{n}\left(\frac{1}{r_1} - \frac{1}{r_2}\right)$$

If this quantity $S$ is negative, the principal points are crossed.

The variation of the positions of the principal points with thickness yields interesting information on the way a lens functions. We shall thus consider a typical case. In Fig. 14 is shown a series of lenses of increasing thickness. These all have the same radii and differ solely in thickness. Case (a) represents the average lens, with just sufficient thickness to avoid a sharp edge, it being necessary to avoid such an edge for manufacturing reasons. Case (b) shows what happens when the lens has been increased sufficiently in thickness to bring the centers of curvature into coincidence. The principal points fall together at the common center of curvature. The thickness of the lens in this case is obviously

$$t = r_1 - r_2 \tag{21}$$

If it is desired to have the second focal point coincide with the second vertex of the lens, the thickness should be determined from

$$t = \frac{n}{n-1}r_1 \tag{22}$$

This case is illustrated in Fig. 14c. Two parallel incident rays have been traced through the focal point to show the functioning of the lens. Note that these rays cross the axis at the second vertex. This means that the second surface makes no contribution to the power of the lens, i.e., the lens would have the same focal length regardless of the value of $r_2$. Thus by substituting Eq. (22) in (17) we get *for this particular case*

$$\frac{1}{f'} = (n-1)\frac{1}{r_1} \tag{23}$$

This is of course independent of $r_2$.

This case is an interesting example of a fundamental rule: Whenever any real image is formed in the plane of a refracting surface, the surface has no effect on that image, *i.e.*, the surface makes no contribution to either the power or the aberration characteristics (except field curvature) of the system. As this rule holds reasonably well for surfaces located very *near* the plane of a real image, we see that *any lens located in the plane of a*

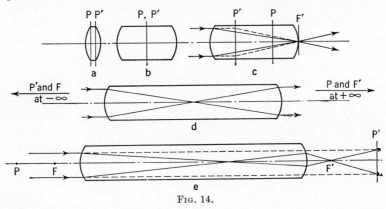

Fig. 14.

*real image has no effect on the power or aberration properties* (except curvature of field) *of the system.* We shall make repeated use of this particular property of lens systems.

The cases illustrated in Figs. 14*b* and 14*c* are not necessarily different. Both can occur at once.

If it is desired to make the first focal point coincide with the first vertex of a lens, the thickness is made equal to

$$t = \frac{n}{n-1}(-r_2) \tag{24}$$

*For this particular case*, the focal length is given by

$$\frac{1}{f'} = -(n-1)\frac{1}{r_2} \tag{25}$$

If a lens is made very thick, it is possible to have a beam of parallel rays come to a focus inside the lens and be made parallel again by a second refraction in the manner shown in Fig. 14*d*. The thickness *in this case* is given by

$$t = \frac{n}{n-1}(r_1 - r_2) \tag{26}$$

Inasmuch as the rays enter and leave this lens parallel, it is evident that it functions as a telescope. In the case illustrated the two radii are equal and the device functions at unit magnification. Although this lens gives no magnification, it does invert the image and thus could be used as a form of erector. It would be too long, however, for practical purposes.

In the case shown in Fig. 14d the focal points and the principal points are at infinity. If the lens is made still thicker, the principal points will be found to be located well outside the lens and the focal points somewhat closer to it. Thus the second

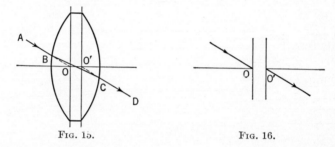

FIG. 15.                    FIG. 16.

principal point is located farther to the right than the second focal point, and the distance $P'F'$ is thus negative. Therefore, the lens is now negative even though it is biconvex in shape! This case is illustrated in Fig. 14e. Note that the parallel incident rays actually diverge upon leaving the lens.

It will be remembered that we defined the principal points as points of unit positive linear lateral magnification. There are also, in each lens, two points of unit positive angular magnification, i.e., if an object is placed at one, it is seen at the other under unit angular magnification. These are known as *nodal points*. They are shown as $O$ and $O'$ in Fig. 15. The representative ray $AB$, directed at the first nodal point $O$, is *parallel* to $CD$, emerging from $O'$, and this relationship holds for any ray aimed at $O$. Note that the ray does not actually pass through $O$ and $O'$, but only appears to do so. Also, note that we could represent this system by Fig. 16. The type of illustration used here is often employed in optics, and the relationship between it and Fig. 15, which shows the actual system, should be carefully studied. The lines through the nodal points are known as *nodal surfaces*, or, more commonly but less correctly, as *nodal planes*.

The previous remarks concerning the suitability of the term "principal plane" also apply here.

The distance from the first focal point to the first nodal point is equal to $f'$, the second focal length. The distance of the second nodal point from the second focal point is equal to the first focal length $f$. The relationship of the nodal points to the focal points is, therefore, the reverse of that for the principal points. When a lens is in air, its first and second focal lengths are equal in magnitude, although opposite in sign. Therefore, *for a lens in air the nodal points coincide with the principal points.*

In Fig. 17 the lens shown in Figs. 15 and 16 is redrawn. The ray $AO$ from an infinitely distant object is incident upon the lens, being directed at the first nodal point. The ray $O'D$ emerges from the lens, apparently coming from the second nodal point. Thus, by the definition of nodal points, $AO$ is parallel to $O'D$. Now let the lens be rotated about the second nodal point $O'$ to the position shown by the dotted lines. The entering ray that strikes the first nodal point is $EG$; this is parallel to $AO$, *i.e.*, it comes from the same infinitely distant object. The emergent ray is still $O'D$. Thus, in spite of the rotation of the lens about $O'$, the image does not shift. This is a very important property of nodal points. If parallel light entered this lens from the right and were aimed at the second nodal point $O'$, rotation of the lens about $O$ would similarly produce no shift of the image. Thus we can mount a lens on a slide capable of rotation about a vertical axis, and form an image of an infinitely distant object. The slide, called a *nodal slide,* may be rotated. If any image shift is observed, the lens is not being rotated about the nodal point. The lens may then be moved back and forth along the slide until rotation of the slide produces no motion of the image. The vertical axis of the slide then coincides with the nodal point of the lens located on the emergent side. The lens is now reversed on the slide and the other nodal point is similarly found. It so happens that nodal points, per se, are of little use in optical design, but the principal points, being the reference points for all optical measurements, are of great value. However, as we have

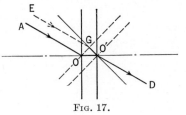

Fig. 17.

just seen, the nodal points may be found with ease. The principal points cannot be easily located empirically. As we have already seen, for a lens in air, the principal points and the nodal

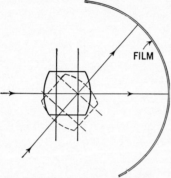

points coincide. Thus for a lens in air we locate the nodal points in the manner described and then use these as the principal points. This is the standard method of locating principal points in the laboratory.

It has been shown that, if a lens is rotated about its second nodal point, there will be no shift of image. Thus, if we take a camera lens and pivot it at its second nodal point, we can rotate

FIG. 18.—The panoramic camera.

the camera and take, on a long circular strip of film, a continuous picture covering a very wide angle. This device is shown in Fig. 18. As the image is always formed a distance $-f$ from the

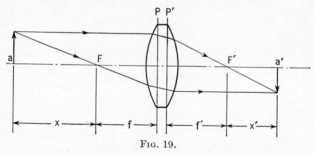

FIG. 19.

second nodal point, the film is placed along the arc of a circle whose center of curvature is at that point. This instrument is known as a *panoramic camera.*

In our consideration of thin lenses we saw that the linear lateral magnification was given by $l'/l$. This expression also holds for thick lenses, $l'$ being measured from the second principal point and $l$ from the first principal point. If the distance from the second focal point to the image is $x'$ (Fig. 19), the linear lateral magnification is given by

$$M_{lat} = -\frac{x'}{f'} \qquad (27)$$

This may be derived from similar triangles in the illustration. Similarly, if the distance from the first focal point to the object is $x$, the magnification may be expressed by

$$M_{lat} = -\frac{f}{x} \tag{28}$$

These two equations may be combined to give the general expression (originally stated by Newton)

$$xx' = ff' \tag{29}$$

Inasmuch as $f$ and $f'$ always have opposite signs, $x$ and $x'$ will also be different in sign. Thus, if an object lies outside the first focal point, the image will be outside the second focal point, and conversely.

**Combinations of Lenses.**—Thus far we have considered the optical properties of single lenses. Now we shall consider briefly the characteristics of optical systems consisting of several lenses.

First, let us deal with the problem of computing the equivalent focal length of a system of two thin lenses. The lenses have equivalent focal lengths $f'_a$ and $f'_b$ and are separated by a distance $d$. The equation giving the required focal length is

$$\frac{1}{f'_{ab}} = \frac{1}{f'_a} + \frac{1}{f'_b} - \frac{d}{f'_a f'_b} \tag{30}$$

$f'_{ab}$ is of course the equivalent focal length of the system. The equation may be solved directly for this focal length, giving

$$f'_{ab} = \frac{f'_a f'_b}{f'_a + f'_b - d} \tag{31}$$

From what point in the system is this focal length to be measured? The system cannot be assumed to be "thin," for the lenses are spaced by a finite distance that might be quite large. The answer to this question is that a system of two (or any number) of lenses may be treated like a thick lens in that it has two principal points. Thus this focal length is measured from the second principal point of the system. If the system consisted of thick lenses instead of thin ones, the same equations could have been used. In this case $d$ would have been the distance from the second principal point of the first element to the first principal point of the second. The principal points, in the case of a system of lenses, are located in the same way as they are for a single lens: a ray parallel to the axis is traced into the system from the left, and the intersection of the entering and emerging branches of this ray gives the location of the second principal point. The first principal point is similarly found by tracing in a ray from the right. This procedure is indicated in Fig. 20.

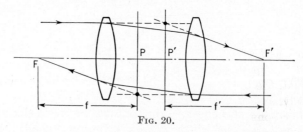

FIG. 20.

The locations of the principal points of a combination of two thick lenses are easily calculated from the constants of the system. Thus the distance of the first principal point of the combination from the first principal point of the first lens is given by

$$K = \frac{df'_{ab}}{f'_b} \tag{32}$$

The distance of the second principal point of the system from the second principal point of the second lens is obtained from

$$K' = -\frac{df'_{ab}}{f'_a} \tag{33}$$

If the system consists of two thin lenses, the distances of the principal points from the elements themselves, instead of from their principal points, are given by these equations.

If the lens combination under consideration consists of more than two elements, the principal and focal points of the first two are calculated by the foregoing formulas; then this combination is treated as a single thick lens and combined with the next element in the system, and so on until all elements have been used. This process is tedious at best. In practice, the principal points of a complicated system are located by tracing rays parallel to the axis into the system and thus locating the focal points. From the ray tracing data the focal lengths may be calculated.

Then, by measuring off distances equal to the focal lengths from the focal points, the principal points are located.

Once the principal points of a system of lenses have been determined, the position of the image formed of any object may be determined by the application of Eq. (6). Object distances are measured from the first principal point of the system; image distances from the second. The magnification introduced by the system is calculated from Eq. (8). If one does not wish to locate the principal points, he can determine the position of the image formed by the first lens, through application of Eq. (6). He then uses this image as the object for the second lens, taking due account of its location with regard to the *second* lens, and determines its image. This is carried on throughout the entire system to the final image. The magnification produced by each lens may be obtained from Eq. (8), using the values of $l$ and $l'$ for that lens. The magnification produced by the entire system is the product of the magnifications introduced by the individual lenses.

The theory thus far considered, known as *Gauss theory*, holds only for perfect (*i.e.*, aberrationless) lenses. With the lenses encountered in practice it holds only for paraxial rays. Thus, although in the various illustrations we have shown rays through all zones of the lens converging toward the image points located by the methods just described, in an actual case only the rays passing through the center of the lens would act in this fashion. Inasmuch as this theory holds only for a very small region near the axis and as the principal surfaces are practically plane in this region, they are commonly shown as planes. They are drawn, as a matter of convenience, across the entire lens; as a matter of fact they only approximate planes very near the axis.

We have tacitly assumed in developing this theory that any wave front after refraction is a spherical surface (including the case of a sphere with an infinite radius). If this were true, we should obtain perfect point images. Unfortunately it is essentially never the case. After refraction the wave form is always slightly aspherical. Each portion of the wave front crosses the axis at its own center of curvature, and, as different portions of the wave front have slightly different centers of curvature, they cross the axis at slightly different points. They thus do not give a true point image. Deviations, of this and other types, from ideal performance are termed *aberrations*.   We shall consider this phase of lens performance in Chap. II.

## REFERENCES

ELSER: "Light for Students," Macmillan & Company, Ltd., London, 1931.
HARDY and PERRIN: "The Principles of Optics," McGraw-Hill Book Company, Inc., New York, 1932.
MARTIN: "An Introduction to Applied Optics," Vol. I, Sir Isaac Pitman & Sons, Ltd., London, 1930.
MONK: "Light: Principles and Experiments," McGraw-Hill Book Company, Inc., New York, 1937.
Also consult the references at the end of Chap. XXIV.

## PROBLEMS

**1.** Given a thin lens of $+20$ cm focal length and an object 2 cm high located 30 cm to the left of the lens, find the position and size of the image. Is the image erect or inverted? real or virtual?

**2.** Let the object in Prob. 1 be located 10 cm to the left of the lens. Solve as before.

**3.** Consider an equi-concave (negative) lens of index $n = 1.5$.   Assume the thickness to be so small that terms of $t/r^2$ may be neglected.   Find $f'$ as a function of $r$.   Locate, in terms of $t$ and $r$, the focal points and principal points.

**4.** Find the focal length and principal points of the following lens:

$$r_1 = +4.0 \qquad t = 1.0$$
$$r_2 = +3.0 \qquad n = 1.5$$

Note that the centers of curvature of the two surfaces coincide.   Make a scale drawing of the lens, plotting the focal and principal points.

**5.** Do the same for the following lens:

$$r_1 = +4.0 \qquad t = 1.0$$
$$r_2 = +6.0 \qquad n = 1.5$$

**6.** Do the same for the following lens:

$$r_1 = +2.0 \qquad t = 1.0$$
$$r_2 = +2.0 \qquad n = 1.5$$

Note that both surfaces have the same radii.

**7.** Find the principal points, focal points, equivalent focal length, and back focal length of the following combination of thin lenses:

$$f'_a = +4.0 \qquad f'_b = -4.0 \qquad d = 2.0$$

Note that the finite spacing gives this combination positive power in spite of the fact that the sum of the powers of the individual components is zero.   This is a good example of a telephoto lens.

Make a scale drawing of this system, locating the above named points.

**8.** Solve for the above-named points and make a drawing of this thin lens combination:

$$f'_a = +1.0 \qquad f'_b = +1.0 \qquad d = 2.0$$

This is a unit power telescope.

**9.** Make the same solution, as in Prob. **7,** for this combination of thin lenses:

$$f'_a = +1.0 \qquad f'_b = +1.0 \qquad d = 6.0$$

Note that a combination of two positive lenses can have a negative focal length.

**10.** Compute the locations of the focal and principal points of the following lens:

$$r_1 = +10.0 \qquad t = 15.0$$
$$r_2 = -5.0 \qquad n = 1.5$$

Make a scale drawing of the lens showing the locations of these points.

**11.** Find the focal length and locate the principal points of a sphere of radius $R$ and index 1.5.

# CHAPTER II

## LENS ABERRATIONS

The performance of any lens or lens system is limited by the presence of defects of the image known as *aberrations*. As the diameter or aperture of any lens system is increased (the focal length being held constant), the aberrations generally become worse. Thus the usable aperture of a given system is usually determined by the amount of aberration that can be tolerated. As the number of lens elements in an optical system is increased, more variables are made available to the designer, and these can be used to obtain a higher state of correction of image defects. Thus a larger aperture can be used for the same focal length as more elements are added to a system. For this reason *fast* systems having a large ratio of aperture to focal length are quite complex.

In the discussions of several of the aberrations reference will be found only to the effect of these aberrations on images of point objects. The reader might wonder as to their effect on extended objects. The fact that should be kept in mind is that any extended object consists only of an infinitely large number of point objects, and the optical laws governing the location and quality of the image of a certain point object will also hold for the neighboring image point. Suppose we consider the effect of spherical aberration on the border between the white and black portions of a certain image. This aberration causes a blurring of each image point. The uniformly black and white portions of the image would look the same whether the lens was afflicted with this aberration or not, because the blurring of the (similar) points would overlap, giving a uniform appearance. At the border, however, some of the blurring of the points in the white part of the image would extend over into the black part. Thus the border itself would not be distinct if the lens were afflicted with spherical aberration. Some of the light from the white parts of the image would be directed into the dark parts, reducing contrast.

In this chapter, and elsewhere in the book, will be found illustrations of lenses with various rays diagramed as passing through them.  Aberration will be explained in terms of the behavior of these rays.  In the design of lenses, aberration is actually measured by tracing such rays through the optical system by certain standard equations derived from Snell's law. This procedure is known as *ray tracing*, which is a fundamental technique used in lens design.  It is described in Chap. XXIV. It need not be studied in detail at this point, but its significance should be comprehended.

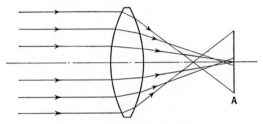

Fig. 21.—Spherical aberration.

In considering the performance of a lens, we usually study the action of rays passing through it at different distances from the axis.  A continuous ring of points on the surface of the lens, all located equal distances from the axis, is called a *zone*.  The action of light passing through different zones is determined.

The subject of lens aberrations is extremely complex when optical systems of high aperture ratio (see Chap. XIV) are considered. However telescopic systems, the simpler photographic objectives, and similar optical systems have fairly small ratios.  For such systems the aberrations may be classified under the following descriptions: spherical aberration, coma, astigmatism, curvature of field, distortion, longitudinal chromatic aberration, and lateral chromatic aberration.

**Spherical Aberration.**—Consider the lens shown in Fig. 21. Parallel light from a distant point object on the axis is incident upon it.  If the lens were perfect, all the rays would be converged upon a single point focus.  No single positive lens can act thus, but, as can be proved mathematically, it must function as shown in the illustration.  The rays from the marginal zones of the lens come to a focus closer to the lens than do the rays from the central zones.  Thus rays through different zones come to a focus at different distances from the lens. If a screen were placed at $A$, there would be formed upon it a sharp image due to the rays from the center of the lens, and this would be surrounded by a halo of light from the rays from the other zones that crossed the axis at various other points. Thus the image might be blurred and contrast would be lost. If a picture were being imaged on $A$, much detail would be lost because a haze of misplaced light would cover it. The black parts of the image would appear gray because of this phenomenon. If the screen were moved so as to bring rays from the marginal zone into focus, the image would become more blurred.

Spherical aberration for any zone is usually measured as the difference between the axial intercepts of a paraxial ray (passing near the center of the lens) and the ray through the zone under consideration. The aberration thus defined varies as the square of the zone height. Thus, if we double the aperture of a single lens, we increase the marginal spherical aberration four times.

When it is desired to state quantitatively the spherical aberration for a lens, the difference in intercept length of the paraxial and extreme marginal rays is given. A single positive lens usually causes the marginal rays to focus closer to the lens than the paraxial rays, in the fashion shown in the illustration. Therefore this type of aberration is called *positive*, *i.e.*, it is written with a plus sign. A lens afflicted with this type of aberration is termed *spherically undercorrected*. If, for any lens system, the marginal rays focus farther from the lens than do the paraxial rays, the aberration is termed *negative* and the lens is said to be *spherically overcorrected*.

If we were to take bundles of rays from other points on the object (*i.e.*, points off the axis), we should find that the spherical aberration was just about the same as that on the axis. In other words, the spherical aberration of a lens is essentially constant throughout its field. Because it is much easier to determine the spherical aberration for an axial object point instead of an extra-axial point it is universal practice so to measure it. Appropriate rays are traced, and the difference between their axial intercepts is determined by subtraction.

By combining a positive and a negative lens, always made of different glasses,[1] it is possible to correct this system for spherical

[1] It is possible to construct a spherically corrected lens made of two com-

aberration for some one zone, *i.e.*, the rays through a zone at some one height from the axis can be made to coincide in focus with the paraxial rays. A lens so corrected is shown in Fig. 22. This is a typical telescope objective. At the right is plotted the curve of spherical aberration vs. the zone height of the incident ray. It will be noted that this lens has been corrected for the marginal zone (the usual state of correction), and thus the extreme marginal and paraxial rays are brought to the same focus. This lens is termed "corrected for the marginal zone," but in spite of this correction it will be noted that a residual of spherical aberration

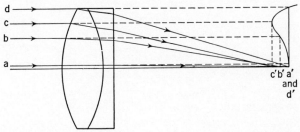

Fig. 22.—Doublet telescope objective corrected for spherical aberration.

remains for the other zones. This is typical of any system corrected for spherical aberration. As far as this aberration is concerned, the performance of the lens is limited by this residual. It would be possible to increase the aperture of the lens and correct the new form for the marginal ray. In this case the intermediate zonal aberration would be found to have greatly increased. Thus the aperture cannot be increased indefinitely. We shall see later that the aperture may be increased only up to a certain calculable limit and no farther.

It will be noted that the zonal aberration of the lens of Fig. 22 is positive. This is the case for practically all the lenses of any type one encounters in practice. A few very unusual photographic objectives and flint-in-front telescope objectives have negative zonal aberration, but these are about the only exceptions to the general rule.

This aberration will be considered in much greater detail in Chap. XXV when we shall deal with the fundamentals of lens design.

ponents of the same glass. This lens could not be corrected for longitudinal chromatic aberration, however, and would therefore be of little use.

**Coma.**—Coma is an aberration affecting only points off the optical axis. Its character may be understood by reference to Fig. 23. The lens is forming an image of the extra-axial object point *A*. It will be noted that the rays through the marginal zone come to a focus at a different point in the image plane from

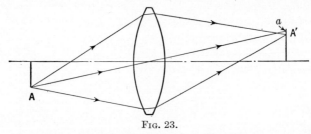

Fig. 23.

the focus of the rays passing through and near the center of the lens. The lateral distance from the focus of the extreme marginal rays to the intercept *a* of the central ray, which we shall call the principal ray, is taken as a measure of the aberration. It will be noted that, whereas spherical aberration was measured longitudinally (parallel to the axis), this aberration is measured laterally (perpendicular to the axis). In the illustration the principal ray strikes the image plane above the focus of the outer rays. This form of aberration is designated *positive*. If the principal ray ends below the outer rays, the aberration is called *negative*.

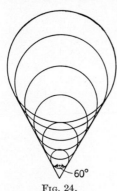

Fig. 24.

Fig. 25.

Coma is somewhat complex in character and may be understood better by reference to Fig. 24. The cone of rays through each zone of the lens (and a zone has been defined as a ring on the surface of the lens, all points of which are equidistant from the optical axis) comes to a focus in a circle rather than at a point. The largest circle in the illustration contains the locus of the foci of all rays passing through the outermost zone. The smaller circles are formed by rays passing through successively smaller zones of the lens. The smallest circle (of zero diameter) at the vertex of the figure contains the principal ray through the center of the lens. When the actual image is viewed, it will not appear like Fig. 24 because more light is concentrated toward the vertex of the figure than at the upper end. Thus when actually seen the comatic image will appear more like Fig. 25. The coma shown in Figs. 24 and 25 is opposite in sign from that shown in Fig. 23.

The size of the comatic image varies as the square of the aperture. So, in selecting a lens, some care should be taken to see that too wide a lens is not used. As various image points removed from the axis are considered, it will be found that the coma is directly proportional to their distance from the axis. Thus it is obvious that image points on the axis will have no coma. As the field increases (*i.e.*, as we select image points farther from the axis), the coma increases quite rapidly so that for optical systems to be used even with fairly narrow fields it is necessary to obtain correction for this aberration.

Coma is a function of the shape of a lens. The coma in a given optical system is usually eliminated by making systematic changes in the shapes of the elements, *i.e.*, by bending.

This aberration will be discussed in much greater detail in Chap. XXVII.

**Astigmatism and Curvature of Field.**—In order to understand the nature of astigmatism it is necessary to comprehend the concept of a fan of rays. Consider Fig. 26. Here is shown a lens forming an image of point $A$ on an extra-axial object $XA$. The points $P$, $O$, and $T$ on the lens define a line parallel to $XA$. If we were to widen slightly the line $POT$ to a narrow band and consider all the rays passing through this linear segment of the lens, we should have a *fan* of rays. The plane containing the point $A$ and the line $POT$ also contains the optical axis, and we shall define this plane as the *tangential plane*. The reason for this name will become evident shortly. The fan of rays in this plane will be called a *tangential fan*. Now let us consider the line $LOM$, which is perpendicular to $POT$ The plane containing point $A$ and the line $LOM$ we shall define as the *sagittal plane*. A fan of rays in this plane is a *sagittal fan*. The tangential plane is sometimes designated as the *meridional* or *primary plane*, and the sagittal plane is sometimes called the *secondary plane*.

With these concepts in mind Fig. 26 should again be consulted. It will be noted that the tangential fan of rays (of which *AP* and *AT* are representative) comes to a focus at *A'*. Although *A* is a point object, the image at *A'* is not a point but rather a short line perpendicular to the tangential plane. It will be further noted that the sagittal fan of rays (of which *AL* and *AM* are

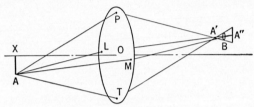

Fig. 26.—Astigmatism.

typical) comes to a focus at *A''*. Here again the image is not a point but rather a short straight line, oriented perpendicular to the sagittal plane. If the image of *A* were to be formed on a screen, the best location for the screen would be at *B* between *A'* and *A''*. At *B* the image would be a disk known as the *circle of least confusion*. If the object being considered were a wheel in a plane perpendicular to the axis and with its center at *X*, the rim would be found to be in focus in the plane of *A'*, *i.e.*, on the

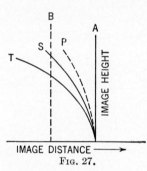

Fig. 27.

tangential image surface. It is for this reason that the term "tangential" is applied to this surface. The spokes would be focused on the sagittal image surface passing through *A''*.

If we were to study a single positive lens and measure the shape of the tangential and sagittal image surfaces for the various object points in a single plane perpendicular to the axis, we would obtain curves of the type shown in Fig. 27. The sagittal image points would be found in focus along the paraboloidal surface marked *S*, and the tangential points along the paraboloidal surface marked *T*. The astigmatism at any point in the field is measured by the longitudinal distance between the *T* and *S* surfaces at that point. It will be noted that for images on the axis there is no astigmatism. This is a common property of all properly centered lens systems. An incorrectly centered system, or one containing cylindrical or toroidal surfaces, will show axial astigmatism, but that fact is of no importance in this discussion.

The astigmatism, as shown in Fig. 26, is independent of the aperture of the lens but varies with the square of the image height. Astigmatism is designated *positive* when the sagittal surface is to the right of the tangential surface as is shown in the Figs. 26 and 27. If these curves represented some particular optical system and if the designer had altered the system by the various means at his disposal (bending of elements, shifting of stop, etc.) to eliminate astigmatism, the tangential and sagittal surfaces would of course coincide, for astigmatism is a measure of the distance between them. In this case however, they would not fall along a plane surface perpendicular to the axis but rather would fall along the dashed paraboloidal surface marked *P*. This is known as the *Petzval surface*. This surface exists (mathematically) for any optical system, but it has physical significance only in the absence of astigmatism, for this is the only time when an image is formed on it. The distances of the sagittal and tangential surfaces from the Petzval surface are always in the ratio of 1:3, *i.e.*, the tangential surface is always three times as far from the Petzval surface as is the sagittal surface. Once an optical system has been roughly laid out and the powers of the lenses fixed, the location of the Petzval surface is fixed and nothing can be done to change it. The astigmatism, however, may be changed. The curvature of the Petzval surface is known as the *Petzval curvature*, which is thus an invariant for any given system. It is usually measured as the longitudinal distance, at some point in the field, from the paraxial image plane to the Petzval surface. It is determined by a quantity known as *Petzval sum*.

If a screen were placed in position *A* in Fig. 27, the center of the field would be in sharp focus, but the edge would be out of focus because of the effects of astigmatism and curvature of field. If the screen were moved to *B*, the edge of the field would come more nearly into focus, as is seen in the illustration, but would be blurred because of astigmatism. The center of the field would obviously be out of focus. If the system were corrected for astigmatism, its characteristics would be represented by Fig. 28: the Petzval, tangential, and sagittal surfaces would all fall together. In this case the center of the field would be sharply imaged on a screen at $A$, the edge of the field being well out of focus. The edge of the field would be focused sharply on a screen at $B$, but the center would not be in focus. Thus it is evident that a system corrected as in Fig. 28, *i.e.*, a system with zero astigmatism, will not give good imagery throughout the

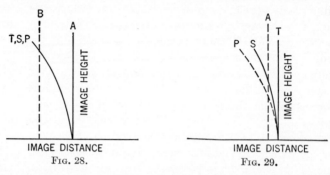

FIG. 28.    FIG. 29.

field. Now suppose that by adjusting the astigmatism we push the two image surfaces behind, *i.e.*, to the right of, the Petzval surface. In this case, because of the fixed 3 to 1 ratio of the tangential and sagittal surface distances from the Petzval surface,

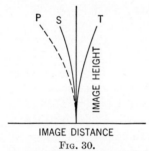

FIG. 30.

the tangential surface must be to the right of the sagittal surface. In other words, to get these two surfaces to the right of the Petzval surface, we have had to introduce *negative* astigmatism. Suppose we have introduced just sufficient negative astigmatism to bring the tangential surface back into coincidence with the paraxial image plane, *i.e.*, the plane, perpendicular to the axis, containing the focus of the paraxial rays. Then we shall have the situation shown in Fig. 29. Now if we place a screen at the compromise position $A$, we shall find that all the images throughout the field are reasonably well in focus. This is the state of correction that is used extensively for the simpler types of photographic objectives. Of course we could have introduced still more negative astigmatism, giving the situation shown in Fig. 30, in which the tangential and sagittal surfaces are symmetrically placed about the paraxial image plane. In order to get this state of correction, however, it is obviously necessary to introduce more negative astigmatism than was used to obtain the situation shown in Fig. 29, and experience has shown that this consequently gives worse imagery. This state of correction was occasionally used with the old types of photographic objectives intended for wide-angle work. Under conditions of poor lighting it was not possible to see the edge of the field clearly to focus the objective, and it was necessary to have an objective in which it was possible to focus the center of the field sharply and then be certain that the edge of the field would also be in focus.

The remarks concerning the inability of the designer to control field curvature apply to telescopic systems and the simpler types of photographic objectives. In the more complicated types of photographic objectives, however, it *is* possible to control the Petzval curvature because high-order aberrations come into play at large relative apertures. Experience has shown that a well-corrected system is not obtained if the Petzval curvature is made zero; if it is made slightly positive (and *positive curvature* is defined as that curvature in which the edge of the field is in focus closer to the lens than the center, *i.e.*, the edge of the field bends toward the lens), a good state of correction may be achieved.

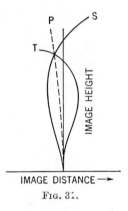

Fig. 31.

In this case the lens has characteristics of the type shown in Fig. 31. The scale of abscissas is enlarged relative to that of the foregoing graphs. Note that the astigmatism is actually zero at only one point of the field. This point is known as the *node*, and because of the positive Petzval curvature it is located in front of (*i.e.*, on the side toward the lens) the paraxial image surface. The astigmatism gets rapidly worse outside the node, and the lens is thus generally not used far outside this point. This type of lens, in which astigmatism is zero at one point in the field, is called an *anastigmat*. Complex systems are required to attain this state of correction, so anastigmatic lenses have been rarely encountered outside the photographic field.

If a telescope or similar instrument is being examined to determine its state of correction, focus the center of the field sharply and then note whether the periphery of the field is out of focus.

If it is, the lens is probably afflicted with curvature of field. In this case attempt to focus the periphery of the field. If it can be brought into sharp focus and the center of the field simultaneously goes out of focus, it is obvious that the situation shown in Fig. 28 exists. If the edge of the field comes into better focus but is still not so sharp as was the center, then both astigmatism and field curvature are probably present, and a situation something like that of Fig. 27 probably exists. If the case shown in Fig. 28 were encountered, the user of the instrument might be deluded into thinking the field was flat if its edge was in focus, because his eye would automatically accommodate as it traveled from the edge to the center of the field. The center, as well as the edge, would therefore appear to be in sharp focus if the Petzval curvature were not too great. If the center were focused sharply, the edge would not appear clear because negative accommodation would be required (see page 85).

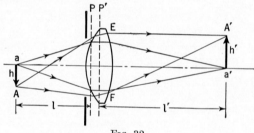

Fig. 32.

**Distortion.**—In Fig. 32 is shown a lens with principal surfaces $P$ and $P'$. Suppose we have an object $aA$. By applying Eq. (6) we can locate the image $a'A'$; or, more specifically, we can thus locate point $a'$ of the image. We can then easily compute the linear lateral magnification by taking the ratio of $l'$ to $l$. By multiplying the object height $h$ by this magnification we get the image height $h'$. It should be noted that the magnification computed here was based solely on data associated with paraxial rays, and thus may be called the *paraxial magnification*. Now suppose that by tracing rays such as $AEA'$ and $AFA'$ we locate $A'$ exactly. By taking the ratio of this actual image height to the object height we get a

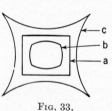

Fig. 33.

measure of the actual magnification. This may be found to be different from the paraxial magnification, in which case the lens is said to be afflicted with *distortion*.

If a lens were free of distortion, it would image a rectangle as shown at *a* in Fig. 33. If the lens had a paraxial magnification greater than the actual marginal magnification, it would have *positive distortion*, and in this case the rectangle would be imaged as shown in *b* in Fig. 33. Because of the shape of this image positive distortion is often called *barrel distortion*. If the paraxial magnification were less than the actual marginal magnification, the lens would be said to have *negative distortion*. The rectangle would now be imaged as shown in Fig. 33*c*. For obvious reasons this type of distortion is frequently called *pincushion distortion*.

A sign convention for distortion that is the reverse of the one given in the previous paragraph is often used. An example of the use of the reversed convention is in the plotting of distortion, as a function of field angle, for a photographic objective. It is common practice to use such a curve in considering the optical performance of an objective. In this case distortion is measured in percentage, the defining equation being

Distortion in per cent
$$= \left( \frac{\text{zonal magnification} - \text{paraxial magnification}}{\text{paraxial magnification}} \right) \times 100$$
$$= \left( \frac{\text{zonal image height} - \text{paraxial image height}}{\text{paraxial image height}} \right) \times 100$$

For any point in the field we can determine (by ray tracing) the location of an image point with both paraxial and true magnifications. The difference in the distances of these image points from the axis is taken as a measure of the distortion. This value varies with the cube of the image height, and this variation explains the formation of the shapes illustrated in Fig. 33. The aberration is independent of aperture. If the distortion, as defined above, is divided by the paraxial image height, the result is the distortion in per cent.

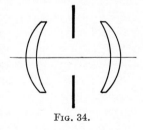

FIG. 34.

It should be remembered that distortion affects only the relative locations of the various image points; it does not affect their sharpness.

An optical system of the type shown in Fig. 34, which is symmetrical about some central point in that the lenses and distances on both sides of this point are identical, is called a *symmetrical system*. When such a system is used at equal conjugates (*i.e.*, image and object distances are equal), it is wholly free of distortion. When used at other object distances, such a system is usually reasonably free of this aberration. The old Rapid Rectilinear photographic objective was of this type and was designated rectilinear because of its comparative freedom from distortion.

In objectives intended for aerial photography distortion should, of course, be kept at a minimum. However, the equipment used for preparing maps from aerial photographs may be adjusted to compensate for distortion in the objective. Lenses intended for copying work also should be free from distortion. With some types of fire-control instruments the situation is not so critical. Gun-sighting telescopes, for example, are generally used only at the center of the field, which is always distortion-free. On the other hand, since rangefinders might be used at any part of the field, they are commonly equipped with special distortion-free eyepieces known as *orthoscopic* eyepieces because of this property. With telescopic systems, for psychological reasons, straight lines viewed near the edge of the circular field sometimes appear curved even though no distortion is present. In this case it is advantageous purposely to introduce a small amount of distortion of the opposite sign to compensate for that effect.

**Chromatic Variation of Aberrations.**—In the foregoing discussion it has been tacitly assumed that monochromatic light was used in the optical systems under consideration. If rays of different wavelengths had been considered, the aberrations would generally have been found to change only slightly. Thus these aberrations are usually corrected for only one wavelength. The occasional exception to this rule is spherical aberration. This varies more with wavelength than do the other aberrations, and it is sometimes necessary to make a special effort to correct the aberration at more than one wavelength. This can be done by proper adjustment of the airspaces between the lenses. The variation of spherical aberration with wavelength in a system computed by the author is shown in Fig. 35. No attempt was made in this optical system to control this variation.

**Longitudinal Chromatic Aberration.**—Equation (2) shows that the focal length of any lens is a function of the index of refraction of the glass used. As this index is a function of wavelength, it is

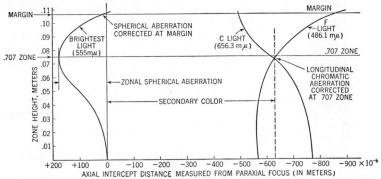

FIG. 35.—Curves showing chromatic variation of spherical aberration, longitudinal chromatic aberration, and secondary color for a three-element aplanatic telescope objective of 1-meter focal length and of speed $f/4.7$. In the usual doublet telescope objective these three curves would be so close together as to overlap because of the greater zonal aberration it would possess.

evident that focal length is also a function of wavelength. Thus the white rays from the point object in Fig. 36 are broken up inside the lens and come to foci that depend for their position on wavelength. The blue rays focus at $a$, the yellow-green at $b$, and the red at $c$. If a screen were placed at $b$, the image formed upon

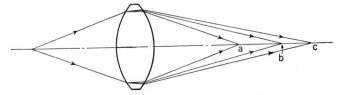

FIG. 36.—Longitudinal chromatic aberration.

it would be surrounded by a purple halo due to the circles of confusion formed by the red and blue rays (*cf.* Fig. 58).

The aberration is commonly measured as the difference in focus between light of the wavelengths of the $C$ (red) and $F$ (blue) lines of hydrogen because these lines are near the ends of the visible spectrum. The aberration is called *positive* when the red focus lies to the right of the blue, *i.e.*, the blue focus is nearer the lens. This is the type of aberration associated with a single positive lens. A lens possessing aberration of this description is called *chromatically undercorrected*. A lens that focuses the red rays to the left of the blue is called *chromatically overcorrected*. This type of aberration is called *negative*.

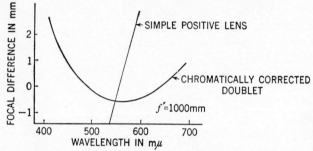

Fig. 37.—Curve showing variation in image position with wavelength for doublet corrected for longitudinal chromatic aberration.

Longitudinal chromatic aberration is one of the most objectionable lens defects and is corrected even in the simplest doublet telescope objectives. When any lens is corrected for this aberration generally all that one can do is to make the lens have the same axial intercepts for two wavelengths, usually those of the *C* and *F* lines of hydrogen. In this case the other wavelengths will still

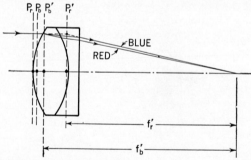

Fig. 38.—Doublet telescope objective corrected for longitudinal chromatic aberration but suffering from lateral chromatic aberration (greatly exaggerated).

focus in other planes, giving rise to a residual aberration known as *secondary color* or *secondary spectrum*. This residual, illustrated in Figs. 35 and 37, is much smaller in magnitude than the aberration of an uncorrected single lens. Nevertheless, it is sufficiently serious to place a definite limitation on the focal length to which a lens may be computed, for it is a constant fraction of focal length. This will be discussed at greater length in a subsequent section.

Longitudinal chromatic aberration is independent of the aperture of a lens and is constant (approximately) throughout the field. It is, therefore, corrected only for an axial image point and is also generally measured in terms of rays arriving at an axial image point.

**Lateral Chromatic Aberration.**—In Fig. 38 is shown a doublet corrected for longitudinal chromatic aberration; *i.e.*, the focal points for two colors (designated "red" and "blue") have been made to coincide. The principal points are located by equations involving the index of refraction, and as this is a function of wavelength the location of the principal points similarly varies with wavelength. The principal "planes" for the two colors are shown. The distance between $P'_r$ and $P'_b$ has been exaggerated for the sake of clarity. Because the principal points do not coincide even though the focal points may, the image distances (which are measured from the principal points) vary with color. We saw that magnification was measured as the ratio of image distance to object distance. Although the object distance may also vary with color, generally it will not vary in the same ratio as the image distance. Thus the magnification is different for different colors. Consequently, the images formed with the different color rays are different sizes. This aberration, measured in terms of the difference in image sizes, is called *lateral chromatic aberration* or, more commonly, *lateral color*. As this aberration is a matter of magnification, it is proportional to image height. It does not exist at all for axial image points and thus may be distinguished from longitudinal chromatic aberration, which is constant throughout the field. It does not vary with aperture.

Since this aberration can cause great trouble in telescope eyepieces unless it is corrected, it is one of the first things considered in their design. It is normally corrected for $C$ and $F$ rays.

We shall consider this aberration and the methods of correcting it in much greater detail in a subsequent section.

**Variation of Aberrations with Image Position.**—With the exception of Petzval curvature, all the foregoing aberrations must be corrected for a given object position. Generally speaking, a lens corrected for one object position will not work well for a radically different object position. A telescope objective is usually corrected for an infinite object distance and works well over a fairly wide range of distances. However, it probably would not be very satisfactory for use in viewing objects a few feet distant. For the same reason a camera lens designed to work with an "infinitely distant" object might not function properly when used as an enlarging lens. Thus considerable caution should be used before attempting to adapt a lens designed for one set of conditions for use in a totally different set. This is all too frequently attempted, often with disastrous results.

**Variation of Aberrations with Image Height and Aperture.**— It is often necessary to know how the various aberrations differ with aperture (usually expressed in terms of the semiaperture, or half aperture, $y$ measured from the axis), or with image height as given in Table I. For an image distance $l'$, measured from the second principal point, and an image height $h'$, the relationship between the image height and the half angle $\alpha$ of the field is

$$\tan \alpha = \frac{h'}{l'} \tag{34}$$

TABLE I.—ABERRATION TABLE

| Aberration | Variation with image height, $h'$ | Variation with aperture, $y$ |
|---|---|---|
| Spherical aberration | Independent | $y^2$ |
| Coma | $h'$ | $y^2$ |
| Astigmatism (difference in focus) | $h'^2$ | Independent |
| Length of astigmatic focal lines | $h'^2$ | $y$ |
| Petzval curvature | $h'^2$ | Independent |
| Distortion | $h'^3$ | Independent |
| Longitudinal chromatic aberration | Independent | Independent |
| Lateral chromatic aberration | $h'$ | Independent |

**REFERENCES**

See lists at the ends of Chaps. I and XXIV.

**PROBLEMS**

**1.** A certain positive lens has an amount of spherical aberration between the marginal and paraxial rays of $+0.01$ cm. What will be the spherical aberration of rays passing through a zone midway between the center and the edge? Suppose we double the diameter of the lens, holding the focal length constant. What will the spherical aberration be for the marginal rays in this case?

**2.** A certain lens gives, at a point 10° out in the field, a comatic image of 1 mm with a point object. What will be the size of the image at a point 20° out in the field? What will it be on the axis?

**3.** A certain telescope objective has a Petzval curvature of +0.4 mm at a point 3° out in the field. At this point the sagittal image surface is 0.2 mm to the left of the Petzval surface. Where is the tangential image surface? Has the lens positive or negative astigmatism?

**4.** A simple photographic objective has +0.5 mm Petzval curvature at a point 10° out in the field. Should one introduce positive or negative astigmatism to get a flat tangential field? If the tangential field is flattened, where will the sagittal image surface be located at this point in the field? What will be the astigmatism? How much astigmatism will there be at a point 5° out in the field?

**5.** With a certain thin lens an object located 10 cm to the left of the lens gives an image (paraxial) 30 cm to its right. For an object 1 cm in height the actual image is −3.1 cm high. Is the distortion positive or negative? What is the distortion? What is the percentage distortion?

If the aperture of the lens is doubled, what will be the distortion? If the object is made 2 cm high, what will be the height of the actual image?

**6.** You are given a lens with the following constructional data: $r_1 = +50$ mm, $r_2 = -30$ mm, $t = 15$ mm. The lens is made of a borosilicate crown glass with $n_F = 1.5222$, $n_D = 1.5164$, and $n_C = 1.5142$. For an infinitely distant object how much (paraxial) longitudinal chromatic aberration is present?

**7.** Let an axial point object be located 50 mm to the left of the first vertex of the lens given in Prob. 6. Compute the (paraxial) longitudinal chromatic aberration in the image. Compare this result with the answer to Prob. 6. (*Hint:* Locate the principal points in $C$ and $F$ light.) If the aperture of this lens is doubled, what will be the longitudinal chromatic aberration? If the object is moved 10 mm off the axis, how much will the longitudinal chromatic aberration change?

**8.** Compute the lateral chromatic aberration of the lens given in Prob. 6 with a point object 50 mm to the left of the first vertex and 10 mm off the axis. What will be the lateral chromatic aberration for point objects on, and 20 mm off, the axis at a point 50 mm to the left of the first vertex?

# CHAPTER III

## THEORY OF STOPS

In the entire field of optics few subjects are of greater importance, and are understood less, than the theory of stops. As this theory is quite simple, there is no good reason why confusion should exist. Before considering it directly we shall refresh our minds with a few simple details of the first-order theory of image formation, *i.e.*, the theory outlined in Chap. I. In Fig. 39 is shown a positive lens forming an image $a'A'$ of an object $aA$ which is located a greater distance from the lens than its focal point. Note should be taken of the marginal ray $aba'$. It will be seen that this ray crosses the axis of the system at both object

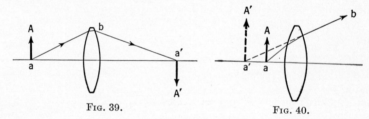

Fig. 39.                          Fig. 40.

and image, and the axial points $a$ and $a'$ are conjugate to one another, *i.e.*, an object placed at one will be imaged at the other. This is an illustration of the extremely important fact that, whenever a ray crosses the axis of an optical system at some point $a$ and then later recrosses the axis at some point $a'$, any object placed at $a$ will be imaged at $a'$, and conversely. If the ray should cross the axis again at a third point, all three points will be conjugate, *i.e.*, an object placed at any one will be imaged at the other two.

Next consider Fig. 40. Here we have the same lens as in Fig. 39, but the object $aA$ this time is located closer to the lens than the first focal point. The lens images $aA$ at $a'A'$, giving an erect virtual image. Note that after traversing the lens the ray $ab$ appears to emanate from $a'$, *i.e.*, it appears to cross the axis at $a'$. This is another example of the case illustrated in Fig. 39. $a$ and *a'* are related in that a virtual image of an object located at *a* will be found at *a'*, although an object placed at *a'* will not be imaged at *a* (why?).

With this preliminary material fixed in mind we are now ready to consider Fig. 41. Parallel light is incident on the lens shown and is focused by it at the focal point. Because of the presence of the stop S, some of the rays do not reach the final image. If this diaphragm were not present, the edge of the lens would act as the limiting aperture of the system, *i.e.*, it would determine which of the rays emitted from the source would reach the image. Every optical system has

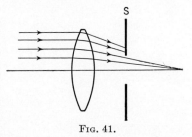

Fig. 41.

such a limiting aperture, whether it is some diaphragm, lens periphery, or other physical object. This limiting aperture is designated the *aperture stop* and controls the brightness of the image.

Now consider Fig. 42. Here is shown a bundle of rays from an infinitely distant extra-axial object point. This particular bundle emanated from the point on the object corresponding to *A'* in the image; the angle at which it arrives at the lens is merely the angle at which point *A* is located. Similar bundles from other points on the object are also incident on the lens at various angles depending on the locations of the points from which they were emitted. These form corresponding image points. Each of these bundles consists of parallel rays; the only thing distinguishing one bundle from another is the angle at which it arrives. Note that each point in the image receives light from many zones of the lens.

Of all the bundles of rays incident on the lens from various points in the object, the one in which we are most interested is the one shown, *i.e.*, that from the part of the object at the *edge* of the field. This bundle will have the worst aberration characteristics of all (in general). Consequently, if we can get this bundle to perform properly, the rest will act reasonably well. Again, if we design our instrument so that sufficient mechanical clearance is left at all points to accommodate this bundle, the other bundles closer to the axis will also be accommodated without difficulty.

This bundle is defined in terms of the angle at which the light arrives, and this corresponds to the angle (known as the *half-field angle*) covered by the instrument.  Generally, in drawing or considering a system it is desirable to represent this bundle by a single typical ray.  The central ray of the bundle is obviously the one to choose.  It is easily seen from Fig. 42 that this is not necessarily the ray through the center of the lens, but rather the one through the center of the aperture stop.  We call this ray passing through the center of the aperture stop the *principal ray*

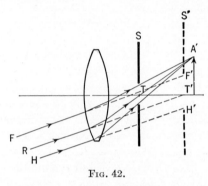

Fig. 42.

or *chief ray*.  This is the ray $RTA'$ in the figure.  Of course we normally use the principal ray from the edge of the field although a principal ray emerges from each point of the object.

We usually trace a ray into the system from the left, *i.e.*, from the object.  In so tracing a principal ray we wish that ray to strike the center of the stop.  If the stop is behind one or more lens elements, there arises the question as to where to direct the entering ray so as to strike the center of the stop.  The angle at which this ray arrives (which we take as the half-field angle) is known, but we do not know at what point to let it strike the first lens.  We could trace a number of rays through the system and find by trial and error the one through the center of the stop, but this is a tedious process.  The solution of this problem can be understood by referring again to Fig. 42.  Note that the principal ray $RTA'$ is aimed, prior to entering the lens system, at point $T'$.  Also note that the ray $A'TR$, if drawn from right to left, forms a virtual image of $T$ at $T'$ because the ray crosses the axis at $T$ and appears to cross it at $T'$ (see the discussion at beginning of this chapter).  Inasmuch as $T'$ is the image of

$T$, $S'$ is the image of $S$ formed by the lens.    Thus, if we knew the location of $T'$, we could aim our entering principal ray at it and would be assured that it would strike the center of the stop. We have seen, however, that $T'$ is merely the image of $T$ formed by the lens, and its location is thus easily determined.    $S'$ is termed the *entrance pupil* and is defined as the image of the stop formed by the elements to its left.    The point $T'$ is called the *entrance pupil point*.    In order to locate the entrance pupil we merely find the image of the stop formed by the lenses to its left. Another important property of the entrance pupil is shown in Fig. 42.    Note that the upper ray $FA'$ is aimed at point $F'$ prior to its passage through the system.    Thus this ray, which touches the edge of the stop, is aimed at the edge of the entrance pupil. Similarly the lower ray $HA'$ is aimed at $H'$ before it passes through the system.    Thus the entrance pupil limits the entering rays (*i.e.*, defines the edge rays) just as definitely as the stop limits the rays that get through the system.    In other words, any ray entering the system in such a fashion that it cannot pass through the entrance pupil will not pass through the stop. Therefore, if we know the position and size of the entrance pupil (and these are easily determined), we know instantly what rays will pass through the system, and we do not have to trace rays experimentally through the system to see whether or not they will get through the aperture stop.    Thus by knowing the size of the entrance pupil we know the size of the bundle of light that will get through the system.    This is obviously of primary importance for it means that the brightness of the image is controlled by the size at the entrance pupil as well as by the size at the stop.

We are often interested in knowing the size of the bundle of light that leaves an optical system.    We can determine this by determining the location of the image of the aperture stop formed by the elements to its right.    This image is termed the *exit pupil*. It limits the diameter of the departing bundle as effectively as does the aperture stop itself and it therefore determines the image brightness in the same way as does the stop.    The point at which the plane of the exit pupil is pierced by the optical axis is known as the *exit pupil point*.

The relationship between entrance and exit pupils is shown in Fig. 43.    $S$ is the aperture stop.    $S'$ is the image of the aperture stop formed by the first lens and is thus the entrance pupil.

$S''$ is the image of the aperture stop formed by the second lens and is thus the exit pupil. The ray entering the system is directed at the entrance pupil point $T'$. Inasmuch as $T'$ is the image of $T$, this ray must pass through $T$, *i.e.*, through the center of the stop. It is thus a principal ray. As $T$ and $T''$ are also

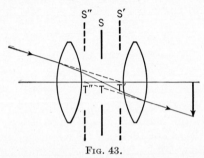

Fig. 43.

conjugate ($T''$ is also an image of $T$), the emergent ray appears to emanate from the exit pupil point $T''$. These relationships hold for any principal ray passing through any optical system.

Another important type of stop is illustrated in Fig. 44. Here is seen a lens forming an image of an infinitely distant object.

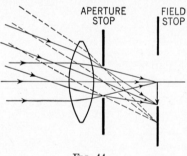

Fig. 44.

Two bundles of rays, from two different points of the object, are shown. Each bundle consists of parallel rays because the object is at an infinitely great distance. The only property in which these bundles differ is the angle at which they arrive at the lens. We could let rays come through the lens at very great angles to the axis, thus permitting the lens to cover a very wide field. However, we should find that these rays that came in at great angles would give poor imagery because of aberrations; thus the periphery of the image would be of poor quality. It is generally desirable to eliminate this region of poor imagery at the edge of the field because it distracts the attention of the user of the device from the center of the field. Thus means are provided to limit the field. Note that in Fig. 44 is shown a diaphragm in the plane of the real image formed by the lens. If another bundle of rays (dotted in the illustration) were to pass through the aperture stop at a greater angle than those bundles shown forming the image, it would not get into the image because it would be stopped by this diaphragm. Thus this diaphragm limits the field covered by the instrument and is therefore termed a *field stop*. A field stop need not necessarily be located in the plane of a real image, but this is generally desirable because it can be distinctly seen and gives a sharp, clean margin to the field of view. Thus in a telescope the field stop is placed in the plane of a real image, when possible, in order that it might be in sharp

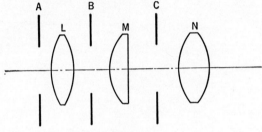

Fig. 45.

focus, as seen through the eyepiece, at the same time that the image itself is in focus.

The rays entering a system are limited in field angle by the *image* of the field stop in the same fashion as the principal rays are diaphragmed by the image of the aperture stop. The image of the field stop formed by the elements to its left is known as the *entrance window*. Any ray arriving at an optical system that cannot get through the entrance window will not be able to get through the field stop for the same reason that a ray that does not get through an entrance pupil cannot get through an aperture stop. Thus, by determining the size and position of the entrance window, we can determine the field that will be covered by the instrument. The emerging rays are similarly controlled by the image of the field stop formed by the lens elements to its right. This image is known as the *exit window*.

Now that we know what the various stops are it is advantageous to consider how they may be located in any optical system. For this purpose let us consider the optical system shown in Fig. 45. This consists of several diaphragms (*A*, *B*, *C*) and several lenses (*L*, *M*, *N*). Since the periphery of any one of the lenses might function as the aperture stop, we must consider these peripheries, as well as the diaphragms, as possible stops. We now find the location and size of the image formed by the elements to its left of each of these potential stops. The resulting images are the potential entrance pupils. These various images are shown in Fig. 46. Any ray that strikes one or more of the stops cannot get through the system. This is equivalent to saying that any entering ray that strikes the image of one of the stops cannot get through the system. Therefore the stop that

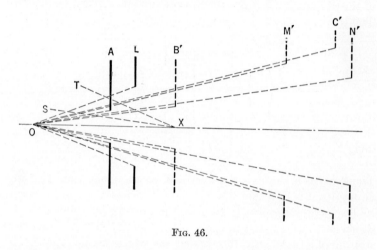

Fig. 46.

permits the fewest rays to get through the system is the aperture stop, and its image will limit the entering rays. Thus we consider the angle subtended at the object point by the various stop images, and the image subtending the smallest angle will of course transmit the fewest rays. This image is the entrance pupil, and the physical object of which it is the image is the aperture stop. In Fig. 46 the angles subtended by the various images at the object point $O$ have been shown. Obviously, image $B'$ subtends the smallest angle and thus is the entrance pupil; $B$ is the aperture stop. If an object much farther to the left had been considered, stop $A$ would obviously have subtended the smallest angle and would have been the aperture stop. Thus we see that the aperture stop may change with a change in object position for any system. In a well-designed system, however, the stop will not change over the range of object positions to be covered by the instrument. The reason why stop *A* and the periphery of lens *L* have been shown in Fig. 46 instead of their images is of course the fact that these objects coincide with their images because there are no lens elements to their left. In other words, an observer at *O* would see *A* and *L* themselves, while he would not see any of the other stops or lenses but would see their images instead. In practice a drawing, such as Fig. 46, is not prepared, but the position and size of the stop images are calculated by the usual methods, and the tangents of the angles they subtend at the object point are then computed. The image giving the smallest tangent is of course the entrance pupil, and the object of which it is the image is the aperture stop.

Inasmuch as *B'*, in Fig. 46, is the entrance pupil, *X* is the entrance pupil point. All principal rays must pass through this point because it is the image of the center of the stop, *i.e.*, all rays that cross the axis at the center of the stop must also cross it at *X*. Principal rays passing through this point must get through the various other stops if they are to appear in the final image. It is evident that an arriving ray such as *TX* could not get into the system because it would be stopped by diaphragm *A*. The ray *SX*, on the other hand, can get through the system. It is thus obvious that some physical object in the system serves to limit the principal rays. As we have seen, this object is called the field stop. From the illustration, it is evident that the stop or lens image that subtends the smallest angle at the entrance pupil point is the one that limits the angle at which principal rays can enter the system, *i.e.*, it limits the field. *Thus, the image subtending the smallest angle at the entrance pupil point is the entrance window, and the object of which it is the image is the field stop.* In the illustration it is evident that *A* is the entrance window. Because there are no lenses to its left, the stop and its image (as seen from the left) are coincident; so *A* is also the field stop.

In addition to aperture and field stops, various other stops, often called *glare stops*, are commonly placed in some types of optical systems to eliminate stray light. Stops for this purpose are sometimes placed in the tube of a telescope between the objective and the erector. Wherever an image of the aperture stop is formed, it is customary to place a stop that helps eliminate stray light and thus improves the contrast of the image. This is usually called an *erector stop* because it is commonly located within the erector system. Additional stops are also placed in the planes of the various images of the field stop. All these latter are, of course, sharply defined in the field of view; so they are made of such size as to give an image in the field of view somewhat larger than the calculated size of the image of the field stop in order that any irregularity in their contours or positioning might not cause them to intrude upon the field of view and render it elliptical. These stops are useful in controlling stray light in long narrow instruments like submarine periscopes.

A difficulty encountered in practically all optical systems that cover a wide angle is shown in Fig. 47. It will be noted that, as the edge of the field is reached, the combined effect of the stop and the lens diameter causes some rays to miss the lens. This effect which is not encountered near the center of the field, is called *vignetting*, and it results in a decrease in illumination at the border of the field. It is not often encountered in military optical instruments, which cover relatively small fields of view, but it is very common in photographic objectives. It helps the performance of the lens in one way, for it has the effect of a diaphragming action (*i.e.*, a reduction in aperture ratio) for extra-axial object points. This improves the quality of the image somewhat, although only at the sacrifice of brightness. In multi-element objectives of the modern complicated types this effect is very pronounced and is a source of some trouble. It will be noted in many of the illustrations in this text that the diameter of the lens is much larger than that required for the axial pencils, *i.e.*, it is much larger than that of the stop. This is to accommodate the extra-axial pencils of light and reduce the effect of vignetting. Figure 42 is a good case in point; Fig. 44 is another. In both cases, if the lens had been made the diameter of the stop, the rays from the edge of the field would not have been accommodated.

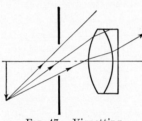

FIG. 47.—Vignetting.

### REFERENCES

See list at the ends of Chaps. I and XXIV.

### PROBLEM

You are given an optical system consisting of two thin lenses, the first being of +4 in. and the second of +2 in. focal length. Both are 4 in. in diameter. The lenses are separated by a distance of 2 in. Midway between them is a diaphragm containing a circular aperture 3 in. in diameter. Assume that an object is located 20 in. to the left of the first lens. Which of the three elements is the aperture stop of the system? Where are the entrance and exit pupils located, and how big are they? Make a scale drawing of the system, showing the locations of the aperture stop and the pupils as well as the optical elements. Repeat the problem with an object located 1 in. to the left of the first lens. What is the aperture stop for an infinitely distant object?

# CHAPTER IV

## BRIGHTNESS OF IMAGES IN OPTICAL INSTRUMENTS

In the design of optical instruments in the past little attention has been given to the *quantity* of light passing through the optical system. Although this is not always an important consideration, it not infrequently dictates the ultimate success or failure of the device. This is particularly true of instruments such as motion-picture projectors, searchlights, and other projection devices. The author has seen a prominent manufacturer of projectors attempt to make a machine to certain performance specifications when a few simple calculations would have shown the project to be physically impossible. The optical engineer should understand fully the factors controlling the amount of light passing through optical systems even though in many cases he will be able to exert little control over these factors.

**Photometric Definitions.**—The design of optical instruments is an engineering study and should be considered on a quantitative basis. Even when dealing with light, the question "How much?" is of fundamental importance. To be able to answer this question in specific cases, it is necessary to know the standard terminology of the field of photometry.

If the eye were equally sensitive to radiant energy regardless of wavelength, *i.e.*, if *equal* quantities of red, blue, green, etc., light (energy) all appeared *equally* bright, the amount of energy radiated from a source per unit time (radiant flux) would be a useful measure of the light flux. However, energies of various wavelengths affect the eye to different extents; some do not affect it at all. Thus a certain source might be radiating large amounts of energy per unit time in the ultra violet, but the source would not seem to be radiating because the eye is wholly insensitive to ultra violet energy. Thus we require some quantitative means of expressing the visual effect of the radiant flux. In order to obtain such an expression, it is necessary to know how the sensitivity of the eye varies with wavelength. This is shown in Fig. 48. It is seen that the eye has its maximum sensitivity at 555 mμ (yellow-green) and that the sensitivity drops to zero at approximately 400 mμ on the short wavelength side and at approximately 720 mμ on the long wavelength side.  Thus, if we had three light sources radiating equal amounts of energy (*i.e.*, at equal radiant intensities), one of which was radiating light (energy) at 420 mμ, another at 500 mμ, and the third at 700 mμ, the first and third would appear much less intense than the second.   The curve shown in Fig. 48 was obtained experimentally and is known as the *relative luminosity curve.   Relative luminosity*

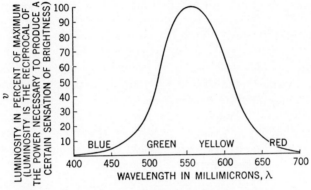

Fig. 48.—Relative luminosity curve: spectral sensitivity of the average eye to equal radiant fluxes.

is the reciprocal of the radiant flux associated with a certain sensation of brightness, this reciprocal being expressed relative to its maximum value.   The function giving this property of the eye is expressed in mathematical equations by the symbol $v_\lambda$,[1] this symbol expressing the fact that the luminosity $v$ is a certain function of wavelength ($\lambda$).   An arbitrary unit of luminous flux has been adopted from consideration of this curve, the unit being the *lumen*.   The important thing to remember concerning this term is that 1 watt of "monochromatic" (*i.e.*, spectrally homogeneous) green light at 555 mμ is equivalent to 650 lumens.[2]   This will serve as a defining equation for the

---

[1] In colorimetry this function is designated by the symbol $\bar{y}_\lambda$.

[2] Prior to a recent determination of the black body constant $c_2$, 1 watt of radiant energy at 555 mμ was considered to be equal to 621 lumens.   If a recently proposed *international lumen* is adopted, 660 lumens will be the equivalent of 1 watt of radiant energy at this wavelength.

term. Thus, for a light source radiating energy of many wavelengths, the *luminous flux*, measured in lumens, may be obtained from

$$F = 650 \int_0^\infty v_\lambda P_\lambda d\lambda \qquad (35)$$

$P_\lambda$ represents the radiant flux (as a function of wavelength) emitted from the source, while $v_\lambda$ is the relative luminosity shown in Fig. 48. In practice the two curves are plotted, and a number of points at the same wavelengths are taken on each. The ordinates are multiplied together and the sum of these products is obtained. (This process is known as point-by-point integration.) Equation (35) shows that we take the actual amount of radiant flux at each wavelength and multiply it by 650 times the relative luminosity (sensitivity of the eye) at that wavelength to obtain the luminous flux for that portion of the spectrum. These values for all parts of the spectrum are then added together to get the total luminous flux for the source under consideration. A little thought will show the logic of this process. The *total radiant flux* $P$ emitted by a given source is obviously the sum of the fluxes in all the different parts of the spectrum and thus may be written

$$P = \int_0^\infty P_\lambda d\lambda \qquad (36)$$

This is commonly expressed in watts.

In considering light sources, the term "luminous efficiency" is sometimes used in two different ways. According to one meaning it gives the amount of (visible) light for a given total amount of power consumed by the source, *i.e.*, it gives the ratio of luminous flux to power input. According to the other definition it is the amount of (visible) light that the source can produce for a given radiant flux, *i.e.*, the ratio of luminous flux to radiant power output. According to this latter view, luminous efficiency is the ratio of luminous flux to radiant flux, and this turns out to be identical with luminosity. The luminous efficiency, or luminosity, of a source in lumens per watt is given by

$$K = \frac{F}{P} = \frac{650 \int_0^\infty v_\lambda P_\lambda d\lambda}{\int_0^\infty P_\lambda d\lambda} \qquad (37)$$

For *small sources* we are usually interested in the amount of flux radiated per unit solid angle in a given direction. The flux radiated per unit solid angle might vary with direction depending on the characteristics of the radiating material and the geometrical construction of the source. Thus supports or other structural members will always affect the amount of light radiated in some directions. The *luminous intensity* or *radiant intensity* of a point source in a given direction is measured by the number of lumens per unit solid angle radiated in that direction and is defined by the equation

$$I = \frac{dF}{d\omega} \tag{38}$$

where $I$ is the intensity in *candles* and $dF$ is the number of lumens of flux within a small solid angle $d\omega$. From this equation it follows that, if 1 lumen per unit solid angle is emitted in a specified direction, the intensity in that direction is 1 candle. *Candlepower* is the luminous intensity expressed in candles. The total solid angle about a point source is of course $4\pi$ steradians, so that if this source emits light uniformly in all directions it radiates $4\pi$ lumens per candle. A light source of 50 candles may be one with an intensity of 50 candles in some particular direction or one emitting an average of 50 candles in all directions.

The definition we have used for intensity assumes that a point source is to be used. If the source has finite area, it is necessary to define another analogous term, and for this purpose we use the concept of *luminance* or photometric *brightness*.[1] With sources of finite area we are interested in the amount of light emitted from a given area, and we thus take the luminance or brightness in a direction making an angle $\theta$ with the normal to a very small element of surface of area $da$ and luminous intensity $dI_\theta$ as

$$B = \frac{dI_\theta}{da \cos \theta} \tag{39}$$

and this may be measured in candles per square centimeter or similar units. For most diffuse radiating (or reflecting) materials, the intensity at an angle $\theta$ is related to the intensity $dI_n$ in

---

[1] The adjective "photometric" is used to distinguish this *physical* concept of brightness from the psychological concept referring to the visual sensation. The physical quantity is sometimes called the *radiance*.

the direction of the normal of the radiating or reflecting surface by

$$dI_\theta = dI_n \cos \theta \tag{40}$$

Any surface obeying this law is known as a *Lambert's law radiator* (or reflector, as the case may be). For a source obeying this law the brightness (or luminance) may be obtained by substituting this expression in Eq. (39), giving as a result

$$B = \frac{dI_n}{da} \tag{41}$$

Thus an extended source obeying Lambert's law appears equally luminous or bright from all directions of observation. Most commonly encountered sources (tungsten, carbon arc, etc.) obey this law quite closely. It is evident from the foregoing equations that brightness (luminance) is expressed in candles per unit area.

The concepts defined (luminous intensity, luminance, or brightness) have dealt with the amount of light radiated *from* various types of light sources. Now let us consider the term expressing the result of having this light fall upon some surface. In this case we wish to know the amount of flux incident *upon* unit area, and we call this quantity *illumination* (often referred to in modern technical literature as *illuminance* or *irradiance*). The illumination $E$ is commonly expressed in lumens per square foot or lumens per square meter.

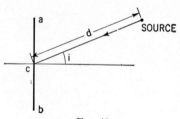

Fig. 49.

**Photometric Computations.**—The usual problem encountered in instrument design is to start with a light source of certain characteristics and a specific optical system, and from these to compute the illumination in a given image plane.

The simplest type of problem is encountered when one has a point source of light of a certain intensity $I$ and he wishes to compute the illumination produced upon a distant surface. This situation is illustrated in Fig. 49. $ab$ is the surface upon which the illumination is being measured. Since it is evident that the illumination will vary over this surface, we must compute it at some specific point, such as $c$, which is a distance $d$ from the source. The angle of incidence of the light, measured between the arriving ray and the normal at the point of incidence, is $i$. In this case the illumination is computed from the inverse square law, *viz.*,

$$E = \frac{I}{d^2} \cos i \qquad (42)$$

If $I$ is expressed in candles and $d$ in feet, the illumination will be expressed in lumens per square foot. (Why?) A commonly used unit of illumination is the foot-candle, which equals numerically the illumination in lumens per square foot. The term "foot-candle" implies that illumination is the product of distance and intensity and is therefore dimensionally incorrect. It is thus necessary to avoid falling into error in the use of this term.

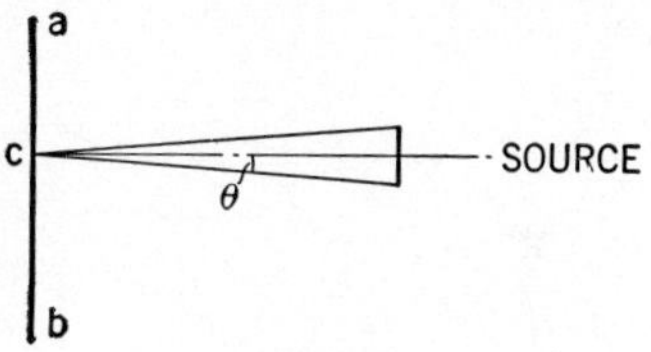

A question arises as to how small a source should be to be considered sufficiently close in size to a point source for Eq. (42) to hold. Generally speaking, if the maximum

Fig. 50.

dimension of the source is not greater than 5 to 10 per cent of $d$, this equation may be used. If the source is larger than this, it should be considered as having finite area. In this case the illumination it will produce on a given surface facing it is given by

$$E = \pi B \sin^2 \theta \qquad (43)$$

This expression of course gives the illumination at some specified point on the surface. $B$ is the (photometric) brightness of the source and $\theta$ is half of the angle subtended by the source at the point at which the illumination is being measured (see Fig. 50). Unfortunately this formula holds only for a disk-shaped source and thus is not of general application. However, for reasonably small values of $\theta$ the following approximate formula holds

$$E = B\omega \qquad (44)$$

where $\omega$ is the *solid* angle subtended by the source at the point under consideration. Since $\omega$ can be evaluated for any given case, the equation is of general utility for illuminance on surfaces facing sources of not too great angular extent. It holds quite well for any reasonable case. If the source is an infinitely large plane, the maximum error occurs, and the result given by Eq. (44) is twice the correct value.

In the cases considered above, we have studied the laws governing the computation of the illumination produced upon a surface by a given light source. Now we shall consider the case where an optical system of some sort is forming an image. Given the characteristics of the light source, the problem is to determine the illumination of the image or any other point in the system. This case is illustrated in Fig. 51. $A$ is the source of brightness $B$. $L$ (shown here as a single lens) represents the

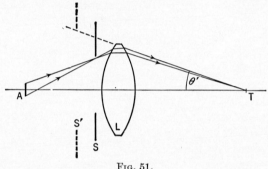

FIG. 51.

optical system, which may consist of any number of lenses. The aperture stop of the optical system is $S$, and the exit pupil is $S'$. We are interested in determining the illumination on a plane perpendicular to the axis at some point $T$ on the axis of the system. This point does not have to be in the plane of the image; it can be at any desired spot on the axis. $\theta'$ is the angle which the ray passing through the edge of the aperture stop (and thus also through the edge of the exit pupil) and the point $T$ makes with the axis. In this case the illumination at $T$ is given by

$$E = \pi B \sin^2 \theta' \qquad (45)$$

Again, for small values of $\theta'$, we can make a useful approximation, for if $\omega'$ is the solid angle subtended at the point $T$ by the exit pupil $S'$ the illumination at $T$ may be expressed by

$$E = B\omega' \qquad (46)$$

Thus, as a general rule, we may state that the illumination at any point on the axis of an optical system is the product of the (photometric) brightness of the source and the solid angle subtended by the exit pupil at this point.

There are certain limitations on the application of Eqs. (45) and (46) that should be kept in mind. First, the source must obey Lambert's law, expressed by Eq. (40). As has been pointed out, most sources commonly encountered do fill this requirement. Furthermore the lens system must be coma free in that it fulfills a condition called the *sine condition,* which will be discussed in a subsequent chapter. The foregoing equations have taken no account of the light lost through reflection at each glass-air interface and through absorption in the glass. The

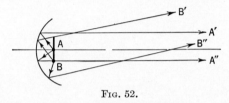

Fig. 52.

reflection loss is easily computed (it is about 4 to 5 per cent per surface), while the absorption loss is usually negligible.

The equations given for the illumination on any plane perpendicular to the optical axis have assumed the source to be of finite size. They apply essentially to all sources encountered in practice (except stars), for even the smallest sources have finite dimensions. In this case they cannot be assumed to be approximately points. Consider the case of a searchlight with a paraboloidal reflector. Any point source at the focus will give a truly parallel beam. When a small (but finite) source is placed at the focus, each point gives a parallel beam, but the different beams emanate in different directions. Thus, in Fig. 52, point $A$ on the source gives rise to the parallel beam $A'A''$, while point $B$ emits the parallel beam $B'B''$. Because these various parallel beams diverge, the illumination along the axis of the light is not constant, as is often assumed, but, as may be shown by the use of the foregoing equations, decreases inversely with the square of the distance from the source. An increase in the size of the source *does not* increase the illumination at any distant point; it merely increases the angular spread of the beam. This point is of fundamental importance in the design of any projection apparatus.

Occasionally one does encounter a case in which a true point source is encountered. In this case the illumination on the entrance pupil of the system is calculated by means of Eq. (42).

If the optical system is perfect, the point will be imaged as a diffraction pattern. The central disk of this pattern has a diameter given by

$$x = \frac{1.22 \lambda}{n' \sin \theta'} \tag{47}$$

$\lambda$ is the wavelength of the light being used, $n'$ is the index of refraction of the medium in which the image is formed, and $\theta'$ has the meaning given in Fig. 51. This central disk alone contains 84 per cent of the total energy in the diffraction pattern, but, for ease in making calculations, we may assume that it contains all the energy. The illumination of the entrance pupil and the sizes of the entrance pupil and diffraction disk are known. As all the energy passing into the entrance pupil (approximately) gets into the diffraction pattern, the illumination of the central disk of this pattern may be determined by multiplying the illumination of the entrance pupil by the ratio of the areas of the entrance pupil and diffraction disk.

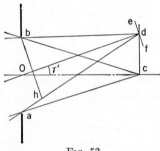

Fig. 53.

Correction may be made for the fact that the central disk contains only 84 per cent of the total energy by taking 84 per cent of the entrance pupil illumination. In these computations reflection and absorption losses within the optical system are neglected.

As will be indicated in Chap. XII, the eye apparently cannot see the outer part of the central diffraction disk. Therefore, when the visually effective diameter of a disk is being computed, the constant 1.22 in Eq. (47) may be changed to 1.0.

Thus far we have derived equations that give the illumination (or illuminance) only at points *on* the axis of the system. Now let us consider how Eq. (46) may be modified to make it applicable to the computation of the illumination at points off the axis, the illumination to be measured on planes perpendicular to this axis. The illumination at point $c$ in Fig. 53 is $B\alpha'$ where $\alpha'$ is the solid angle subtended at $c$ by the exit pupil $ab$ of an optical system. Now consider the problem of determining the illumination at point $d$ at which the exit pupil subtends the solid angle $\beta'$. The illumination given by Eq. (46) applies to surfaces perpendicular to the principal ray (for the case of a point on the axis of the system we merely postulated that the illumination was measured on a plane perpendicular to this axis). Thus, if we attempted to calculate the illumination at $d$ by use of Eq. (46), we should obtain the illumination on plane $ef$, which is normal to $Od$. Inasmuch as the angle between $ef$ and $cd$ is $\gamma'$, we should multiply Eq. (46) by cos $\gamma'$ to give the illumination on plane $cd$, and thus we get for the illumination at $d$

$$E = B\beta' \cos \gamma' \tag{48}$$

This does not give us as much information as we should like to have, for angle $\beta'$ varies with angle $\gamma'$, and we thus do not know how the illumination varies with the angle of obliquity. To evaluate this, let us calculate the illumination at $d$ in terms of $\alpha'$ and $\gamma'$ rather than $\beta'$ and $\gamma'$. As we move the point under consideration off the axis, two effects come into play. In the first place the exit pupil, as viewed from the point on plane $cd$, decreases in (projected) area as we depart from the axis. Thus, as viewed from $d$, the diameter of the exit pupil is $bh$ rather than $ba$. As $bh = ba \cos \gamma'$, it is evident that we must introduce another cosine term because of this effect. Then, too, the solid angle $\beta'$ is actually smaller than $\alpha'$ in the ratio $(Oc/Od)^2$, from elementary principles of solid geometry. Inasmuch as cos $\gamma' = Oc/Od$ it is obvious that a $\cos^2 \gamma'$ must also be introduced. Therefore, combining these cosine terms with Eq. (48), we get for the illumination on plane $cd$ at $d$

$$E = B\alpha' \cos^4 \gamma' \tag{49}$$

Note that we are using the solid angle $\alpha'$ instead of $\beta'$. This derivation has assumed that no vignetting has occurred. In the case of vignetting the illumination falls off even more rapidly than with the fourth power of the angle of obliquity. In fact one might empirically determine the point at which vignetting occurs by measuring the illumination in the image plane at successive extra-axial points and plotting the results together with a $\cos^4 \gamma'$ curve. The point at which the experimental curve begins to depart from the cosine curve is the point at which vignetting begins. The amount of vignetting may be inferred from the distance between the curves.[1]

---

[1] A slightly different method of doing this is described in Research Paper RP1498 of the National Bureau of Standards.

Even without vignetting, the *fourth-power cosine law* stated by Eq. (49) causes a tremendous reduction in illumination for points near the edge of the field in wide-angle photographic objectives, such as are used for aerial photography. At 45°, for example, the illumination is only one-fourth of its value on the axis. Thus, if the exposure time is made correct for points in the center of the image, those near the margin will tend to be underexposed.

**Applications.**[1]—The various equations given here may be applied directly to any optical problem. Care must be exercised to make certain that the units of the various quantities inserted in the equations are consistent with each other.

An interesting case where this theory is applied is that of the photographic objective. The amount of light such an objective (which may consist of one or more lenses) can deliver to an image point is determined by the ratio of the focal length to the diameter of the entrance pupil. This is known as the *focal ratio*. If a given lens has a focal length 3.5 times as large as the entrance pupil diameter, the focal ratio is 3.5. The reciprocal of focal ratio is called the *aperture ratio* or *relative aperture*. For the lens in question the aperture ratio would be 1/3.5. In photographic terms the focal ratio is called the *f-number*. Thus this lens would be rated as $f/3.5$, showing the entrance pupil diameter to be 1/3.5 of the focal length. By substituting the definition of $f$-number in the foregoing equations it may be demonstrated that the illumination on the film, for an infinitely distant object, is inversely proportional to the square of the $f$-number. Thus an $f/1.5$ lens is $(3.5/1.5)^2$ or 5.4 times as fast as an $f/3.5$, the term "fast" being related to the speed with which a certain photographic density can be built up with a given light source by the lens under consideration. An $f/1.5$ lens concentrates so much luminous flux at each point on the film that an exposure is quickly made, and such a lens is termed "fast." An $f/16$ lens would take a much longer time to give an equivalent exposure and would thus be termed "slow." Thus, in general, an optical

[1] Some very interesting examples of applications of this theory to practical problems are given in an article by A. C. Hardy entitled "The Distribution of Light in Optical Systems," in the *J. Franklin Inst.*, Vol. 208, No. 6, December, 1939.

system of high aperture ratio is called *fast*, and one of low aperture ratio is called *slow*.

## REFERENCES

DRUDE: "Theory of Optics," Longmans, Green, and Company, New York, 1929.

HARDY: The Distribution of Light in Optical Systems, *J. Franklin Inst.*, Vol. 208, No. 6, December, 1939.

HARDY and PERRIN: "The Principles of Optics," McGraw-Hill Book Company, Inc., New York, 1932.

HIGBIE: "Lighting Calculations," John Wiley & Sons, Inc., New York, 1934. Also many other books on photometry.

MONK: "Light: Principles and Experiments," McGraw-Hill Book Company, Inc., New York, 1937.

MOON: "The Scientific Basis of Illuminating Engineering," McGraw-Hill Book Company, Inc., New York, 1936.

SEWIG: "Handbuch der Lichttechnik," Julius Springer, Berlin, 1938.

STEINMETZ: "Radiation, Light, and Illumination," McGraw-Hill Book Company, Inc., New York, 1909.

## PROBLEMS

**1.** An electric bulb of 150 cp is located 5 ft above a desk. What is the illumination on the desk, directly under the bulb, in foot-candles? in lumens per square foot? in lumens per square meter?

**2.** You are working with a light source that has an intensity of 50 candles in a known direction. How much flux will be incident upon a camera lens 2 in. in diameter, located 20 ft from the source and in the direction of known intensity?

**3.** You are taking a picture with a lens diaphragm set at $f/1.5$. You wish to reduce the illumination on the film to one-third its present value. What will be the new stop setting?

**4.** What is the focal ratio of the lens system specified in the problem at the end of Chap. III?

# CHAPTER V

## PROPERTIES OF THE EYE

The human eye is a physical image-forming system having lenses of certain curvatures and measurable indices of refraction. These lenses follow the usual laws of image formation in producing an image on the sensitive screen in the eye known as the *retina*. However, if one were to attempt to determine all the properties of the eye from a study of its physical constants, he would be led sadly astray. Many of the important properties

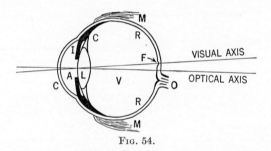

Fig. 54.

of the visual mechanism are of psychological or physiological origin and cannot at present be explained in physical terms. Inasmuch as most of the optical instruments with which we shall deal involve the use of the eye as the receptor, it is necessary that we study in some detail the properties of the eye that influence the design of such devices.

**Construction of the Eye.**—Figure 54 shows a horizontal section through the right eye. Light enters the eye through a thin transparent membrane called the *cornea*. This is shown at *C*. The light then passes through a liquid known as the *aqueous humor* (*A*), which has an index of refraction of about 1.337. It then passes through a capsule of jelly-like material (*L*) misleadingly referred to as the *crystalline lens* (*n* = 1.437). It finally traverses another jelly-like material (*V*) called the *vitreous humor* (*n* = 1.337) and then impinges on the retina (*R*) where it forms a

70

real image.   When focused on an object at infinity, the first focal length ($f$) of the eye is $-15.5$ mm and the second focal length ($f'$) is $+20.7$ mm.   When focused on a near-by object (15 cm away), the first and second focal lengths are $-14.0$ and $+18.7$ mm respectively.

The aperture stop of this optical system is an adjustable diaphragm designated as the *iris* ($I$).   The image of this diaphragm formed by the aqueous humor and cornea is the entrance pupil, which is located 3.05[1] mm behind the cornea for the eye focused on an infinitely distant object and 2.67 mm behind the cornea for a near object.   This iris opens and closes automatically, contracting under very bright illumination and expanding in dim light.   It thus tends to hold the illumination on the retina constant regardless of image brightness.   However, image brightnesses vary over a much wider range than do iris-opening areas, so it falls far short of accomplishing this.   In considering the eye as a part of an optical system we attempt to fill its entrance pupil with light, for this means that we are filling the stop with light.   For practical reasons we are much more interested in the size and position of the entrance pupil than we are in the iris itself.

Most of the refraction of light, in being brought to a focus on the retina, occurs at the first surface of the cornea.   Changes in focus to adjust the eye for various object positions are made by the lens, which changes its shape to make the adjustment.   This process is known as *accommodation*.   Some observers believe, however, that this adjustment is made by a change in the distance between cornea and retina.

The retina $R$ is the sensitive screen on which the image is formed.   The surface of this retina contains a layer of nerve fibers that converge to the optic nerve at $O$ and thence transmit the impulses to the brain.   The retinal ends of these fibers consist of microscopic structures known as *rods* and *cones*.   The visual center of the retina (the fovea centralis, $F$) consists, for most individuals, exclusively of cones.   Outside this center, rods begin to appear and occur with increasing frequency toward the outer

[1] HARDY and PERRIN, "The Principles of Optics," McGraw-Hill Book Company, Inc., New York, 1932.

NUTTING, "Outlines of Applied Optics," The Blakiston Company, Philadelphia, 1912.

portions of the retina. As the rods increase in number in these outer zones, the cones decrease. The cones appear to be associated with acute vision, for in order to study an object closely the eye automatically rotates to bring the image onto the fovea, where the cones exist exclusively and are closely packed. The rods appear to be associated with night vision. As we shall see in a subsequent chapter, when an object viewed at night is so magnified by an instrument (such as a night glass) that its image on the retina extends into the region where the rods predominate, this image appears to increase in brightness. As far as daylight vision is concerned, the field of distinct vision is surprisingly small. Any part of the image formed outside the fovea is seen indistinctly. The field of distinct vision is slightly less than 1° in angular extent. The rest of the visual field is used merely as a finder to pick out objects that are brought onto the fovea for closer examination. Thus, in reading, the eye shifts from word to word, bringing each in turn onto the fovea. The same thing occurs when an image is being studied through an optical instrument. As the eye scans the field of the instrument, the eyeball may rotate in its socket (through motion of the muscles $M$), thus bringing various parts of the image onto the fovea. We should keep this characteristic of the eye in mind in designing any visual instrument. Usually, however, as the instrument is used to scan an extended field it is rotated so that each part of the field in turn is brought onto its optical axis, and the image is therefore formed on the fovea centralis. The user's head moves with the instrument, and the eyeball does not rotate. Because only the central part of the field comes under examination by the most acute part of the eye, it is possible to tolerate poorer performance at the edge of the field with an instrument intended for visual use than can be done with an optical device intended for some other purpose, such as photography.

The rods, which are responsible for night vision, predominate in the peripheral portions of the retina. Therefore these portions are more sensitive than the central portions at low illumination levels. A dim star, too faint to be seen when viewed directly (*i.e.*, when brought onto the fovea), may often be seen when its image is brought near the edge of the retina, *i.e.*, when it is seen "out of the corner of the eye." The star can be located by scanning the sky with the extra-foveal portions of the retina, but, if it is very faint, it will disappear if an attempt is then made to view it directly.

The retina, as we have seen, contains rods and cones on its sensitive surface. In the fovea the cones vary in size from about 0.0015 to 0.0054 mm in diameter. The cones in the outer regions are much larger. These dimensions set a physiological limit to the fineness of detail that can be distinguished, for the cones are "triggered off" by the incident light. Thus, if the light strikes only half the cone, the response is the same as if the whole cone were illuminated. The cones thus tend to limit resolution in the same way that grain does in a photographic film although at times the eye performs better than one would expect from such considerations. In the fovea each cone is connected to a single nerve fiber; thus maximum resolving power for this discrete particle type of receptor surface is obtained. Outside the fovea several cones (and rods) may be connected to a nerve fiber; thus the fiber transmits only an average response obtained from the receptors connected to it. This is believed to be at least a partial explanation of the fact that the peripheral portions of the retina give only indistinct vision both in daylight and at night.

**Resolving Power.**—No perfect (or imperfect) optical system will give a true point image of a point object (such as a star). Because of diffraction phenomena, as explained in any elementary physics text, the image will be a concentric pattern of light and dark rings as shown in Fig. 136. The fact that an image of this type rather than a true point image is obtained means that the image will be blurred to an extent depending on the size of the diffraction pattern. This in turn depends on certain physical constants of the optical system. On the size of the diffraction pattern depends the ability of the system to distinguish between two adjacent points. If the diffraction disks that are the images of two points overlap too much, the points cannot be distinguished as separate entities. If the diffraction patterns are separated sufficiently, the points will be seen separately.

The *resolving power* of a system is its ability to distinguish between two adjacent points and is often expressed in terms of the minimum angle between two points that can just be resolved, or separated. The larger this angle, the smaller the resolving power. One of the limiting factors of resolving power in an optical system is the size of the diffraction disk. Since resolving power is a measure of the ability of an optical system to distinguish fine detail, it is an important property of such a system. The resolving power of the eye, when computed by use of Eq. (47), would be about $\frac{1}{2}'$ if it were a perfect optical system and had an entrance pupil of 4 mm. This means that it would distinguish between two equally bright point objects separated by an angle (whose vertex was at the eye) of only $\frac{1}{2}'$. However, the eye is actually not perfect; in addition the coarseness of the retinal structure imposes still another limitation on the resolving power. In practice *the resolving power of the eye appears to be about* 1'. This figure should be kept in mind because it will recur later. It is known as the *minimum separabile*.

If a luminous object subtending an angle of less than 1' at the eye is viewed it *will* be seen, but it will apparently subtend an angle of 1', *i.e.*, its image will appear to be of the same size as that of an object subtending an angle of about 1'. Thus, if a pattern of points each of which subtends an angle of 1' at the eye and all of which are separated by spaces subtending less than 1' is viewed, the pattern will appear to be homogeneous. Considerations of this character are sometimes used by motion-picture engineers in considering how "grainy" a film may be used under certain circumstances.

It is very important for the optical instrument designer to know the diameter of the entrance pupil of the eye that will give the best resolving power, for this tells him what size of exit pupil his instrument should possess. According to present available data the resolving power appears to be fairly constant when the entrance pupil diameter is between 3 and 5 mm, and 4 mm appears to be about the optimum.[1] If the diameter is reduced below 3 mm, the resolving power is lowered because of the increase in size of the diffraction patterns formed at the images of individual points. When the diameter increases beyond 5 mm, the effects of longitudinal chromatic aberration and spherical aberration, particularly the latter, reduce resolving power. The effect of chromatic aberration was investigated by Hartridge,[2] who found that a 3-mm pupil resolves 56 sec. in white light and 46 sec. in monochromatic light. The 20 per cent difference is presumably due to chromatic aberration.

[1] Cobb, *Am. J. Physiol.*, Vol. 36, p. 335, February, 1915.
  Berger and Buchthal, *Skand. Arch. Physiol.*, Vol. 78, p. 197, 1938.
[2] Hartridge, *J. Physiol.*, Vol. 52, p. 175, 1918.

These data concerning resolving power apply only to objects at the center of the visual field, *i.e.*, to objects whose images are formed on the fovea. As the object moves out in the visual field, *i.e.*, as the image moves off the fovea toward the periphery of the retina, the resolving power decreases, falling to 20 per cent of its maximum value when it is 10° off the axis, and to 10 per cent at about 23°.[1]

Although the periphery of the retina has low resolving power, it is more sensitive to flicker than the fovea, in a dark-adapted eye, but less sensitive in the perception of motion.[2]

A common name for the resolving power of the eye is *visual acuity*.

**Emmetropic and Ametropic Eyes.**—When a normal eye is relaxed, parallel rays entering it are brought to a focus on the

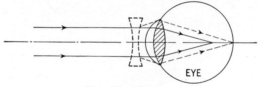

Fig. 55.—Myopia.

retina. Such an eye is called *emmetropic*. All eyes that do not act in this fashion are designated *ametropic*.

In some cases of ametropia (*i.e.*, where parallel rays do not focus on the retina) parallel rays from an infinitely distant object are brought to a focus before the retina. This condition is known as *myopia*. A person afflicted with this ailment must bring objects rather close to the eye to discern them. Thus the condition is known commonly as near-sightedness. Parallel rays focus in front of the retina as shown by the solid lines in Fig. 55. A negative lens is needed to correct the condition and push the image back onto the retina. The functioning of such a negative lens is shown by the dotted lines.

In the opposite case parallel rays converge toward a focus behind the retina. This condition is called *hypermetropia* or *hyperopia*, the more common designation being far-sightedness. It is illustrated by the solid lines of Fig. 56. More power must be

[1] Wertheim, *Z. Psychol.*, Vol. 7, p. 177, 1894.
[2] Ruppert, *Z. Sinnesphysiol.*, Vol. 42, p. 409, 1908.

introduced into the optical system to bring the rays into focus on the retina; thus a positive lens is added.    Its effect is shown by the dotted lines.[1]

Because conditions of myopia and hypermetropia are often encountered, it is necessary to provide ample facilities for focusing optical instruments even though they are intended to be used at a fixed distance.    By proper adjustment of the focusing mechanism it is possible to cause the rays leaving the eyepiece to be sufficiently convergent or divergent to render the image sharp to an ametropic individual.    It is recommended that such individuals

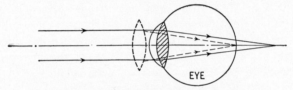

FIG. 56.—Hypermetropia.

use optical instruments with their glasses removed, for they can get the necessary alteration in the convergence of the rays by changing the focusing adjustment.    Because their glasses are removed, they can bring their eyes to the proper eye position as computed by the designer.    If glasses were worn, this could not be accomplished and they probably could not view the entire field of the instrument without motion of the head.

**Astigmatism.**—Certain individual eyes are so constructed that they have different optical powers in different meridians.    This results in the image of a point source being drawn out into a short line, and such a visual defect is termed *astigmatism*.    This can happen even for sources on the optical axis.    In this respect visual astigmatism differs from that encountered in optical instruments because the astigmatism of any properly centered spherical lens system is zero on the axis.

[1] Figures 55 and 56 suggest that myopic and hyperopic eyeballs are of the same size and shape as emmetropic eyeballs, and that the focusing of the rays before or behind the retina is caused either by abnormal radii of the refracting surfaces of the ametropic eye or by abnormal refractive indices of the contents of the ametropic eyeball.    While these cases do occur, myopia and hyperopia are generally caused by the eyeball being abnormally long or short respectively.

Astigmatism is due chiefly to the lack of sphericity of the cornea whose front surface might have different curvatures in different meridians. *Direct astigmatism* is that in which the greater power is in the vertical meridian; *inverse astigmatism* is that in which the horizontal meridian has the greater power. If the meridian of greatest power is inclined, the case is called *oblique astigmatism*.

Of a number of persons examined by an early investigator[1] 9 per cent had no astigmatism. Of the remaining 91 per cent about 78 per cent were afflicted with direct astigmatism, 1 per cent with inverse, and 12 per cent with oblique.

Astigmatism can usually be corrected by the use of cylindrical or toroidal lenses with the axes of the cylinders properly oriented with respect to the axis of astigmatism. In some cases the cornea is so irregular in shape that correction cannot be obtained.

Astigmatic individuals should keep their glasses on while using optical instruments, for there is no practical way of correcting in the instrument for this visual aberration.

**Size of Retinal Image.**—It is occasionally desirable to know the actual physical dimensions of an image formed on the retina. These can be easily computed, for an object $y$ meters in height located $l$ meters from an emmetropic eye produces an image on the retina of a height given in meters by

$$y' = 0.015 \frac{y}{l} \tag{50}$$

If the object is infinitely distant and subtends an angle of $w$ radians at the eye, the size of the retinal image, in meters, is given by

$$y' = 0.015w \tag{51}$$

for an emmetropic eye.

If an ametropic eye is corrected with a spectacle lens, the lens will alter the size of the retinal image. The magnification produced by such a lens is known as *spectacle magnification*. If a spectacle lens of $D$ diopters (it will be remembered that the power of a lens, in diopters, is the reciprocal of the focal length measured in meters) power is placed $x$ meters from the first focal point of the

---

[1] Nordenson, "Ann. Oc.," 1883.

Tscherning, "Physiologic Optics" (trans. by Weiland), Keystone Publishing Company, Philadelphia, 1924.

eye, the spectacle magnification is

$$K = \frac{1}{1 + xD} \tag{52}$$

The first focal point of the eye is located 13 mm in front of the cornea, as shown in Fig. 57.  As distances are measured *from* this point, $x$ will be negative if the lens is to its left; positive, if the lens is to the right of this point.  $K$ is given as a magnification term. Thus the true size of the retinal image is $Ky'$, where $y'$ is calculated from Eq. (50) or (51), and $K$ from Eq. (52).

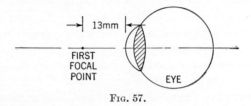

13mm

FIRST
FOCAL
POINT

EYE

Fig. 57.

**Contrast Sensitivity or Intensity Discrimination.**—In the design of instruments for use at night it is often important to know how the ability of the eye to distinguish between two objects of slightly different brightnesses varies with their average brightness.   The eye functions in such a way that the percentage change in brightness that is just perceptible is constant over a wide range of field brightnesses.  We shall call the ability of the eye to distinguish between two sources of nearly equal brightness *contrast sensitivity* or *intensity discrimination*.   If the eye can just distinguish an object whose brightness differs by an amount $dB$ from a large field of brightness $B$, the contrast sensitivity may be measured by $dB/B$, sometimes called *Fechner's fraction*.   The contrast sensitivity will of course vary inversely with this value. The fraction $dB/B$ has a value, for the average eye, of about 2 per cent for a range of brightness from about 1 to 100,000 candles per square meter when small visual fields are considered.   In other words, throughout this range the least perceptible brightness difference is about 2 per cent of the average field brightness. For field brightnesses of less than 1 candle per square meter, the eye loses some of its contrast sensitivity, *i.e.*, the ratio $dB/B$ increases.   At the higher levels above 100,000 candles per square meter the sensitivity appears to remain constant although there is some contradictory evidence.[1]

At normal illumination levels the contrast sensitivity is constant for all wavelengths; at very low levels (less than 0.1 candle per square meter), it is increased for blue light and decreased for red. As will be seen, this fits in with other color properties of the eye.

All these data on contrast sensitivity hold only for an eye adapted to the particular field brightness under consideration.

**Adaptation.**—It should be remembered that after exposure to a bright source it takes a quite appreciable time for the eye to become sensitive to low illumination levels, this increased sensitization being known as *adaptation*. The results obtained differ somewhat with the type of test object used.

The eye ordinarily adapts itself to the average field brightness when an object is being viewed. As the illumination changes, the eye automatically changes its adaptation. Thus, within certain limits, if the field brightness is varied sufficiently slowly that the eye can continuously adapt itself to the changing illumination, very little change in sensation will occur, *i.e.*, the observer will often be unconscious of the change. It is therefore evident that the eye is a highly unreliable photometer.

The ability of the eye to adapt itself to a specific level of illumination varies with wavelength. At the blue end of the spectrum it requires some time for the eye to adapt itself to the new level of illumination when the field brightness is drastically decreased. The rods in the extra-foveal portions of the retina, which are responsible for vision at low illumination levels, are not sensitive to red light, and so adaptation does not occur at the red end of the spectrum. Thus, if a red source of light is not sufficiently bright to be seen with foveal vision, it will not be seen at all. A faint blue source will not be seen when viewed directly, but will be seen if brought onto the extra-foveal portions of the retina, where the rods predominate. These facts are of importance in blackout vision. Practical applications of these effects are described on pages 82 and 83.

**Flicker Sensitivity.**—**Successive Induction.**—When the eye is exposed to a light source, an appreciable time elapses before it

---

[1] König and Brodhun, *Sitz. Akad. Berlin*, July 26, 1888.

Nutting, *Bull. Bur. Standards*, Vol. 5, p. 285, 1908.

Hecht, Peskin, and Patt, *J. Gen. Physiol.*, Vol. 22, p. 7, 1939.

responds. When the source is turned off, there is again a time lag before the sensation ceases. If the source is turned on and off with increasing rapidity, a flicker of higher and higher frequency will be seen (and the frequencies of stimulus and sensation are perhaps unequal) until a critical frequency is reached; then the sensation of flicker disappears and the source appears constant in brightness. This critical frequency increases with the field brightness. At a field brightness of 0.001 candle per square meter the critical (stimulus) frequency is 11 cycles per second; at 10 candles per square meter, it is 39 cycles per second. As has been previously indicated (page 75), the peripheral portions of the retina are more sensitive to flicker than the fovea.

This persistence of vision is of course the basis of motion pictures, for the light reaching the screen is interrupted intermittently by a shutter operating above the critical frequency. Because this change in illumination is above the critical frequency, it is not seen. The frame being projected on the screen is changed during each third dark interval, the other two dark intervals being added merely to keep the frequency well above the critical value.

Another effect that may be of importance in the observation of motion pictures is that of after-images. When the eye has been exposed to a luminous stimulus and the stimulus is removed, the visual sensation persists for a short time, then disappears, and a dark interval follows. After this an after-image appears, then comes another dark interval, and then another after-image. If the appearances of these after-images are phased properly with the periods during which the screen is dark, they may be of considerable importance in the production of the sensation of motion of the pictures seen on the screen.[1]

The effect of persistence varies with wavelength, the persistence being greater for the yellow-green of the center of the spectrum than for the red or blue at the ends.[2]

Let us assume that we have a circular shutter rotating in front of a light source. Let 50 per cent of the shutter be open and 50 per cent closed. Assume that the shutter is rotating well above the critical frequency, so the light seen through the rotating shutter will appear constant in brightness. Under these condi-

---

[1] JUDD, *Am. J. Psychol.*, Vol. 38, p. 507, October, 1927.

[2] In other words, the effect probably depends on brightness alone.

tions the light will apparently be decreased in brightness when compared with its appearance when viewed directly. If we were to measure its apparent brightness, we should find it to be 50 per cent as bright as it would be without the shutter. If the shutter were only 30 per cent open, the light would appear 30 per cent as bright as it was without the shutter. Thus the light would appear to vary in brightness directly with the shutter opening. The law stating this fact, known as *Talbot's law*, has been shown (empirically) to hold over a wide range provided the eye is exposed for at least 3 per cent of a cycle. This particular property of the eye is employed in order to obtain a field of adjustable brightness in the design of some visual photometers and spectrophotometers. A sector disk of variable aperture is employed, and this is rotated above the critical frequency. The variable sector opening is controlled to give a field of continuously variable brightness.

**Color Properties of the Eye.**—As has been indicated in Chap. IV, the eye is not equally sensitive to all wavelengths of light but gives a luminous response in the manner shown in Fig. 48. That this curve does not remain fixed at all brightness levels is suggested by an experiment performed many years ago. This consisted of adjusting bright red and blue fields until they appeared to the eye to be of equal brightness. They were then reduced by equal and quite large amounts. The red field was then found to appear darker than the blue. This phenomenon is known as the *Purkinje effect*, after its discoverer. It strongly suggests that the spectral luminosity curve shown in Fig. 48 changes with the level of illumination, and this has been found to be the case. At low brightness levels the peak of the curve shifts to the left toward the shorter wavelengths, and so does the long wavelength cutoff; *i.e.*, the eye totally loses its sensitivity to the long wavelength (red) light. The short wavelength end of the curve (violet), remains fixed. Thus, generally speaking, as the illumination decreases, the eye becomes relatively more sensitive to the blue end of the spectrum and decreasingly sensitive to the red end. This shift appears to begin at an illumination level of about 1 lumen per square foot.

Because of the fact that the eye has its maximum sensitivity to color in the day (at high levels of illumination) and is quite unresponsive to color at night (at low levels), it has long been suspected that the cones, which are responsible for daylight vision, are also responsible for color vision. The rods, which enable us to see at night, respond by yielding neutral colors. Thus at night we see only various shades of gray.

When photometric measurements are made, the results may be adjusted, by use of the data given in Fig. 48, to take into account the variation of the sensitivity of the average eye with wavelength. Because most eyes, at normal levels of illumination, approach in their relative spectral sensitivities the average eye represented by this curve, the results are of general application. At low levels of illumination this curve no longer is applicable. Unfortunately, for many years such data as had been obtained upon luminosity curves at low levels had not been correlated, and no standard curves were selected. Thus there was no reliable reference scale for photometry at such levels, and photometric measurements, in the commonly understood sense, were not possible.[1] With the outbreak of the present war and the appearance of problems relating to vision in blackouts, this lack of standard data became a serious handicap. For this reason much work is being done at the present time to accumulate and standardize upon luminosity data for use at very low illumination levels.[2]

In the discussion of the ability of the eye to adapt itself to low levels of illumination it was indicated that this power of adaptation was a function of wavelength. For the long wavelengths (red) the power of adaptation is absent because the eye has no sensitivity at low levels to this region of the spectrum. Its maximum sensitivity at these levels lies in the short-wavelength region; it is in this region that the adaptation occurs. The fact that the eye is much more sensitive to blue than to red light at low levels is of importance in selecting, for example, a filter to be placed over the headlight of an automobile for use in a blackout. If a blue filter is used, the light passing through it

[1] "Reports of Progress in Physics," The Physical Society, London, 1942.
*Light and Lighting*, Vol. 33, p. 162, 1940.
"Report of Discussion on Vision," p. 60, The Physical Society, London, 1932.

[2] For the latest available data see "Summary of American Opinion BS/ARP 18, British Standard Specifications for Fluorescent and Phosphorescent Paint," prepared by L. A. Jones of the Eastman Kodak Company, Rochester, N. Y., for the American Standards Association, New York, under date of June 15, 1942.

will be visible to the dark-adapted eye of an enemy pilot much farther away than would be the case if a red filter were employed (see page 79).

Another practical application of these color sensitivity data is seen in a recent U.S. Navy announcement stating that it has been found desirable to furnish pilots preparing to make a night flight with red[1] goggles for use for about half an hour before they take off. This cuts out the light from the region of the spectrum in which adaptation occurs and lets the eye become dark adapted. The pilot is still able to see during this interval by means of the red light transmitted by the goggles and is thus able to study

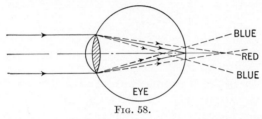

FIG. 58.

maps and charts in a lighted room. As no adaptation can occur in the red end of the spectrum, he loses nothing by using this property of daylight vision. When he goes to his plane to take off, he removes the goggles, and his eyes, having been protected against short-wavelength energy for the past half hour, are dark adapted.

The eye is practically uncorrected for chromatic aberration. Nutting[2] has shown that a curve of focal length vs. wavelength for the eye is similar to the curve one would obtain if it were assumed that the eye contained nothing but water. Under normal circumstances the eye automatically accommodates so as to bring the brightest part of the spectrum into focus on the retina. The blue then focuses in front of the retina; the red, behind it, as shown in Fig. 58. The halo about the image point formed by the blue and red rays is of course purple. It is not ordinarily seen, but by covering part of the entrance pupil it can be brought into view with a point source of light.

When the eye views monochromatic (spectrally homogeneous) light sources of different wavelengths, it can focus on the retina

[1] See, however, Lowry, *J. Optical Soc. Am.*, Vol. 33, p. 619, 1943.
[2] *Proc. Roy. Soc.*, Vol. 90, p. 440, 1914.

all colors in turn except blue. Thus a monochromatic blue source of light cannot be distinctly seen. The image of a blue point source is very large and increases in size as the source recedes from the observer.

Consider Fig. 59, which shows an eccentric stop placed in front of an eye. The point source $O$ emits purple light, *i.e.*, it emits only red and blue. The red image of $O$ is formed at $R$; the blue image at $B$. The light passing through or toward these

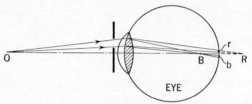

Fig. 59.—Chromatic parallax.

image points strikes the retina at $b$ and $r$, respectively. Thus two diffuse separate images are formed side by side on the retina. As the stop is moved across the eye, the images shift and reverse position. This effect is known as *chromatic parallax*. It can manifest itself in many ways and can be a source of considerable trouble in making precision settings with spectrometers. It is excellently discussed by Guild,[1] and reference should be made to his writings if work with instruments of this sort is contemplated. The difficulty is overcome by placing a fine opaque fiber in the center of the slit of the spectroscope, parallel to its edges. Settings are made on the dark line running through the middle of the slit image, which, being colorless, causes no chromatic parallax.

**Spherical Aberration.**—The chromatic aberration of the eye is similar to that of an undercorrected lens.

The eye is also afflicted with spherical aberration. Most eyes show undercorrection; however, various degrees of correction (including overcorrection) are occasionally encountered. Frequently there are different degrees of correction in different zones. The aberration can even change signs in different meridians. The pupil is sometimes eccentrically placed; in this case, aberration of opposite signs may be encountered at opposite sides, or at top and bottom. Because of this situation it is

[1] "Dictionary of Applied Physics," Vol. IV, pp. 72, 767, Macmillan & Company, Ltd., London, 1923.

*Proc. Phys. Soc.*, Vol. 29, p. 311, 1917.

quite impossible to introduce correction for spherical aberration of the eye into the optical elements of an instrument.

**Accommodation.**—When an emmetropic eye is relaxed (focused on infinity), its power is about 59 diopters. This power can be varied involuntarily by the process of accommodation to bring into focus objects at various distances. The process involves changing the shape of the lens $L$ in Fig. 54 by pulling upon it with the ciliary muscle $C$. The effect thus produced is not uniform throughout the eye but is a maximum at the center, the imagery produced by the peripheral portions being poor. Normally, the eye compensates for this effect by an automatic reduction in the size of the iris to eliminate the peripheral rays. If the pupil is dilated by a drug, such as cocaine or atropine, that does not affect the range of accommodation, the imagery obtained from near-by objects is very poor.

The rods and cones of the retina project perpendicular to its surface. An image may be considered to be sharply focused on the retina if it is located anywhere between the tips and bases of these projecting nerve endings. As an object moves from infinity to a point about 20 ft in front of an emmetropic eye, its image moves from the tips to the bases of the rods and cones. Hence, an object located anywhere from 20 ft. to infinity can be seen clearly without accommodation. The eye must only accommodate to objects located closer than 20 ft.

Accommodation is a very important factor to be considered in the design of visual instruments. If a telescope has a curved stigmatic field in focus at the edge, the eye will automatically accommodate as portions nearer the center are brought onto the fovea; hence, the field will appear flat and in sharp focus. Because the eye accommodates automatically, we cannot tell whether an image we see in an instrument is located 10 in. in front of the eye, or at infinity, or in between. The eye always automatically tends to bring it into focus. Because the eye muscles of an emmetropic eye are relaxed when the eye is viewing an object at infinity, we normally prefer to use an instrument with the eye so focused. This is true even though we can sometimes slightly increase the magnification by bringing the final image close to the eye; for in this case the ciliary muscles are tensed, and therefore fatigue.

The power of accommodation decreases with age. Its range is about 14 diopters at an age of 10 years, 10 diopters at 20 to 25 years, 2.5 diopters at 50 years; and beyond 60 years. it is negligible.

For very small pupil diameters (which may be obtained by placing before the eye a piece of metal containing a very small hole or by using an optical instrument with a very small exit pupil) the range of accommodation of the eye increases greatly, and objects very close to the eye can be seen.   Dust on the eye lens of a microscope having a small exit pupil may sometimes be seen because of this phenomenon, which is called *pinhole vision.*[1]

**Precision of the Eye in Making Coincidence Settings.   Vernier Acuity.**—In the use of many optical instruments the efficiency of performance depends on the ability of the eye to make a setting of some sort, such as aligning a cross hair on a target (gun sight) or bringing two halves of a broken line into coincidence (coincidence rangefinder).   This latter case has been investigated by French and others,[2] and some very valuable data on it have been accumulated.

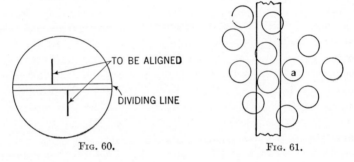

FIG. 60.                    FIG. 61.

Settings were made with varying thicknesses and lengths of line and with various widths of dividing line between the two fields (Fig. 60).   It was found that under favorable conditions coincidence settings could be repeated so closely that the departure of an observation from the mean of a series was only about a half second of arc, or less than a hundredth part of the displacement necessary for the resolution of the two lines.   The angle that the image of the lines subtended at the eye was found to limit the attainable precision.   For images subtending less than 0.6' the power of alignment was negligible.   As the length increased, the precision also increased until the line image subtended an

[1] KINGSLAKE, *J. Sci. Instruments*, Vol. 14, p. 289, 1937.
[2] FRENCH, *Trans. Optical Soc.*, Vol. 21, p. 127, 1919–1920.
SCHULZ, *Z. Instr.*, Vol. 39, pp. 91, 124, 242, 1919.
v. HOFE, *Z. tech. Physik*, Vol. 1, p. 85, 1920.

angle of about 12′; further increases of length thereafter effected no further improvement.

Many people who have done extensive rifle or pistol shooting have found that as precise results may be obtained with a wide-bladed front sight as with a narrow one, and the wide sight is easier to see. Similarly in this investigation the precision was found to be independent of the width of the lines. This probably occurs because the eye brings into alignment one *edge* of the two lines. It was found that the thinner the lines the more rapidly the final setting could be made. As might be expected, an increase in the width of the line separating the two fields was found to cause a loss of precision. When the angular width of the separating line was 4″ the mean error was 1.1″, and when the separating line was increased in width to 19′ the mean error increased to over 5″.

In the best results reported the retinal images were brought to the same relative position to within one-sixtieth of the diameter of a cone. The effect involved may be analogous to that illustrated in Fig. 61, in which the circles represent cones, and the vertical object is a line being positioned. It will be noted that, because of the random distribution of the cones, the line can be moved in either direction much less than the width of a single cone before its position affects another one of these elements. A very slight motion to the right will cause it to affect the cone marked *a*. Only a part of a cone has to be illuminated to cause the whole cone to go into action and respond with a nerve impulse. Thus the effect is the same as if the whole cone had been illuminated. As has been mentioned previously, each cone in the fovea affects a single nerve fiber; thus this part of the retina is particularly well adapted for this type of setting. Again, it will be remembered that the aligning power was found to increase with the length of the line. As an increase in the line length increases the possibility of there being cones in the proper positions to indicate the next slight image shift, this lends contributory support to the hypothesis.

Although the settings have been shown above to be reproducible to a high degree, it was found that the mean of these settings was not always correct. Thus one observer would be found consistently to set one line to the right of the other; another would always do the reverse. The settings were thus characterized by precision (reproducibility) rather than accuracy (correctness). It was eventually discovered that this lack of accuracy was caused by astigmatism of the observer. When the direction of astigmatism was perpendicular or parallel to the line under consideration, the error of setting was found to be zero; when the astigmatism was at 45° to this line, the error was a maximum. This suggests that it is desirable to determine the direction of astigmatism with each observer and then make provision for him to orient his head properly to satisfy the minimum error condition when using a rangefinder. Unfortunately rangefinders do not lend themselves readily to such an adjustment, and it is found more satisfactory to make provision for calibrating an instrument for each observer to take this effect into account.

It has been found by French and other investigators that the precision of alignment does not vary greatly with the level of illumination. It is possible to vary the illumination 1,000 times or more without greatly affecting the aligning ability.

The ability of the eye to make a coincidence setting is designated *vernier acuity*, and it is commonly measured in terms of the angular displacement that can just be detected between two objects. The vertex of the angle is at the eye. If an optical instrument of a certain magnifying power is used to view the objects being brought into coincidence, the angle that these objects subtend at the instrument must be multiplied by its angular magnification to obtain (approximately) the angles that their images subtend at the eye. This fact must be kept in mind in dealing with rangefinders.

With a trained observer the probable error in making a single coincidence setting is about 2″. If we take five or six probable errors we come pretty close to absolute certainty of setting, and thus we say that an observer is very reliable to about 10″ or 12″. This value, representing the performance of an average observer, is called a *Unit of Error*. It is used extensively in rangefinder calculations. We prefer a 12″ Unit of Error; Germans use 10″.

**Stereoscopic Acuity.**—This term refers to the ability of the eye to tell which of two objects is the closer. It is a property of binocular vision, both eyes being necessary to make the determination. Each of the two test objects will subtend a certain angle at the eyes of the observer. When the objects are located so that the observer can just tell which is nearer, the difference between the angles which the interocular distance of the observer subtends at the two objects is taken as a measure of his stereoscopic acuity. As will be seen later, this property of vision is the basis of the stereoscopic rangefinder.

Measurements on many observers show that stereoscopic acuity is fairly independent of illumination or object size. A difference in the sizes of two adjacent objects can be detected to within 7″. As was the case with vernier acuity, about 2″ probable error for a single observation represents the best working performance with stereoscopic acuity. Therefore we use the same Unit of Error for both.

The surprising fact that both types of acuity have the same working limits suggests that both may be manifestations of the same fundamental phenomenon. If one considers the case where the two test objects and one eye of the observer lie in a straight line, it is seen that the difference in the ranges of the two objects is detected in terms of a vernier displacement in the other eye. The reader should sketch this situation to appreciate its significance.

**Spatial Induction.**—This phenomenon is discussed on pages 186 and 187 and will not be considered at this time.

**Stiles and Crawford Effect.**—Stiles and Crawford investigated the visual efficiency of rays entering various portions of the entrance pupil of the eye. They found that the rays entering the peripheral portions of the pupil produced a considerably reduced sensation of brightness compared with those passing through the center.[1] It has long been known from studies on mechanical and optical gun sights that the user of such a device automatically centers the sight aperture or exit pupil in the eye's entrance pupil and the reason for this was not clearly understood. It appears that this *Stiles and Crawford effect* is at least partially responsible, for it is evident that the eye centers itself automatically to find the brightest image, and it finds this image when the rays enter the central portion of its pupil. The fact that the imagery is poorer, because of spherical aberration, with the peripheral rays than with the rays passing through the center of the pupil is also probably a contributory factor. For these reasons the eye automatically centers itself on the exit pupil of any optical instrument when the exit pupil is smaller than the eye's entrance pupil. When the exit pupil of the instrument is larger than the eye's pupil, the eye still centers itself in the pupil, but for a different reason. The peripheral portions of any instrument's exit pupil are generally noticeably more afflicted with

[1] STILES and CRAWFORD, *Proc. Roy. Soc.* Vol. B112, p. 428, 1933.

aberration than the central portion, so the eye centers itself in the region of best imagery provided that the difference in image quality between center and edge is detectable.

**Conclusion.**—The various properties of the eye discussed above, as well as numerous others, play a very important function in the operation of optical instruments. Consequently they should be thoroughly understood before design work is undertaken on such instruments. Our present knowledge of some of the properties of the eye (such as resolving power) that are of fundamental importance in instrument design is not so complete as we would like, and much work of importance must be carried on in this field.

### REFERENCES

"Dictionary of Applied Physics," Vol. IV, Macmillan & Company, Ltd., London, 1923. Article on The Eye.

HARDY and PERRIN: "The Principles of Optics," McGraw-Hill Book Company, Inc., New York, 1932.

HELMHOLTZ: "Physiological Optics" (trans. by Southall), Optical Society of America, 1924.

LYTHGOE: "Illumination and Visual Capacities" (Spl. Report Series, No. 10), His Majesty's Stationery Office, London, 1926.

MARTIN: "An Introduction to Applied Optics," Vol. I, Sir Isaac Pitman & Sons, Ltd., London, 1930.

MOREAU-HANOT: "Photométrie des lumières brèves ou variables," Revue d'Optique théorique et instrumentale, Paris (XVᵉ), 1934.

NUTTING: "Outlines of Applied Optics," The Blakiston Company, Philadelphia, 1912.

POLYAK: "The Retina," University of Chicago Press, Chicago, 1941.

SOUTHALL: "An Introduction to Physiological Optics," Oxford University Press, New York, 1937.

WALLS: "The Vertebrate Eye," Cranbrook Institute of Science, Bloomfield Hills, Mich., 1942.

WRIGHT: "The Perception of Light," Chemical Publishing Company of New York, Inc., New York, 1939.

### PROBLEMS

**1.** A man 6 ft tall is standing 25 ft away from an observer. What is the size of the retinal image of this man formed in the observer's eye?

**2.** An airplane subtends an angle of 1' at an observer's eye. What is the size of the image formed on the observer's retina?

**3.** A myopic observer wears a correcting spectacle of −6 diopters power located 17 mm in front of the cornea. What is the change in the size of the retinal image thus produced? What will be the size of the image of the man considered in Prob. 1?

**4.** Using data given earlier in the chapter, derive Eq. (51).

# CHAPTER VI

## OPTICAL MATERIALS

### GLASS

Optical glass is glass made of specially selected materials, under closely controlled conditions, for use specifically in optical instruments. The required manufacturing technique differs greatly from that employed in the manufacture of ordinary glass, and the chemical composition is generally different, too.

In the early days of the nineteenth century, when high-quality optical systems began to be developed, it was found that ordinary glass did not give satisfactory results because slight inhomogeneities, which resulted in differing indices of refraction throughout a lens, caused serious defects in the quality of the image. It was also found that the presence of small bits of foreign matter or small bubbles were very objectionable for certain types of lens systems. It was then realized that it would be necessary to take special precautions with glass intended for optical use, and the optical glass industry thus had its beginning. At first only a very few types of glass were produced, but it was gradually appreciated that the proper selection of glass for a given optical system provided an additional variable with which the designer could exert some control over its aberration characteristics. However, until 1886, only ordinary crowns and flints were available. It was possible to make simple achromats with these glasses, but it was not possible, with the lens designs then in use, to bring the Petzval sum to zero and still have positive power in the system. Between 1880 and 1886 Abbe and Schott pursued extensive researches in developing glasses that would permit of controlling Petzval curvature, and these were made commercially available in 1886. Achromats made of ordinary crown and flint are called *old* achromats, while those made from the more recently developed glasses are called *new* achromats. With all the old glasses, the indices and dispersions lay on a single line. This restriction was removed with the introduction of the new glasses. There have recently been made available a new series of glasses of very high index that will open a new host of possibilities to the lens designer.

**Characteristics of Optical Glass.**—It will be remembered that index of refraction varies with wavelength. The *way* in which index changes with wavelength, together with the index of refraction itself (measured at some reference wavelength), are the important optical characteristics that distinguish one type of glass from another.

As the eye has its maximum sensitivity at 555 m$\mu$, it was desired to standardize on a wavelength in this region for the measurement of index. By common consent, this reference wavelength is taken as 589.3 m$\mu$, for this is the average of the wavelengths of the two $D$ lines of sodium. These sodium lines are easily obtained from a Bunsen burner and a pinch of sodium chloride or a sodium vapor lamp, and by their use anyone wishing to make index measurements can be sure of obtaining exactly the right wavelength without special apparatus. The index, when measured at this wavelength, is designated $n_D$.

In order to obtain a measure of the way index varies with wavelength in a given sample of glass, the following constant is usually used:

$$\nu = \frac{n_D - 1}{n_F - n_C} \qquad (53)$$

where $n_F$ is the index of the glass at 486.1 m$\mu$, which is the wavelength of the $F$ line of hydrogen, and $n_C$ is the index at 656.3 m$\mu$, the wavelength of the $C$ line of hydrogen. These lines may be obtained from a hydrogen-discharge tube when appropriate filters are employed.

This is called the *reciprocal dispersion* or *constringence* of the glass and is also referred to as *Abbe's number* or *$\nu$-value*. For convenience, it is sometimes referred to, albeit incorrectly, as dispersion.

The two values $n_D$ and $\nu$ are all that are generally needed for design purposes. However, occasionally a designer wishes to compare various pairs of glasses to determine which will give the least secondary spectrum in an achromat; for this purpose he wishes to study various partial dispersions, such as $n_C - n_{A'}$, $n_D - n_C$, $n_F - n_D$, etc., the subscripts referring to the spectral lines at which the indices were determined. Thus these values are also generally given in glass catalogues.

The variation of index with wavelength is the property of glass referred to as *dispersion*. It is pointed out that there are a large number of interpolating formulas that are available if it should become desirable to calculate the index at some wavelength intermediate between those wavelengths at which index data are available (see Eq. 153).

In general the manufacturers of optical glass can usually hold the index of a melt of glass to within about $\pm 0.001$ of the value given in his catalogue and the $\nu$-value to within about $\pm 0.2$ to $\pm 0.4$, depending on the type of glass.

**Composition.**—As has already been indicated, it is very important that optical glass be uniform in composition, not only throughout a single batch but also from one batch to another. This of course requires very close control over manufacturing conditions.

Fundamentally, the manufacture of optical glass consists of melting together carefully measured quantities of very pure ingredients at a temperature sufficiently high to insure enough fluidity to permit bubbles to escape. This mixture should be carefully stirred to insure homogeneity and then be cooled very slowly to room temperature.

Most glasses contain materials, such as silica (as sand), sodium and potassium carbonates and nitrates, calcium carbonate, and aluminum oxide. Then special ingredients are added to give the glass desired properties. Any glass that contains a significant amount of lead is designated a *flint* glass; any not containing this lead is called a *crown*. Various types of flints and crowns are produced with different optical properties. Some of the new high-index glasses contain rare earths, such as tungsten and tantalum, and use no silica.

**Defects of Optical Glass.** 1. *Striae.*—These are streaks or veins in the glass of a composition differing slightly from the average. This difference in composition results in a slight difference in optical properties. Thus the index of refraction of these striae is usually lower than that of the surrounding mass. This index difference usually is confined to the fourth decimal place, but in some cases it can extend to several units in the third place. Very heavy striae (generally pronounced stree-eye) are called *cords*, and these can be as much as 0.007 lower in index than the average. Because of these index differences, refraction occurs within the glass, and this can impair the imagery. On a warm day, when distant objects are seen to shimmer because of the different indices of rising air currents, the index differences responsible for the effect are in the fifth place! Because these defects produce small deflections in the expected paths of the rays, their effect is much worse in high-power instruments where the rays converge under a small angle (as with a long focus objective) than with a low-power instrument where the rays come in at large angles. These defects are thus particularly objectionable in instruments such as rangefinders, panoramic sights, and telescopic sights. With low-power binoculars, trench periscopes, etc., their effect is of less importance. With lenses the importance of striae has been found to depend on their location. A single heavy cord near the margin of a lens would generally not be serious. Fine striae scattered throughout a lens may be quite objectionable for many purposes, although they may not be too bad in low-power elements. These fine striae are much more objectionable than a single heavy cord. With prisms the effect of striae is difficult to predict. They may prove very harmful in one prism and not particularly bad in another. In general, it is necessary to select glass as free as possible from striae for use in prisms.

When plate glass is rolled, the striae are broken up into very fine bands parallel to the direction of rolling. These are called *ream*. If the plane of the ream and the plane of the rolled glass are perpendicular to the light rays, the effect of ream is not serious. Thus reticles, spectacle lenses, and some instrument lenses may be made of rolled glass. Borosilicate crowns, barium crowns, and dense flints may be obtained free of striae.

2. *Bubbles.*—These result from gasses that were trapped in the melt and could not escape. They vary in size from a few millimeters up to several centimeters in diameter. Small bubbles are called *seeds; air bells* are bubbles of irregular shape.

A bubble located in an element in the plane of a real image is very objectionable, for it will cut out part of the image. However, if located in an element some distance from an image plane, it will merely reduce the over-all transmission a negligible amount without producing any other serious effect. Bubbles may thus not be a very serious defect. Occasionally a bubble will be found to mark the end of a short stria, and this type of bubble is definitely objectionable. Borosilicate crown and dense flint glass can be obtained comparatively free of bubbles, but dense barium crown and barium glasses usually contain numerous seeds 0.05 to 0.1 mm. in diameter.

3. *Stones.*—These are small fragments of undissolved material, usually pieces of the pot or spalling of the crown of the pot arch. Their own presence is per se no more objectionable than that of bubbles, and the remarks made of bubbles also apply to stones. However, on cooling, the difference in thermal expansion between glass and the stone usually results in the glass adjacent to the stone being placed in a state of strain, which is a serious defect. The effect may even produce conical fractures. Another objection to stones arises from the fact that as they are swirled about in the melt during stirring they go partly into solution, producing, because of the resulting change in index, striae. For this reason glass containing stones is usually rejected on sight.

Carelessness during the pressing of lens blanks can also result in the introduction of stones and included folds of extraneous material.

4. *Crystallization Bodies.*—When glass cools down to room temperature during manufacture, the solution becomes supersaturated with respect to certain component materials; if given the chance to do so, these will crystallize out. This crystallization destroys the homogeneity of the mass, and large strains are set up adjacent to the precipitated crystals. Such glass is worthless for optical use.

5. *Cloudiness.*—Because of manufacturing difficulties, turbidity sometimes results and the glass becomes cloudy or milky. Such glass is immediately rejected, for obvious reasons.

6. *Strain.*—When a hot piece of glass cools non-uniformly, the glass is placed in a state of heavy strain because of the different rates of thermal contraction in different parts of the glass. This strain may be removed by a process known as *annealing*, in which the glass is heated just enough to permit the slight flow necessary for the strain to release, and it is then carefully and slowly cooled in such a way as not to introduce new strain. If the annealing is not properly performed, strain will remain.

Strain is objectionable because it seeks to relieve itself by slow movement even at room temperature. A piece of strained glass might shatter at any moment because of internal stress. Then too, during the grinding and polishing operations on lenses strain seeks to release itself, causing disfiguration of the lens surface to a sufficient degree to impair the optical performance of the element. Even after manufacture a strained lens will continue to change shape while mounted in an instrument and might either give poor imagery or even shatter while releasing strain.

Strain causes a change in index of refraction of glass, and renders it birefringent (see Chap. VII). Because the material is birefringent, two rays of different velocities are propagated, and the deterioration to be expected in the image is inferred from the magnitude of the retardation between these two beams. Poor glass shows a retardation of as much as 40 to 50 m$\mu$ per centimeter of glass path, while good glass shows 3 to 5 m$\mu$ per centimeter retardation. An effect of strain on glass is a direct change in the index of refraction, this change being such as to make a poorly annealed piece of glass about 0.001 to 0.004 lower in index than a well-annealed piece from the same melt. This reduction in index is not so serious as the direct result of strain in warping the glass. Strain can make glass optically active (see Chap. VII), and this is also objectionable.

7. *Chemical Stability.*—The various types of glasses differ widely in their stability, this being their resistance to attack by atmospheric constituents such as carbon dioxide and water vapor, by perspiration, and by bacteria and plant organisms. These all act to destroy the quality of the polish and in many cases produce a film on the surface of the glass, which greatly reduces light transmission. Glasses thus attacked are evidently not suitable for exposed lenses and windows in optical instruments. In designing an instrument this point should be kept in mind. Borosilicate crown and dense flint glasses have good resistance to this type of attack, while some dense barium crowns and borate and phosphate glasses are bad (see Table II).

8. *Color.*—This defect in optical glasses, which is very noticeable, is caused by the presence of unavoidable impurities in some components. Iron oxide is a chief source of trouble, giving green, yellow, or other discoloration depending on the chemical state of the iron. Oxides of copper, nickel, cobalt, etc., may also cause difficulty. The presence of a small amount of color in a glass can cause a considerable amount of light absorption over a

long optical path. Thus glass intended for the manufacture of large prisms must be particularly free of this defect. The color can be most easily noted by looking through a long piece of it.

Borosilicate crown, barium crown, and dense barium crown glasses are usually free of color while dense flint glasses commonly show a slight amount of yellow and extra dense flints are usually noticeably yellow.

This color is apt to vary from one batch to another; thus an element made from a certain batch might be colored; that from another might be satisfactory. This causes trouble in binocular instruments, particularly rangefinders, because of the obvious difficulty of working with two differently colored fields, as would happen if lenses or prisms with pronounced color were mounted on one side of the device.

**Detection of Defects.**—Visual inspection is sufficient to detect many of the above-mentioned defects. Bubbles, stones, and striae are often found in this way. Striae may be more readily detected by immersing the sample in a liquid of the same refractive index to eliminate the effect of surface irregularities. They may also be found by polishing two plane parallel windows on a test sample and passing a beam of parallel light through them.[1] Seeds, stones, and bubbles are detected by illuminating a block with a beam of light from the side and viewing it normally. The only light from the source seen by the examiner is that scattered by the impurities, which thus appear as bright specks on a dark field. Strain can be observed by viewing the sample between crossed Nicol prisms (see Chap. VII). The strained areas will appear lighter than the unstrained ones. Highly strained samples can be re-annealed in an attempt to release strain. However, the annealing should be closely controlled or the glass will change its optical characteristics. Very close control over annealing conditions is necessary in the manufacture of optical glass because the final optical properties depend to a great extent on the time and temperature schedule used. The transmission of a sample may be measured with a Martens photometer or with photoelectric equipment.

[1] HARDY and PERRIN, "The Principles of Optics," McGraw-Hill Book Company, Inc., New York, 1932.

## COLOR FILTERS

The optical instrument designer often faces a very definite need for a filtering material with which he can exert some measure of control over the spectral properties of the light being admitted to, or transmitted through, his apparatus. The most generally satisfactory method of accomplishing this is through the use of a transparent material containing a dye or other light-absorbing medium. Such a device is designated a *filter*. It may be constructed from glass, gelatin, or a plastic as the base material. Each of these has certain advantages and disadvantages.

Gelatin filters are at present available with greater varieties of transmission characteristics than can be obtained with other materials. They cannot, however, be exposed to high temperatures, such as exist in motion-picture projectors, without decomposing.

Glass filters are much more stable to heat than gelatin, but the transmission characteristics of some types change with temperature. Generally speaking, control over the transmission characteristics is difficult to maintain, and variations in the characteristics of glass filters manufactured at different times are common. Thus, if a given filter is to be duplicated, another piece of the same melt, as well as the same color, should be requested.

The advantages and the disadvantages of plastic filters will be discussed under Plastics, page 103. In general, it may be remarked that the rapid expansion of the plastics industry has not allowed sufficient time to be devoted yet to providing a wide range of plastic filter materials. When this is done, however, they will undoubtedly displace glass and gelatin in many applications.

Before attempting to use filters for any purpose, the optical engineer must have some knowledge of the general appearance of the transmission curves of the various types of filters available. For this reason, the curves shown in Fig. 62 should be studied closely. The ordinate is *transmission* (per cent of light transmitted by the sample) and the abscissa is the wavelength of the light being considered.

These curves may appear confusing at first, but a little consideration shows that they are simple and logical. Note that the green filter, for example, transmits other colors than green, but that the curve has its peak in the green part of the spectrum.

The characteristics of each filter will now be considered individually. The remarks made here, as well as the curves shown, apply in general to filters of a given color and not to any specific filter.

Blue filters generally have peaks between 350 and 450 m$\mu$, and their transmissions generally drop to a low value in the green

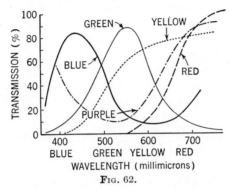

Fig. 62.

and yellow and begin to increase in the red. This increase in transmission at long wavelengths is generally not desired, and it is merely a characteristic of the cobalt used to color these filters. The reason that the red transmission is undesirable is that it detracts from the purity of the transmitted color, this purity being judged by the relative absence of colors other than that for which the filter is intended.

Green filters generally have fairly high purity, their curves dropping at both ends of the spectrum. Note that their curves approximate the spectral sensitivity curve (luminosity curve) of the eye at normal levels of illumination. Such filters are sometimes used in conjunction with photocells to give an over-all response similar to that of the eye.

Reasonably pure yellow filters are practically unknown, for all such filters encountered in practice have high red transmissions and generally good green transmissions. They drop to very low transmission in the blue and are usually opaque to ultra violet. Filters used to eliminate ultra violet light generally have yellow transmission characteristics in the visible spectrum, this being a disadvantage.

Red filters are often quite pure in color, although many transmit some yellow. Their high transmission at the long wavelength end of the visible spectrum usually continues wel' into the infra red. Most red filters change their transmission characteristics as their temperature rises.

There is no spectral purple color, for purple is the visual (subjective) response to a combination of red and blue. Thus a purple filter must have relatively high transmission in both these regions. Either of the components may be the larger, the blue being predominant in blue-purple and the red in red-purple.

When a beam of light passes through a sheet of transparent material, there is a certain loss of light by reflection at each surface. Thus for glass, a normally incident beam loses about 4 per cent at each surface, or 8 per cent for the two surfaces. The equations for computing this loss will be given in Chap. VIII.

When we work with a piece of transparent material and wish to use its light-transmitting qualities, we are usually interested in the amount of light that leaves the second surface expressed as a fraction of that incident upon the first surface. This quantity is at present known as *transmission*, although this name may be changed at the conclusion of the present war in an attempt to develop a more systematic nomenclature of photometric terms. If we eliminate the surface reflection losses and use as a measure of the light-transmitting ability of a material the amount of light incident *upon* the second surface of a sample expressed as a fraction of the light *transmitted by* the first surface, we have the *transmittance*. If we determine the transmittance of unit thickness of the material we have the *transmittancy*.

At any wavelength $\lambda$, where the transmittance is $T_\lambda$, the *density* $D_\lambda$ is given by

$$D_\lambda = \log \frac{1}{T_\lambda} \tag{54}$$

If the density at each of a number of points on a transmittance curve for a certain thickness filter be determined, these data can be used to determine the transmittance curve of a filter of any other thickness, for, at a given wavelength, the density is proportional to thickness, or

$$\frac{D_1}{D_2} = \frac{T_1}{T_2} \tag{55}$$

Thus a new curve for any thickness may be determined.

In dealing with filters one is normally given the measured transmissions. These are reduced to transmittances by computation. Equations (54) and (55) are then applied and the new transmittances are ascertained. These are reduced to transmission by computation.

Filters serve several useful purposes in military optical instruments. They may be used to reduce the amount of visible light entering the instrument so that it can be aimed at or near bright light sources, such as the sun or a searchlight. They may be used to detect camouflage, because colors seen through filters are distorted. They may be used to protect the user of the instrument against ultra violet or infra red radiation, both of which are harmful to the eye. Yellow or red filters may be used to see distant objects on hazy days because they absorb the short wavelengths scattered by the haze.

Most filters that remove the infra red component of the transmitted radiation do so by absorbing these wavelengths. As many common light sources have most of their energy in the infra red, this means that the filter will absorb much of the incident energy and will consequently become hot. If such a filter is mounted in a projection machine, it can easily absorb sufficient heat to cause breakage. Thus means should be provided for cooling such a filter.

Neutral density filters, *i.e.*, filters with flat transmission curves, are very difficult to obtain, most smoked glasses exhibiting absorption in some part of the spectrum. A fogged photographic plate is fairly useful for this purpose. A wire screen is most excellent provided that care is taken to control the light scattered by the wires.

The quality of the surfaces on a filter inserted in any optical system should be comparable with the rest of the surfaces in the system; otherwise they will adversely affect the quality of the image.

## PLASTICS

Plastics are synthetic solid materials that may be used for mechanical or optical purposes. The various types of plastics have different characteristics, and each must be considered individually. However, a few pertinent generalizations can be made, although these apply only to the *present* state of a field that is changing with amazing rapidity.

Plastics belong to two general groups: thermoplastic materials and thermosetting materials. *Thermoplastic materials* become fluid, or semi-fluid, in a certain temperature range and can thus be molded. If the molded article is again raised to the requisite temperature, it can be re-molded. *Thermosetting materials,* on the other hand, are usually loaded into a mold in powder form. When the temperature is increased, this powder fuses into a solid. The article is kept at the elevated temperature for a short time (this is known as *curing*) while a non-reversible chemical reaction occurs; it is then cooled and removed from the mold. If this article is again raised to the critical temperature, no further change will occur, for the original curing process changed the chemical structure of the original molding powder and thus changed its properties. The reaction is thus irreversible.

Generally speaking, it is not advisable to use plastics for important mechanical parts (other than knobs and such items) in precision optical instruments. Nearly all plastics absorb water from the atmosphere and, for this reason, undergo dimensional changes as the moisture content of the air varies. This is obviously highly undesirable when it is desired to define the position of optical elements with great precision. Then, too, all plastics show a tendency to change dimension when placed under any mechanical stress, this property being called *cold flow*. This characteristic is also objectionable in optical instruments. A further objection, applying particularly to thermoplastic materials, is the fact that many such materials begin to soften at temperatures that may be reached in the tropics. Thus the possibilities of plastics for use in the important mechanical parts of optical instruments are not at present particularly encouraging.

Plastics suitable for use in optical elements, such as lenses and prisms, are mostly of the thermoplastic class, and the various objections (distortion under heat, dimensional change caused by humidity, etc.) to the use of such materials for mechanical parts apply to some degree to their application to optical uses. In addition, some plastics exhibit a phenomenon known as *haze*, which is a scattering of light produced by the presence in the base material of colloidal particles of a different index. It results in a loss in contrast in the image of any object viewed through the material. The precautions taken to insure homogeneity in plastics are generally not comparable with those taken in the manufacture of optical glass, and plastics thus exhibit many optical defects, striae being pronounced. A further objection to the use of plastics in optical elements arises from the fact that many of these materials have large thermal expansion coefficients. When given a surface of optical quality by normal polishing processes, the temperature of these materials rises because of the friction involved. When the plastic lenses are removed from the polishing machine and are permitted to cool, the resulting dimensional changes destroy the shape of the surface. This effect might, however, be overcome. Finally, no plastics have a surface hardness comparable with that of glass. Plastic lenses are therefore not durable but are easily scratched, as by injudicious cleaning. The picture presented here is not very encouraging. However, the plastics industry has grown so rapidly that it has spent little time on optical problems, and it is quite possible that many or all of the above-mentioned objections will be overcome when such research is performed. Indeed there is strong indication that this stage has been reached.

Plastics are finding certain limited uses in lens systems. In one small sound motion-picture machine, cylindrical plastic lenses are used in the sound reproduction system. Plastic lenses are also finding an ever-increasing field of application in goggles for civilian and military uses, their high impact strength rendering them preferable to glass for this purpose. Undoubtedly optical instruments with plastic lenses and mechanical parts will be developed during the present conflict, and ample opportunity for judging their value will be offered.

Plastics are now being successfully used to cement lenses. Certain methacrylates are well suited to this application.

Plastic color filters are useful under conditions where the highest optical requirements need not be met. Plastic filters have two advantages over glass: they have higher impact strength and they can be colored with dyes and thus furnished with a wider range of transmission characteristics.  It is possible so to treat some plastics that they will transmit the visible spectrum unimpaired but are entirely opaque to ultra violet.  If high ultra violet transmission is desired, several thermoplastic materials having this property are available.

Having dealt with these general considerations, let us consider a few specific plastics.

*Phenol-formaldehyde Compounds* (Examples: Bakelite, Catalin). These thermosetting materials are commonly furnished with some type of wood flour or mineral filler for economic reasons, and these fillers render the material opaque.  When obtained without fillers, these compounds can be used to make transparent or translucent objects, but their general optical properties are not good.  Their water absorption is fairly low, being about 0.1 to 0.2 per cent for the base material.  They have no specific softening point but begin to distort at temperatures of about 240 to 250°F.  Their impact strength is low, *i.e.*, they are brittle. Their machining properties are fairly good.

*Urea-formaldehyde Compounds* (Examples: Beetle, Plaskon). These again are thermosetting compounds.  They are normally furnished with an alpha cellulose filler and are consequently translucent.  For this reason their optical uses are restricted to such applications as diffusing screens, lamp shades, etc. Although these materials do not distort until temperatures of about 260°F are reached, they will resist continuous temperatures no higher than 160°F.  They have quite high water absorptions and are thus subject to dimensional changes caused by humidity variations.  They are among the heaviest of the plastics, having a specific gravity of about 1.5.  Their impact strength is very low.  They have fair machining properties.

*Vinyl Resins* (Example: Vinylite).  These materials can be supplied in a transparent form and have some optical possibilities. However they undergo distortion at a temperature of about 145°F and such a temperature is attainable if an object is left in the sun in the tropics.  They have fair impact strengths and quite low water absorptions.  They have good machining properties.  The refractive index of the transparent form of the material is 1.53.

*Methyl Methacrylate Resins* (Examples: Lucite, Plexiglas). These thermoplastic materials have very interesting optical properties for they are crystal clear, having transmissions as high as that of optical glass, 90 to 92 per cent. Unfortunately at temperatures around 150°F (or less) they begin to show distortion to heat. They have medium impact strength and medium water absorptions. Their refractive index is about 1.49. They offer the greatest optical possibilities of any of the common plastics. They are at present extensively used for transparent windshields, gun turrets, cockpit enclosures, etc., in aircraft. They have excellent machining properties and can thus be easily shaped by machining methods. Because of their high transmissions, these materials may be used to conduct light through long rods. This property is used in one motion-picture projector sound head in which a plastic rod is employed to conduct a light beam from the film to a photocell located adjacent to the first stage of amplification. The objectionable long high-impedence electrical connection between photocell and amplifier was thus avoided. Cylindrical lenses of the same material were used in the sound head. These materials transmit ultra violet radiations down to wavelengths of about 275 m$\mu$ and can thus be used for ultra violet work. They have very little tendency to scatter light and, for this reason, are particularly well suited to the aviation applications mentioned, as well as general optical uses.

*Polystyrene Resins* (Examples: Lustron, Styron). These thermoplastic materials also have rather interesting optical possibilities. They, too, have very high transmissions (90 to 92 per cent). They have zero water absorption characteristics, being unique among plastics in this respect. They begin to undergo distortion at temperatures of about 150 to 200°F. They are the lightest of the plastics, having a specific gravity of about 1.06. In common with the methacrylates they have medium impact strength. In weathering and machining properties they are inferior to the methacrylates but may displace them in some optical applications because of their superiority in other respects. Their refractive indices lie in the range 1.50 to 1.60. They may be easily recognized by their lightness and the metallic sound produced by flicking them with a fingernail.

*Cellulose Acetate Compounds* (Examples: Lumarith, Plasticele). These materials are used extensively for military and civilian goggles because of their high transmissions (90 to 92 per cent)

and very high impact strength.  Cellulose acetate itself is too
brittle to be of use for practical purposes, so it is combined with
about 30 to 40 per cent of various organic materials (called
*plasticizers*) to give it desirable physical properties.  By proper
selection of plasticizer many combinations of desirable mechanical
properties may be obtained.  These materials transmit ultra
violet light down to about 270 m$\mu$ (the exact value of the cutoff
depends on the plasticizer used), but, as has been proven by the
author, this ultra violet transmission can be eliminated by proper
treatment without affecting the transmission of the visible
portion of the spectrum.  Cellulose acetate plastics have several
adverse characteristics: high water absorption, a tendency to
distort at temperatures of 130 to 200°F, and a pronounced
amount of haze (enough to scatter several per cent of light).
They are used for cockpit housings and other aircraft enclosures
in competition with the methyl methacrylates and are also
employed for molded gas mask lenses, military goggles, etc.
Their refractive indices vary from 1.47 to 1.50.  They are
moderately heavy (sp. gr. about 1.3) but have very good machining properties.

*Cellulose Nitrate Compounds* (Examples: Celluloid, Pyralin).
These materials are similar in some respects to the acetates.
They, too, require plasticizers to make them usable practically,
and the most commonly employed material is camphor.  They
have less haze than the acetates and somewhat less water absorption, this depending on the plasticizer.  Their light transmission
properties are equally good.  Their impact strength is rather
high.  They soften at around 160 to 190°F and of course are
very inflammable.  Their machining properties are reasonably
good.  The fact that they have less water absorption than the
acetates has caused some manufacturers of light airplanes to
use them in preference to the acetates for windshields.  Their
lower cost is also a factor here.  The chief objection to their use
for this purpose is their tendency to discolor and "craze" (become
covered with fine cracks) under exposure to the sun.  Because
of their inflammability they are not generally molded, an exception to this being their use in a process known as *blow* molding
by which toys, ping-pong balls, etc. may be fabricated.  The
index of refraction of the nitrates is about 1.50.  Besides being
used in aircraft windshields, they are employed in goggles.

## MISCELLANEOUS MATERIALS

**Quartz.**—Most optical glasses do not transmit wavelengths shorter than about 300 m$\mu$. Instruments such as spectrographs designed for use at shorter wavelengths must thus have their optical elements constructed of some other material. If the instrument will not be used at wavelengths much shorter than 200 m$\mu$, quartz will be the material selected.

Quartz is a form of silicon dioxide. It is very hard and is thus very durable, although for the same reason it is more difficult to work optically than is glass. Although it is very widely distributed geographically, only a few localities are capable of furnishing quartz sufficiently flawless for optical use. Because of its scarcity and the difficulty experienced in working it, optical elements constructed of this material are much more expensive than similar elements made of glass.

Because crystal quartz is so scarce and because it occurs generally only in small pieces, several attempts have been made to prepare fused quartz of a grade satisfactory for optical use. This work has not yet met with the desired success for the material produced has contained many striae and bubbles. In addition, it has been found difficult to anneal the product, and the residual stresses are usually of far greater magnitude than would be tolerated in glass. Small pieces of fused quartz free of striae and bubbles can be prepared, but pieces of crystal quartz of the same size are available in quantity, so the fused quartz is of little advantage. If the various difficulties of manufacture can be overcome, there seems little doubt that fused quartz will find wide application. It is superior to natural quartz in that it is isotropic and does not give the various troubles with polarized light experienced with natural quartz that will be mentioned below. Then, too, its low coefficient of expansion would make it useful for condenser lenses to be used in motion-picture projectors, for such lenses when made of fused quartz would show less tendency to break because of thermal expansion than do similar elements made of glass. It is much softer than natural quartz and is therefore easier to work optically.

Natural quartz is crystalline in structure and has optical properties common to certain types of crystals. In the first place, it is *doubly refracting*, or *birefringent*. This means that a beam of unpolarized light incident on the quartz is broken up, inside the material, into two divergent beams, polarized perpendicularly to one another.    The index of refraction is different for these two beams.    Thus, if an object is viewed through such a birefringent material, two images are seen.    It is evident that this is a very serious drawback for optical purposes.    However, these birefringent materials have a certain direction, known as the *optic axis*, along which light may travel without breaking up into two polarized beams.    It is evident that if a lens were to be made of crystal quartz it would be necessary to locate the optic axis and let the axis of the lens lie parallel to it.    The birefringence of quartz is very small compared to that of Iceland spar (see page 109) and can be neglected in some cases.

The second adverse optical property of crystal quartz is its ability to rotate the plane of polarization of a beam of polarized light when the beam is traveling parallel to the optic axis.    A material that does this is termed *optically active*.    Because of this property, quartz elements have a tendency toward forming double images even when the light travels parallel to the optic axis.    Because of its high ultra violet transmission, quartz is used extensively in the construction of the optics of spectrographs, and this effect of forming a double image must be eliminated in such instruments.    This is done, in the construction of spectrograph prisms, by combining a piece of quartz that gives right-hand rotation to the beam (*dextrorotatory*) with a piece giving left-handed rotation (*levorotatory*).    Thus a 60° Cornu prism is made up of two 30° prisms of opposite rotations.    In Littrow-type spectrographs this difficulty is overcome by reflecting the beam traversing the prism straight back through the prism to the photographic plate.    The rotations occurring during the two passages through the prism compensate one another.

**Fluorite.**—Fluorite is a form of calcium fluoride, sometimes called *fluorspar* in its transparent form.    It is crystalline in structure, but, because its optical properties in all directions are the same, it acts as though it were isotropic and is thus not birefringent.    It transmits wave lengths nearly as short as 100 m$\mu$ and is thus used for work in the far ultra violet.    It is somewhat softer than glass and is thus more easily worked but less durable.    It is much more rare than quartz and is available only in very small pieces; thus fluorite optical elements are comparatively expensive. Because of its optical properties, it is ideally suited to achromatize quartz, and quartz-fluorite doublets could find many important applications. However, it is not available in sufficiently large pieces to make such lenses practical.[1] Its optical properties are such as to make it well suited to use with glass in the reduction of secondary spectrum, and it is widely used for this purpose in microscope objectives. The minute size of such objectives makes it practicable to construct lenses for them of the tiny available pieces of high quality fluorite. Microscopic objectives so constructed are called *semi-apochromats*.

**Calcite.**—Calcite is a natural form of calcium carbonate. It is very strongly birefringent, but it does not rotate the plane of polarization. Its strong birefrigence eliminates it as a possible material for the production of spectrograph prisms. However, this same birefringent property is used to advantage in the construction of polarizing prisms. In its transparent form it is known as *Iceland spar*.

**Canada Balsam.**—Canada balsam is obtained from the sap of the North American balsam fir. It is soluble in xylol. Its index of refraction varies from specimen to specimen, 1.54 being a typical value.

Achromats are commonly cemented with a stick of balsam. In this process the lenses are first carefully cleaned with ether and then placed on an electric hot plate covered with an asbestos pad. They are heated enough to evaporate all moisture on their surfaces, and a small amount of balsam is then applied with the balsam stick. The two elements are now placed in contact and are manipulated by sliding them over one another until all air trapped between them is removed. To center the elements, the doublet is now placed between V-blocks, but this technique is successful only when the two elements are of the same diameter and this is not always the case. The lenses are permitted to cool and the cement hardens, completing the operation.

**REFERENCES**

BELL: "The Making and Molding of Plastics," Hutchinson & Co., Ltd., London, 1936.

DELMONTE: "Plastics in Engineering," Penton Publishing Company, Cleveland, 1942.

[1] Rock salt is sometimes used to achromatize quartz.

"Dictionary of Applied Physics," Vol. IV, Macmillan & Company, Ltd., London, 1923. See articles on Optical Glass, Quartz, Light Filters, etc.

HARDY and PERRIN: "The Principles of Optics," McGraw-Hill Book Company, Inc., New York, 1932. (Optical materials.)

HOUWINK: "Chemie und Technologie der Kunstoffe," Akademische Verlagsgesellschaft m.b.H., Leipzig, 1939.

HOVESTADT: "Jena Glass" (trans. by J. D. and A. Everett), Macmillan & Company, Ltd., London, 1902.

KAUSCH: "Handbuch der künstlichen plastichen Massen," J. F. Lehmann, Munich, 1931.

MARTIN: "An Introduction to Applied Optics," Vol. I, Sir Isaac Pitman & Sons, Ltd., London, 1930. (Optical glass.)

SASSO: "Plastics for Industrial Use," McGraw-Hill Book Company, Inc., New York, 1942.

SIMONDS: "Industrial Plastics," Pitman Publishing Corporation, New York, 1941.

WOOD: "Physical Optics," The Macmillan Company, New York, 1934. (Glass, filters.)

"Wratten Light Filters," Eastman Kodak Co., Rochester, N. Y. (Filters.)

WRIGHT: "The Manufacture of Optical Glass and of Optical Systems," Ord. Dept. Doc. 2037, Government Printing Office, Washington, 1921. (Glass.)

## PROBLEMS

**1.** Refractometer measurements show a piece of borosilicate crown glass to have the following indices: $n_D = 1.5164$, $n_C = 1.51423$, $n_F = 1.52218$. What is the reciprocal dispersion of this glass? A piece of dense flint glass is found to have these indices: $n_D = 1.6465$, $n_C = 1.64095$, $n_F = 1.65999$. What is its constringence? Why are the $C$ and $F$ indices given to one more significant figure than the $D$ index?

**2.** Measurements made upon a certain filter of 1 mm thickness, when corrected for reflection loss, show it to have a transmittance of 80 per cent at 550 m$\mu$ and 20 per cent at 680 m$\mu$. Compute the transmittances at these wavelengths of filters 3 mm and 5 mm thick. What will be the colors of these filters?

# CHAPTER VII

## POLARIZED LIGHT

Light has the characteristics of a wave motion in which the waves vibrate in all possible planes perpendicular to the direction of propagation. Such waves are called *transverse*. It is possible to analyze these transverse wave motions into components along two axes perpendicular to each other and the direction of propagation. If one of these components is removed, the remaining component is called *plane-polarized light*. The *plane of vibration* is taken as the plane parallel to the direction in which this component exists. The plane containing the incident and reflected beams is called the *plane of polarization*, this being perpendicular to the plane of vibration.

A simple method of obtaining polarized light is by reflection from a plate of glass set at such an angle that the incident and refracted beams are perpendicular. This property is expressed in *Brewster's law*, and another way of stating it is to say that for complete polarization of the reflected beam the angle of incidence must equal the arc tangent of the index of refraction of the glass, or

$$I = \text{arc tan } n \tag{56}$$

where $I$ is the required incidence angle for total polarization and $n$ is the index of refraction of the glass. For ordinary glass the angle $I$ is about 57°. As the amount of light reflected at this angle is small, it is customary to use a pile of glass plates when attempting to polarize light with this technique.

When a ray of unpolarized light is incident normally on certain anisotropic crystals, as shown in Fig. 63, it is broken up within the crystal into two components. One obeys the ordinary laws of refraction and is undeviated. This is called the *ordinary ray*. This ray has a constant velocity regardless of the direction in the crystal in which it is traveling. The other ray is generally deviated and thus does not obey Snell's law. This is designated the *extraordinary ray*. Its velocity varies with the direction of

111

propagation in the crystal; in a certain direction, known as the *optic axis*, its velocity equals that of the ordinary ray. In *positive crystals* the velocity of the extraordinary ray is, for directions other than that of the optic axis, greater than that of the ordinary ray; for *negative crystals*, the reverse holds.

The types of crystal used most extensively in optical instruments for the production of polarized light, such as calcite, have a single optic axis and are thus called *uniaxial* crystals. Many

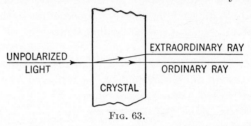

Fig. 63.

other crystals have two optic axes and are accordingly called *biaxial*.

The ordinary and extraordinary rays are polarized in planes perpendicular to each other. Crystals that produce polarized light in this fashion are known as *birefringent*, or *doubly refracting*. It is obvious that if one of the beams could be removed, leaving only the other, the crystal could be used as a source of plane-polarized light. Tourmaline is birefringent and has the additional unusual property of absorbing the ordinary ray, if the

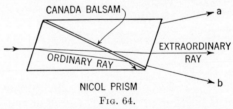

Fig. 64.

crystal is more than 2 mm thick, and transmitting the extraordinary ray almost undiminished in intensity. However, the absorption is not uniform for all wavelengths, and the emergent beam is thus rather strongly colored.

Calcite is strongly birefringent and is widely used for the production of polarized light. It is possible to cement together two pieces of calcite with Canada balsam in such a way that one of the beams (the extraordinary ray) passes through the crystal while the other (the ordinary ray) is reflected off to the side into an absorbing layer of black paint (Fig. 64). The beam that gets through is of course polarized. The device has thus produced polarized light by the removal of one of the components of the original beam. Such a device is known as a *Nicol prism*. The field of one of these prisms, *i.e.*, the angle between rays *a* and *b* in Fig. 64, is rather small (24°) and is unsymmetrical about a line through the center of the prism.

These Nicol prisms have been modified in various ways to make the field symmetrical or reduce the amount of calcite

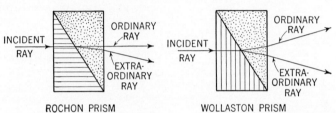

ROCHON PRISM                    WOLLASTON PRISM

Fig. 65.—Two popular forms of polarizing prisms. The crosshatching indicates the directions of the optic axes of the two calcite components of each prism.

required. The *Glan-Thompson*, which resembles the Nicol in appearance except for the fact that the end faces are square and perpendicular to the sides, is the most popular variation in present use. It has a much wider field (40°) than the Nicol. The Glan-Thompson and various other polarizing prisms are commonly called *Nicols*. The various modifications of the Nicol are more expensive than the original form because of manufacturing difficulties.

These prisms all transmit about 25 to 40 per cent of the incident light.

The face of a Nicol prism, being inclined to the incident beam, can reflect a suitably oriented polarized component of that beam. This can cause error in photometric equipment in which such prisms are used. Errors of this sort can be reduced by coating the faces of the Nicol by means of the techniques described in Chap. VIII.

The above-described prisms transmit only one of the two polarized components. It is occasionally desirable, as in the design of photometric or spectrophotometric apparatus, to use both beams and have the polarizing prism separate them. Two pieces of calcite may be cemented to form a prism in which one of the polarized beams is transmitted undeviated and the other is deviated, this being known as a *Rochon prism*. It is also possible to cement the two pieces of calcite to make a prism in which the two emergent (mutually perpendicularly polarized) beams are deviated (nearly) equal and opposite amounts. This device is called a *Wollaston prism*. Because the emergent beams are deviated symmetrically, it is more popular than the Rochon. These two prisms are shown in Fig. 65.

If a beam of light is passed through a Nicol prism, the emergent component will be polarized. If this component is passed through a second Nicol, the emergent beam passes through

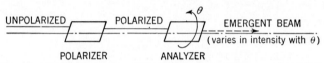

Fig. 66.—Two Nicol prisms arranged to give a beam of (plane-polarized) light of continuously variable intensity.

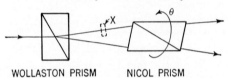

Fig. 67.—Simplified schematic diagram of a *Martens photometer*. Certain extra glass optical elements to make the device convenient to use have been omitted.

maxima and minima as the second prism is rotated about its longest axis. Thus such a setup (shown in Fig. 66) may be used to obtain a continuous change in light intensity. When the prisms are so aligned that no light emerges from the second, they are said to be *crossed*. If the second prism is now rotated 90°, the emergent beam will have maximum intensity and the polarization planes of the two prisms are said to be *parallel*. It is evident that the intensity of the emergent beam is a function of the angle $\theta$ between the two polarization planes. If $I_0$ is the intensity with the two polarization planes parallel, the intensity $I$ at any angle $\theta$ (neglecting reflection and absorption losses) is given by

$$I = I_0 \cos^2 \theta \qquad (57)$$

In *polarization photometers* of the *Martens* type, two mutually perpendicularly polarized beams are produced by a Wollaston prism and are passed parallel to one another through a Nicol prism, as shown schematically in Fig. 67. As the Nicol is rotated, both beams will vary in intensity, and these intensities will be equal when the Nicol is set at an angle of 45° to the planes of polarization. If an object $X$ whose transmission is to be measured is inserted in one of the beams, the intensity of this beam will be decreased relative to the other and the Nicol will have to be rotated to make the two intensities equal again, the angle of the Nicol being $\theta_1$. If the object is now transferred to the other beam, the Nicol must again be rotated to balance the two beams in intensity, and its angle is now $\theta_2$. In making these settings one balance point will always be found at an angle greater than 45°; the other, at an angle less than 45°. The term $\theta_1$ refers to the angle greater than 45°, and $\theta_2$ to the other. From these data the transmission of the unknown is easily computed by use of the formula

$$T = \cot \theta_1 \tan \theta_2 \qquad (58)$$

This type of photometer finds wide application in photometry and spectrophotometry. It was stated in Chap. VI that glass in a state of strain is birefringent and optically active. Thus if any of the optical elements in a polarization photometer should be strained, they will introduce polarization errors.

It is well known that there are now various types of polarizing films available for the production of polarized light.[1] These are not, generally speaking, as efficient as Nicols, for they transmit less light. In addition, they transmit some light even when crossed, while crossed Nicols are quite opaque. However, they can accommodate beams of much greater cross-sectional area than Nicols and can also accommodate fields of much greater angular extent. They are in addition much less costly than Nicols. These polarizing films are generally opaque to the violet and ultra violet; some of them transmit red and infra red light without polarizing it. The Nicol, however, is equally effective at all wavelengths. Two Nicols can be crossed so effectively that no light whatever is transmitted, but this adjustment must be made very carefully.

Polarized light is used for various photometric purposes, the Martens photometer already described being a typical example. This type of photometer may be used to measure the visible light transmission of pieces of glass, or of glass filters, or even of com-

[1] See, for example, Grabau, *J. Optical Soc. Am.*, Vol. 27, p. 420, 1937.

plete optical instruments.[1]    It is also used to measure the density of photographic images.

If a piece of strain-free glass is placed between two crossed Nicols, no light will be seen through the instrument because the incident light is polarized by the first Nicol and is thus completely blocked out by the second.   However, if the glass is stressed, it will be birefringent, and the birefringence will be a function of the stresses involved.   The birefringence results in light being transmitted through the second Nicol.   Thus the stressed areas of the glass can be seen.   In this way strain in glass is detected.[2] It is possible to make a model of an engineering structure, (such as a bridge) out of a transparent material (such as a plastic) and hang weights on it to simulate various loading conditions. By studying the stressed model in polarized light the parts of the structure that become heavily stressed under load are indicated by the polarization patterns.

A scientifically sound method of producing three-dimensional motion pictures is to take two pictures of an object by means of two cameras, these being spaced in a fashion similar to the eyes of an observer.   Two projectors throw the images on the screen.   In order that the picture that was taken by the right-hand camera might be permitted to reach only the right eye of the observer the light from the right-hand projector can be vertically polarized, and this light can be directed to the observer's right eye provided that it is covered with a piece of polarizing material with its polarization plane vertical.   If the left eye is covered with a disk of horizontal polarizing material, no light from the right projector can reach it.   If the left projector projects images in light that is horizontally polarized, light from this projector will reach the left eye only.   Thus each eye sees a slightly different image.   In this way perspective may be obtained.   According to a recent announcement there has now been developed a technique for recording the two images on a single film, and incorporated in the film are means for properly

---

[1] For information on light-transmission measurements see McRae, *J. Optical Soc. Am.*, Vol. 33, p. 229, 1943.

[2] By use of this technique the author was able to trace an error in the annealing procedure employed in a radio-tube plant.   An average breakage of over 1.5 per cent of the total production of tubes that resulted from improper annealing was reduced to less than 0.1 per cent.

polarizing the light through the two images. Thus, only a single projector is required. It is even claimed that sufficient images to give a three-dimensional color picture have been recorded on a single film.

Because light specularly reflected from glossy surfaces such as wet pavements or automobile hoods is partly polarized, goggles containing polarizing materials so oriented that their vibration plane is vertical will eliminate such glare. Some sky light is partially polarized, and thus, sky glare may sometimes be reduced to some extent by such goggles. In a similar fashion, polarizing materials may be used for eliminating polarized glare in photography.

Two polarizing materials (either Nicols or films) may be arranged as in Fig. 67 so that rotation of one gives a means of controlling intensity continuously. Two polarizing films may be used and may be placed in contact, thus giving a light and compact method of varying illumination. Such a device is being used to control the brightness of dashboard lights in military aircraft, for it is much ligher than the bulky rheostat normally used.

### REFERENCES

"Dictionary of Applied Physics," Vol. IV, Macmillan & Company, Ltd., London, 1923. Article on Polarized Light.

DRUDE: "Theory of Optics," Longmans, Green and Company, New York, 1902.

FÖRSTERLING: "Lehrbuch der Optik," S. Hirzel, Leipzig, 1928.

HARDY and PERRIN: "The Principles of Optics," McGraw-Hill Book Company, Inc., New York, 1932.

MARTIN: "An Introduction to Applied Optics," Vol. I, Sir Isaac Pitman & Sons, Ltd., London, 1930.

SCHUSTER: "Theory of Optics," Longmans, Green and Company, New York, 1924.

WOOD: "Physical Optics," The Macmillan Company, New York, 1934.

### PROBLEMS

**1.** You wish to produce a beam of polarized light by reflecting an unpolarized beam from a piece of glass of index 1.523. At what angle to the beam would you place the glass plate?

**2.** Two Nicol prisms are crossed so that no light passes through them. One is then rotated 20° with respect to the other. Express the intensity of transmitted light as a fraction of the intensity when the Nicols have their polarization planes parallel.

# CHAPTER VIII
## LOW-REFLECTANCE LENS COATINGS

It is a general physical property of transparent materials that, when a beam of light passes through a boundary of two media having different indices of refraction, a certain percentage of light will be reflected back by this interface instead of passing through. The phenomenon is known as *Fresnel reflection*. In order to find the amount of light reflected in any specific case it is necessary to determine the angle of incidence $I$ and then, by application of Snell's law, to determine the angle of refraction $I'$. With these data it is possible to calculate the intensity of light reflected (expressed as a fraction of the incident light) from the following equations, derived by Fresnel:

$$R = \frac{\sin^2 (I - I')}{2 \sin^2 (I + I')} + \frac{\tan^2 (I - I')}{2 \tan^2 (I + I')} \tag{59}$$

where $R$ is the *reflectance*.

For the special case of normal incidence at a glass-air interface, the amount of reflection (reflectance) is expressed by

$$R = \frac{(n - 1)^2}{(n + 1)^2} \tag{60}$$

Equations (59) and (60) refer to intensity, which is the square of the amplitude of the light waves.

In the case of a single glass-air interface $R$ (for glass of $n = 1.5$) is 0.04, and thus 4 per cent of the incident light is reflected at the surface. A lens or glass plate has two glass-air surfaces, and thus slightly less than 8 per cent of the incident light is lost through reflection. There is of course also some loss through absorption in the glass, which is generally negligible. In a cemented lens the reflection loss at the cemented surface is usually very small because of the small index difference.

Because of the fact that there are a large number of glass-air surfaces in photographic objectives and instruments such as rangefinders, gun sights, bombsights, and periscopes, it is evident that a marked loss in transmission must result through reflection. In a typical rifle telescope sight the over-all transmission is not greater than 40 per cent, the other 60 per cent being reflection loss. Because the human eye and photographic plates respond more or less logarithmically to illumination, losses of even 60 per cent are not very serious under average conditions. Under twilight conditions a loss of this magnitude might of course be quite harmful. One of the chief objections to reflection loss is that the light thus lost is reflected from other surfaces in the system, and much of this light eventually gets into the image where it causes loss of detail and contrast. If the illumination is particularly intense, this light can cause ghost images. This phenomenon is often noticed in motion pictures when a flashlight is directed into the camera lens. Several images of the flashlight bulb can be seen on the screen. Photographers who have occasion to take pictures with their cameras pointing at the sun often obtain distressing results because of reflected light.

Although light reflection had been a source of annoyance for many years, it was not until 1892 that a first hint was received as to the way the reflection might be reduced. In that year the famous British lens designer, H. Dennis Taylor, made a study of tarnished lenses and found to his astonishment that they transmitted *more* light than clear ones! Evidently the tarnish in some way reduced reflection. He set about finding ways of artificially tarnishing lenses and found that this could be accomplished[1] by immersing them in an aqueous solution of ammonia and hydrogen sulphide. This work was followed by other developments along the same lines by Kellner, Kollmorgen,[2] Wright,[3] and others. The explanation for the effect was published by Dr. Katherine Blodgett,[4] and more data were contributed by C. H. Cartwright and A. F. Turner.[5]

Consider Fig. 68. Let $B$ be a block of glass coated with a thin layer $A$ of material of lower index than the glass. At surface 1 there will be a certain amount of light reflected back

[1] "The Adjustment and Testing of Telescope Objectives," Cooke, York, England, 1896.

[2] *Trans. Ill. Eng. Soc.*, Vol. 2, pp. 220–234, 1916.

[3] *Ord. Dept. Doc.* 2037, Government Printing Office, Washington, 1921.

[4] Reflection of Light from Glass, *Phys. Rev.*, Vol. 55, p. 391, 1939.

[5] U.S. Patent 2207656.

toward the light source.   Because there is also an index difference at surface 2, there will similarly be reflection at this interface.   Now assume that we have selected the index of refraction of the material comprising the coating $A$ so that equal
amounts of light are reflected at surfaces 1 and 2.   As we increase
the thickness of this coating, the two reflected components,
being wave motions, will be alternately in and out of phase.
Suppose we select this thickness so that the two components are
out of phase.   Then they will cancel
one another by destructive interference.
The energy cannot be destroyed.   It
actually appears in the transmitted
beam as an increase in transmission.

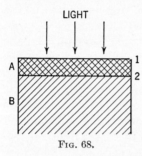

FIG. 68.

It has been found that to give equal
reflectances at the two surfaces the coating must have an index of refraction
that is the geometrical mean of that of
the air and the glass.   Thus, if we let
$n_g$ be the index of the glass and $n_a$ that of the air, the index $n_c$
of the coating is given by

$$n_c = \sqrt{n_g n_a} \tag{61}$$

We may take $n_a$ as unity, and then $n_c$ will be seen to be the square
root of the index of the glass.

The critical thickness for the coating that will give destructive
interference is one quarter of a wavelength of the light used
(the reflected beam travels through the coating twice, giving a
path difference of one-half wavelength), or any odd integral
number of quarter wavelengths.   Of course the thickness can
be made correct for just one wavelength, and there will be
some reflection at adjacent wavelengths.   If the coating thickness is taken as one quarter wavelength, the reflectance at wavelengths adjacent to that for which correction was obtained will
be found very small.   If the reflectance is made zero near the
center of the visible spectrum, the reflectance at the two ends will
be about 0.6 per cent.   If the coating is made some odd *multiple*
of one-fourth wavelength in thickness, the reflectance will still
be zero at the wavelength of correction, but it will be appreciably
greater at adjacent wavelengths.   For this reason, the coating
should only be made one quarter wavelength thick.   If a single

surface of an instrument intended for visual use were being coated, the wavelength chosen for complete correction would of course be at the center of the visible spectrum, at about 555 m$\mu$. If several surfaces were being coated, it would be possible to place the zero-reflectance wavelength of each at a different point in the visible spectrum; in this case the emergent light would be achromatic. Lenses that have been treated to give zero reflectance at the center of the visible spectrum can be easily detected in reflected light. These lenses will of course show no reflection in the green portion of the spectrum but will reflect some light at the ends of the spectrum, in the red and blue. Thus the reflected light will be purple. This purplish cast in reflected light is the easiest way of detecting a coated lens. If the coating is one-fourth wavelength in thickness, its color will be a light purple. If the coating is three or more quarters of a wavelength thick, the purple will be correspondingly darker. If the reflectance is made zero at too short a wavelength, the coating will appear reddish; if at too long a wavelength, the coating will be bluish.

Summing up, then, we see that the reflectance at a glass-air interface can be substantially reduced, and the transmission of this surface substantially increased, by coating the surface with a material having an index of refraction equal to the square root of the index of the glass. The coating should be some odd multiple of $\lambda/4$ in thickness and preferably should be $\lambda/4$ units thick. This means that for coating a piece of optical glass the coating should have an index of about 1.24 and a thickness of about 0.000014 cm. It is very difficult to find a material of the proper index. When a material has been found, it is necessary to work out a technique with which accurately to control the application of a thickness of the magnitude given. Considerable ingenuity has been utilized in solving these problems, and three general techniques have been developed.

One was developed by Dr. Katherine Blodgett, who applied very thin coatings of organic substances to the glass by a dipping process. She repeatedly dipped the glass in the coating material until a layer of the desired thickness had been formed. Monochromatic light was reflected from the surface being coated, and the thickness of the coating was increased until no more light was reflected. Since the organic materials applied to the glass by each dipping had too high an index to be useful, certain components of the coating were dissolved out, after application to the glass, leaving a low index film. The materials used were barium stearate and cadmium arachidate. Although excellent control over light reflection is possible by means of this process, it has two drawbacks, which have thus far barred it from practical application. The first is that each lens must be coated individually, and the process requires very careful control. It is therefore not a production process. Second, these organic films are not hard but may be removed from the glass by wiping. For this reason, too, the method is at present eliminated from consideration for practical application.

Another method is a direct development of the work by Taylor, Kollmorgen, and Wright already described, *i.e.*, it is an artificial tarnishing process.

Most optical glass is composed of a large percentage of silicon dioxide (silica), the residuum being oxides of lead, barium, zinc, calcium, sodium, potassium, and other metals. The method consists, in brief, of dissolving out of the glass the metallic oxides in a thin layer near the surface, leaving in this layer only a porous structure of silica. It is believed that air enters the cavities left by the removed oxides and thus lowers the average index of refraction of the layer. In this way a thin layer of material of reduced index of refraction is formed on the surface of the glass. The chemical used to dissolve out the oxides should be chosen from a consideration of the properties of the glass being treated. Dilute solutions[1] of any of the common strong acids[2] may be used, nitric acid being the most popular. For certain glasses, such as dense barium crowns, weaker acids, such as phosphoric or boric, are employed. Some glasses, like soda-lime-silica crowns, resist the action of the acids, and a long time is required to form the film. The fact that different types of glasses require different treatments, and some resist treatment, is something of a disadvantage.

The same ingredients of the glass that are removed through the action of acids are also dissolved out, at a slower rate, by water.

[1] JONES, Some Properties of Polished Glass Surfaces, *J. Soc. Motion Picture Engrs.*, Vol. 37, p. 256, 1941.

JONES and HOMER, Chemical Methods for Increasing the Transparency of Glass Surfaces, *J. Optical Soc. Am.*, Vol. 31, p. 34, 1941.

[2] A recently developed variation of this technique involves the exposure of the surface to be treated to hydrofluoric acid fumes (Nicoll, *R.C.A. Review*, Vol. 6, p. 287, 1942).

This results in the dimming of glass surfaces in the tropics and in the tarnishing of lead and barium glasses. With the foregoing in mind, it is quite evident why Taylor, back in 1892, found that tarnished lenses had higher transmissions than clean ones, for the tarnish was merely the same surface film that is now used to reduce reflection. The color of the tarnish is of course caused by interference. It is evident that the presence of such a tarnish is not particularly objectionable, provided it is not associated with corrosion or pitting of the surface. Surface haze, of the type formed in the tropics, results from a different chemical reaction. This haze can easily be wiped from the glass when it is first formed, and this should always be done because surface pitting may result from the continued presence of the haze. The dense barium crowns are particularly susceptible to this formation, while the borosilicate crowns resist it well.

Laboratory tests have been developed that show the tendencies of various types of glass to form the type of tarnish associated with low-reflection films and to undergo dimming in the tropics. Results of such tests are given in Table II, where the glasses are rated from 1 to 5, those in class 1 being very resistant and those in class 5 being easily affected.

The fact that water has a dissolving action on some components of the glass means that when a lens has been treated by the acid process to form a film of low-index material one quarter of a wavelength in thickness, exposure of the lens to the elements will result in a gradual increase in the thickness of the low-index layer. This is objectionable for two reasons. First, as we have already seen, one quarter of a wavelength is the optimum thickness for reduction of reflection, and an increase in thickness will result in a decrease in transmission. Second, if too thick a layer of silica is formed, it is possible that this layer will crack away from the underlying glass because of shrinkage. Thus it is necessary to guard against the possibility of atmospheric moisture attacking the glass. The necessary protection is obtained by heating the glass immediately after the formation of the silica layer to densify the silica. This greatly reduces the rate at which water attacks the glass.

Every time a thin layer of moisture is left on a lens by a finger or by other means a thin silica film is formed. Thus the surface of any lens is covered with an irregular silica film. If an attempt

TABLE II*

| Type of glass | Refractive index | $\nu$-value | Dimming test | Tarnish test |
|---|---|---|---|---|
| Borosilicate crown | 1.511 | 63 | 1 | 1 |
| | 1.516 | 64 | 1.5 | 1 |
| | 1.516 | 64 | 1 | 1 |
| | 1.517 | 64 | 1 | 1 |
| | 1.518 | 64 | 1.5 | 1 |
| Crown | 1.523 | 59 | 1.5 | 1 |
| | 1.512 | 60 | 1.5 | 1 |
| Light barium crown | 1.572 | 57 | 2 | 3 |
| | 1.572 | 57 | 2 | 4 |
| | 1.573 | 57 | 1.5 | 3 |
| | 1.574 | 57 | 1 | 1 |
| Dense barium crown | 1.608 | 59 | 3.5 | 5 |
| | 1.609 | 59 | 3 | 5 |
| | 1.611 | 59 | 3 | 5 |
| | 1.611 | 60 | 3 | 5 |
| | 1.610 | 57 | 1 | 4.5 |
| | 1.611 | 57 | 2 | 5 |
| | 1.611 | 59 | 3 | 5 |
| | 1.612 | 57 | 2 | 5 |
| Crown flint | 1.526 | 51 | 3 | 1 |
| | 1.528 | 52 | 1 | 1 |
| | 1.528 | 52 | 1 | 1 |
| | 1.529 | 52 | 1 | 1 |
| Barium flint | 1.581 | 46 | 1.5 | 3 |
| | 1.583 | 47 | 1 | 1 |
| | 1.584 | 46 | 1 | 1 |
| | 1.588 | 46 | 2 | 2.5 |
| | 1.605 | 44 | 2 | 2 |
| Extra dense flint | 1.717 | 29 | 3 | 3 |
| | 1.717 | 29 | 2 | 3.5 |
| | 1.720 | 29 | 1.5 | 3 |
| | 1.721 | 29 | 2 | 5 |
| | 1.648 | 34 | 3 | 2 |
| | 1.649 | 34 | 2 | 2 |
| | 1.650 | 34 | 2 | 2 |
| | 1.650 | 34 | 2 | 2 |

* JONES, Some Properties of Polished Glass Surfaces, *J. Soc. Motion Picture Engrs.*, Vol. 37, p. 260, 1941.

were made to form a low-reflectance layer on such a lens by the acid process, the results would be apt to be disappointing, for the irregular silica layer would cause the acid to affect differently various areas on the lens surface. It is, therefore, necessary to apply these low-reflectance treatments to lenses immediately after they are polished. If the glass has been polished just sufficiently well to remove all visible scratches but not well enough to remove the invisible ones, the small invisible scratches will be made visible by the acid process. Thus lenses to be treated in this way should be polished for a longer time than ordinary lenses.

The increase in transmission to be obtained by this acid technique is not so great as may be obtained from the fluoride process, to be described. A light barium crown glass of an index of 1.57 normally has a transmission of about 90 per cent; when treated, the transmission is increased to 95.5 per cent. As a general rule the reflection loss is reduced to about 20 per cent of its original value by the acid process when high-index glasses are treated; it is reduced only to about 75 per cent of its initial value with low-index glasses. Thus a borosilicate crown of 1.52 index would have its transmission increased from 92 to 95 per cent upon being treated.

A third process of applying low-reflectance coatings to glass is the evaporation onto the glass, in a vacuum, of metallic salts of low refractive index. The first work in this direction was undertaken by Strong[1] who used calcium fluoride as the coating material. He realized that, if he could vary the index of the coating material so that it was equal to that of the glass at the glass-fluoride interface and then progressively decrease it to equal that of the air at the air-fluoride interface, he would obtain zero reflectance at all wavelengths. He was not able to vary the index in the desired fashion but nevertheless obtained marked decreases in reflection. The significance of thickness was appreciated by Cartwright and Turner,[2] who were able to obtain transmissions for a glass plate (two surfaces) of up to 99.6 per cent.

Calcium fluoride films of the type applied by Strong have an index of refraction of about 1.22. This gives quite large reduc-

[1] *J. Optical Soc. Am.*, Vol. 26, p. 73, 1936.
[2] *Phys. Rev.*, Vol. 55, p. 391, 1939.

tions in reflection, and transmissions of 99 per cent with samples coated with this fluoride are common. However, these films do not resist abrasion well and are easily scratched. They are not soluble in water.

Sodium fluoride was one of the materials applied by Cartwright and Turner. This material has an index of about 1.29. It does not give quite so high a reduction in reflection as the previously mentioned substance, the transmission of a glass plate treated with it being about 98 per cent. The material gives tougher films than does $CaF_2$, but they can be removed by rubbing with a cloth.

Lithium fluoride produces films that have considerable abrasion resistance. They also give about 98 per cent transmission on glass plates. However, they are soluble in cold water.

Various other substances, such as magnesium fluoride and cryolite (sodium aluminum fluoride), have been applied successfully. As each of these has its own optical and mechanical properties, the individual intending to have a lens coated should be sure that the material applied to his lens will give the desired properties. As has been indicated, some of the coating materials have poor mechanical properties. Others are soluble either in plain or salt water. Some fog readily in humid atmospheres. Generally speaking, magnesium fluoride appears to be the most suitable material for use on exposed surfaces.

One method of obtaining good mechanical properties is suggested by Cartwright and Turner in U.S. Patent 2207656. They evaporated a film of a metallic fluoride just a little less than one quarter of a wavelength thick onto glass and then evaporated over this a very thin protective layer of zircon or quartz. They also found that the ruggedness of a layer of a metallic fluoride could be increased by precoating the glass with a very thin layer of chromium and then permitting air to oxidize the metal and form a transparent oxide. The fluoride coating was found to adhere strongly to this layer.

The utility of this fluoride treatment for any particular application can be determined only after a study is made of the requirements involved. For some applications it will be found economically justified; for others, the reverse will hold. Some sound recording systems,[1] for example, were treated. These con-

---

[1] MILLER, *J. Soc. Motion Picture Engrs.*, Vol. 37, p. 265, 1941.

tained 10 glass-air surfaces. Gains in transmission of 50 per cent were obtained. This proved useful because the recording lamps could be run at lower voltage, and appreciable increases in lamp life resulted. The gain in transmission has also been used to make possible the employment of slower, finer grained films, and an increase in recording quality was thereby obtained.

Camera lenses have been treated with some success. In one specific case an $f/2.0$ motion-picture lens of 3-in. focus had a transmission of 69.5 per cent. The lens was treated and the transmission was thus increased to 95.1 per cent. The reflection loss was thus reduced from 30.5 to 4.9 per cent. A pronounced increase of contrast and brilliance of picture also results from this treatment and flare is greatly reduced.

Treated lenses are also being used successfully in projection systems, and increases in screen illumination of 30 per cent have been attained. One of the most important results of this treatment when applied to photographic objectives is the decrease in flare, *i.e.*, the ghost images of a bright source of light near the optical axis of the objective. As has been previously mentioned, this is caused by multiple reflections from lens surfaces. It is possible to take pictures directly toward bright light sources with treated lenses without being disturbed by flare. Undesired light (flare) can reach a photographic image in several ways: by Fresnel reflection of the type considered above, by scattering from finger marks, etc., on the surface of a lens, and by reflection from lens cells, shutter, diaphragms, and bellows or camera walls. The application of a low-reflectance coating to a lens can exert control only over the first of these. However, this is the only type of flare that results in the formation of ghost images; the others merely cause loss of contrast because light is scattered generally over the image. The formation of ghost images has been studied by Goldberg[1] and reported in English by Mees.[2] In this book we shall restrict our definition of flare to include only the light undergoing Fresnel reflection.

The use of treated lenses in instruments intended for visual use is still the subject of considerable controversy. Because of

---

[1] GOLDBERG, *Der Aufbau des photographischen Bildes*, p. 81, W. Knapp, Halle, 1922.

[2] MEES, *Theory of the Photographic Process*, The Macmillan Company, New York, 1942.

the various physiological considerations previously mentioned, changes of 40 or 50 per cent in the illumination on the eye are not of great significance, and it is thus felt in some circles that the increase in the efficiency of an instrument that would result from this treatment is not worth the expenditure of time and money involved. People holding this view claim that the usefulness of the coating is apparent only when an object is viewed through an instrument under twilight conditions, and twilight occupies such a small portion of the day that the treatment is not justified. Others claim that, particularly with military instruments, viewing must often be accomplished under conditions of poor visibility, and that for instruments intended for such use treatment of lenses is essential. The whole question is further complicated during the present emergency by the fact that the available facilities for treatment are somewhat limited in capacity. There seems little doubt, however, but that coated lenses will be quite commonplace for many applications in the near future.

This whole field is comparatively new, and a process of orientation is taking place. There have been rumors that lenses have been damaged by some companies who apparently tried to coat them with but inadequate experience. It is consequently recommended that anyone intending to have lenses coated examine the facilities of the company that is expected to do the work and satisfy himself that they are competent to do the job before letting a contract.

In arranging to have work of this type done, bear in mind that it is possible to have the outside surfaces of a lens system coated with a material of high mechanical strength giving moderate transmission, such as magnesium fluoride, and to have the protected inner surfaces coated with a material giving high transmission but having indifferent abrasion resistance.

### PROBLEM

The aperture of a rangefinder is covered with a window made of ordinary crown glass of index 1.525. Light from a target strikes the window perpendicularly. How much is lost at the first surface through reflection? how much at the second surface? If a fluoride coating were to be applied to reduce reflection what index of refraction should it have? How thick should it be? What physical characteristics would be imperative for a coating for this application?

# CHAPTER IX

## PHOTOGRAPHIC OBJECTIVES

The study of photographic objectives is fascinating and instructive, for these lenses represent the most highly corrected types of lens systems. Since their designer is faced by the most complex task in the field of optics, an individual becomes adept at designing such objectives only through long study and experience.

We shall pursue our study of these objectives chronologically, starting with the earliest type of lens and working toward the modern complex optical system. We shall consider only a few representative types because of limitations on space.

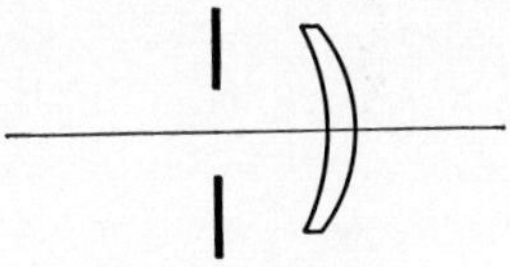

**Photographic Objectives.**—The simplest type of photographic objective is the Landscape lens, developed about 1812. This consists of a single positive meniscus lens equipped with a stop.

LANDSCAPE LENS
FIG. 69.

Inasmuch as only a single lens is used, no correction for chromatic aberration can be obtained. These lenses were used with the old types of film that were sensitive to such a narrow region in the blue end of the spectrum that satisfactorily results could be obtained without color correction. The stop is used to correct coma, and it so happens that favorable astigmatism correction is obtained at the same time by bending the lens. The aperture is limited by spherical aberration, and the lens is not used at more than $f/11$. A half field of about 20° can be covered (any field angle given in this chapter is half of the total field). These lenses are still used in some inexpensive cameras, although not nearly so extensively as a few years ago. They are very cheap to manufacture. The Landscape lens is illustrated in Fig. 69. In this illustration, as well as in the others, light enters the lens from the left and comes to a focus at the right.

One of the great objections to the use of Landscape lens is that it cannot be focused by the use of the eye, for the focal plane of the photographically most active rays (about 400 m$\mu$) does not

129

coincide with the focal plane for the visually brightest light (555 mµ). To overcome this difficulty simple achromats were introduced. These are known as Chevalier lenses, S.A. (simple achromatic) lenses, and achromatic landscape lenses. Instead of having the usual $CF$ achromatism (*i.e.*, the $C$ and $F$ rays brought to the same focus), they were corrected by bringing together the photographically active rays $(G')$[1] with the visually

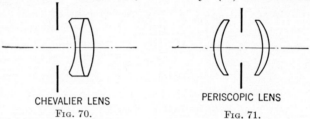

CHEVALIER LENS            PERISCOPIC LENS
Fig. 70.                   Fig. 71.

brightest rays $(D)$. This is called $DG'$ achromatism. Achromats of the "old" and "new" types were used (see Chap. VI). Experience taught the designer that the "new" achromats gave much less secondary spectrum and a flatter field and they could be used as anastigmats if the crown and flint components were separated by an air space. If properly designed, a Chevalier lens will cover a 45° field at $f/16$, the 45° angle being measured from the optical axis, and thus, to be precise, is the half-field angle. However, a certain amount of distortion will be unavoidable. Such a lens is shown in Fig. 70. It cannot be corrected for spherical aberration, and this limits the aperture.

After the development of the landscape lens, the field of lens design was static for a few years until it was discovered by Steinheil and Dallmeyer that a symmetrical lens was free of distortion, lateral color, and coma. Actually, such a lens is free of distortion, lateral color, and coma only for equal conjugates, *i.e.*, at unit magnification. However, it is reasonably free of these aberrations at most working distances; at the time it was developed, it was believed to be free of them for all distances. The first of these symmetrical objectives to appear (see Fig. 71) was developed by Steinheil. The coma, lateral color, and distortion introduced by the two elements were of equal magnitude and opposite sign and thus balanced themselves out. This gave the designer an additional degree of freedom:

[1] The $G'$ line of hydrogen has a wavelength of 434.0 mµ.

movement of the stop, but there was not much he could do with it. This type of lens had only the advantage of distortion correction over the landscape lens, for its speed ($f/14$ to $f/16$) was very similar and its field was only 20°. It was known as the Periscopic lens.

The Periscopic lens was developed still further by making the two elements into doublets (see Fig. 72). Spherical aberration and longitudinal color could thus be corrected. Such lenses were introduced in 1860–1870. Typical representatives of this lens were the Busch Pantoskop and the Harrison and Schnitzer Globe.

A lens of this type that was widely used until 1920 under the name Rapid Recti-linear (or R.R.) has been developed to as high a speed as $f/8$. This lens differs from the one in Fig. 72 by having the positive elements facing the stop. Fields up to 22° can be covered by it.

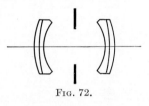

FIG. 72.

This Rapid Rectilinear modification of the original lens was introduced by Dallmeyer in 1866–1867. Other lenses of this class were the Voigtländer Euryscope, the Universal Aplanat, the Ross Doublet, and the Wide Angle Aplanat. This type of lens has now been replaced by the Triplet.

Two other lenses similar to the Periscopic are of interest. The first of these, the Panorama lens, was developed before the Periscopic, in 1859. This lens, developed by Sutton, had all its

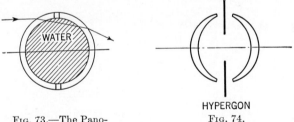

FIG. 73.—The Pano-rama lens.

HYPERGON
FIG. 74.

surfaces concentric and symmetrical. It was filled with water (see Fig. 73) for the purposes of achromatization. This gave it terrific curvature of field and it therefore had to be used with a curved film gate; but it gave reasonably good imagery out to 30 to 40° when so used. The lens shown in Fig. 74 represents the Periscopic lens carried to an extreme. This system, developed in 1900 by van Höegh of Goerz under the name Hypergon, has a very wide field that is flat and free of astigmatism. It can be used up to 75° on each side of the axis! Its aperture is small, being of the order of $f/20$ to $f/35$. The fourth-power cosine law takes a strong toll of illumination at points removed from the optical axis, and a rotating star diaphragm must be used to overcome this loss. This lens is still used and has been improved somewhat by adding two small extra negative elements (uncemented), one on either side of the stop. This form of the lens, which covers a 45° field at $f/6.3$, was developed by Richter in

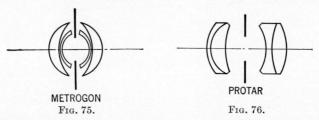

METROGON
Fig. 75.

PROTAR
Fig. 76.

1933 and is marketed under the names of Topogon and Metrogon (Fig. 75). This lens was developed still further by the Ross company, which broke up the last lens into two elements. Such lenses are corrected for curvature of field, astigmatism, coma, color, and distortion, and cover fields up to 45° at speeds up to $f/5.6$. They are widely used for aerial photography.

In about 1890 Rudolph, of Zeiss, combined an old achromat with a new one (Fig. 76). He left the old one sufficiently overcorrected for spherical aberration to balance the spherical of the new one. He then had five degrees of freedom with which to work:

        1. Distribution of power
        2, 3. Two bendings
        4, 5. Two stop positions

A system like this is not easy to compute, but Rudolph successfully designed several: an $f/8$ (35°), an $f/12$ (40°), an $f/18$ (45°). The astigmatism was removed at one point of the field, and the lens was thus called the Anastigmat. It is now called the Protar and is extensively used as a wide-angle lens. The two halves of the lens cannot be used independently as is possible with some other types of design. In a typical solution the first element has no power but a large amount of aberration, which compensates for aberration in the second doublet. This was the first real anastigmat objective of high speed.

Rudolph next thought of constructing an anastigmatic landscape lens, the Amatar, using three different types of glass (Fig. 77). With this he could correct spherical aberration, curvature of

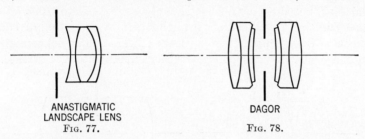

ANASTIGMATIC
LANDSCAPE LENS
Fig. 77.

DAGOR
Fig. 78.

field, and astigmatism. He could not control coma, lateral color, and distortion. He then found that by putting two of these systems face to face he could correct these three aberrations by the symmetrical principle, giving a fully corrected system (Fig. 78). This is a particularly difficult lens to compute. Lenses of this type run from $f/6.3$ (32°) to $f/4.5$ (25°) and are very useful for wide-angle photography. In this form the lens was developed

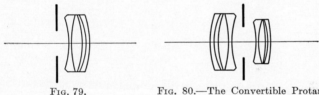

Fig. 79.

Fig. 80.—The Convertible Protar.

simultaneously by Rudolph of Zeiss and van Höegh of Goerz. Rudolph called it the Triple Protar and Van Höegh the Double Anastigmat. From the first letters of the words "Doppel Anastigmat Goerz" came the initials D.A.G. for the name Dagor applied to this type of lens. A modification of this lens, the Goerz Aerotar, covers a 34° field at $f/6.8$. This type is not *convertible* in that the two halves cannot be used separately. A demand for such a convertible lens arose, however, and Rudolph undertook the solution of this problem. It was rendered difficult by the fact that the two halves of the objective had to be corrected individually. This was accomplished by the four-element lens shown in Fig. 79. Two such elements were used symmetrically about the stop (Fig. 80), the combination being known as the Convertible Protar, Quadruple Protar, and Double Protar. The reason that convertible lenses were popular was that the two halves had different focal lengths; thus, when used individually or in combination, they gave a variety of characteristics. This lens, brought out in 1894, is used at speeds up to $f/6.3$. In 1906 Rudolph developed a convertible Protar consisting of two cemented triplets with the stop between them, each triplet consisting of a positive lens with a negative element cemented to each face.

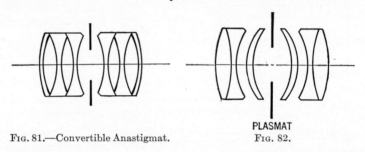

| FIG. 81.—Convertible Anastigmat. | PLASMAT<br>FIG. 82. |

The same type of lens was developed still further to contain five cemented elements (Fig. 81) by van Höegh in 1897. Lenses using two five-element cemented components are still manufactured for photo-engraving work, a typical example being the Turner-Reich objective.

Another representative type of lens is shown in Fig. 82. This may be looked on as a development of the Periscopic or Dagor lenses. It was developed by Rudolph in 1920 under the name Plasmat. It was made symmetrical in spite of the fact that by this time designers had learned that by departing from symmetry somewhat they were able to increase the amount of correction. Such a large depth of focus was claimed for the lens that some suspicion exists that it actually possessed no

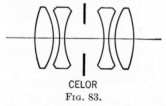

CELOR
FIG. 83.

sharp focus. Recently the Zeiss people took this up again, making it unsymmetrical. It was sold as an aerial surveying lens ($f/4$) covering 35° under the name Orthometar. It was calculated in this form by Merté in about 1930 and proved very successful. A lens similar to this is the Ross $f/4$ Wide-Angle Xpres.

Another type of double anastigmat may be constructed by separating two positive and negative elements (see Fig. 83). Each half of the lens must be corrected for spherical and chromatic aberration, and the whole must be corrected for curvature and astigmatism. Distortion and lateral color are pronounced in each half of the system, but these are removed when two symmetrical halves are used. There are six variables that may be used to control aberration on each side in such a system, and these are usually sufficient to control all the aberrations mentioned. Two such halves are computed and then combined. One half is varied symmetrically with respect to the other to make the final adjustment. This type of lens was developed by van Höegh under the name Celor in 1898. An $f/6.3$ and an $f/3.5$ were developed under this name, and an $f/4.5$ under the name Dogmar. Another lens of this type was developed by Steinheil in 1901 under the name Unofocal. During the last war the Taylor, Taylor, and Hobson Company brought out an $f/4.5$ aerial photography lens called the Aviar, which was also of this general class, and the Eastman Kodak company has produced lenses of this type under the general name Kodak Anastigmat. It should be remembered that this type of lens can be used only to cover a certain field angle; when this field angle is exceeded, the image goes bad very suddenly. For this reason such a lens should not be employed in a camera with a rising front. The field covered by this lens is about 22 to 25°. It may be looked upon as the logical successor to the Dagor, having an "air lens" in the center of each half.

A further variation of this lens was produced in 1900 by Rudolph under the name Unar, from which emerged the famous Tessar, also produced by Rudolph. This is shown in Fig. 84. It was developed in 1902. It can cover fields up to 28° at speeds up to $f/3.5$. It will be noted that the first two elements in this system have practically no power but just make contributions to the aberrations.

Another independent start in lens design was made by Rudolph who started out with a system of two positive and two negative lenses, somewhat similar to the Celor, and developed this into an anastigmat of the type shown in Fig. 85. This lens, developed in 1895–1896, is known as the Planar. It is symmetrical and is useful for copying at unit magnification. Its speed is about $f/4$.

This lens was neglected for many years and then was revived in
1922 by Lee.   He made it asymmetrical and developed it into a
very nice system under the name Opic.   This was used at speeds

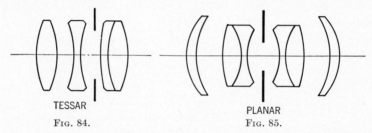

TESSAR

FIG. 84.

PLANAR

FIG. 85.

up to $f/2$ and covered fields up to 25°.   After Lee's work, many
further developments of the lens were made.   One of the most
famous of these is the Zeiss Biotar (Fig. 86), computed by Merté

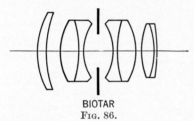

BIOTAR

FIG. 86.

who first made the last element
single; then changed it to a
doublet.   This is sometimes
used at $f/1.4$ to cover a 14° field,
but it is not usually employed
at speeds greater than $f/2$.   It
works well with aspheric surfaces.   The Leitz Summar and
Summitar, the Schneider Xenon, and the Kodak $f/1.9$ Ektar are
of this general type.   In the Kodak and Summitar versions the
doublet is in front; the single element behind.

Another independent start in lens design was made by H.
Dennis Taylor in 1895.   He realized that the power that a
given lens contributes to a lens system is proportional to the
height at which a marginal ray strikes that lens.   On the other
hand, the contribution that each lens makes to curvature of
field is proportional to the power of the lens regardless of the
height at which rays strike the lens.   He thus reasoned that if
by spacing his lenses properly he could make the marginal rays
strike a negative lens in the system so low that this lens would
not nullify the positive power of the system, he could introduce
such a negative lens to control curvature without having the lens
increase the focal length of the system inordinately.   All previously designed objectives had been afflicted with positive
Petzval curvature; by the introduction of this negative lens

Taylor was able to introduce sufficient negative Petzval curvature to give the objective a flat anastigmatic field. Taylor's objective, known as the Cooke Triplet, or more commonly as the Triplet, is shown in Fig. 87. Note how the marginal ray strikes the negative lens much lower than it strikes the positive elements.

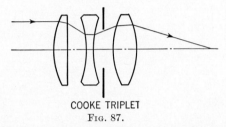

COOKE TRIPLET
Fig. 87.

This lens has just enough degrees of freedom to clear up all the aberrations. It is much cheaper than the Rapid Rectilinear and has thus displaced it entirely. The Triplet can be made with speeds up to $f/3.5$, or better, and can cover fields up to 20 to 25°. The vast majority of contemporary inexpensive photographic objectives are of this general type. It will be noted that the Tessar may be considered as a modified Triplet, with

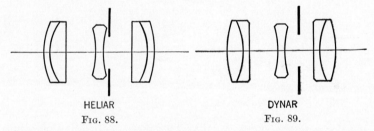

HELIAR
Fig. 88.

DYNAR
Fig. 89.

the last positive element replaced by a doublet. The Tessar was, however, developed independently of the Triplet.

Although the Tessar was not developed directly from the Triplet, various other lenses were. In 1902, Harting, of Voigtländer, produced a lens of the Triplet type in which both positive elements were doublets instead of single lenses. This lens, known as the Heliar, is shown in Fig. 88. A further development of this lens was the Dynar, shown in Fig. 89. This came out in 1903. It covered fields up to about 30° at a speed of around $f/7$. The present Heliar is of the Dynar type.

A still further development of the general principle of the Triplet is credited to Bertele, of the Ernemann Co. He started with the idea of aplanatic points (see Chap. XXV) and broke the first element into two separate positive lenses, one of which was aplanatic. The resulting lens is shown in Fig. 90. It covered fields up to 15° at $f/2$ and was useful for motion-picture

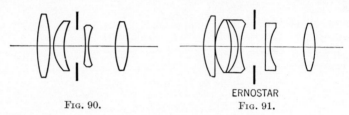

FIG. 90.

ERNOSTAR
FIG. 91.

photography. This was developed into a more elaborate form by Bertele in 1925, the result being the Ernostar. This lens, shown in Fig. 91, covers fields of 20° at a speed of $f/1.8$. The idea was pushed still further by Zeiss in 1934, the result being the Sonnar shown in Fig. 92. This covers fields up to 25° at a speed of $f/1.5$. The first cemented triplet in this very elaborate lens is negative in power; the second is positive. Thus the lens

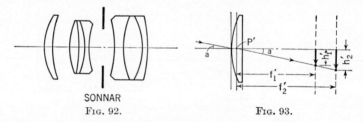

SONNAR
FIG. 92.

FIG. 93.

consists of a negative component between two positive ones and is just an elaboration of the old Cooke Triplet. A whole series of these Sonnars has been developed for various purposes.

**Telephoto Lenses.**—In Fig. 93 is shown a single positive lens functioning as an objective. The second principal point is at $P'$. A field of half angle $a$ is being covered. Note that, if the focal length of the lens is $f_1'$, the image height is $h_1'$; if the focal length is $f_2'$, the image height is $h_2'$. From the illustration it is evident that for a given field angle, the size of the image is proportional to the distance of the film from the second principal point of the objective, i.e., it is proportional to the focal length $f'$.

Thus we can obtain a large picture of a certain object by using a lens of long focal length. Unfortunately, if we tried to get a large picture of a small distant object by using a lens of very long focal length, the lens would have to stick far out in front of the camera, and this would be inconvenient. The distance from the vertex of the last surface of the last lens in an objective to the focal plane is known as the *back focal length* in comparison with the real focal length, called the *equivalent focal length*. Thus in a telephoto lens we desire long equivalent focal length, to give a large picture, coupled with short back focal length to give a compact arrangement. To arrive at this end it is obviously

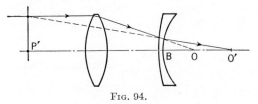

FIG. 94.

necessary to push the second principal point well out in front of the lens. The means by which this is accomplished is indicated in Fig. 94. Note that the rays leaving the positive lens are converging to a focus at $O$ but are diverted to $O'$ by the negative element. It will be remembered that the second principal point is located by tracing a ray from an infinitely distant object through the lens to its focus. The intersection of the entering and departing rays is located, and a line is passed through this intersection perpendicular to the axis. The axial intercept of this line is the second principal point. By following this procedure, the second principal point of the system in the illustration is found at $P'$. It is thus seen that the system has a large equivalent focal length $P'O'$ and therefore gives a large image, but has a short back focal length $BO'$ and is consequently compact. Such a system is known as a *telephoto lens*.

It is common practice to make both elements of such lenses doublets or triplets in order to obtain a high state of correction. A typical telephoto lens is shown in Fig. 95. This will cover a field of about 15° at $f/5.6$. Some of the more complicated forms are as fast as $f/3.5$. These lenses usually have an equivalent focal length about two or three times as great as the back focal length, this ratio sometimes being called the *telephoto effect*.

Telephoto lenses are commonly given anastigmatic correction, but they are normally afflicted with pincushion distortion. Lee, of Taylor, Taylor, and Hobson, got around this trouble by separating the components of the negative lens. This procedure introduced sufficient astigmatism to overcome the distortion.

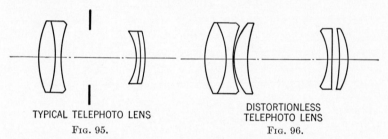

TYPICAL TELEPHOTO LENS
FIG. 95.

DISTORTIONLESS
TELEPHOTO LENS
FIG. 96.

The residual astigmatism was removed by dividing the front lens into two meniscus-shaped components. One of the two front components was made a doublet for the purpose of achromatization. The lens is shown in Fig. 96.

**Projection Objectives.**—Most present projection objectives are direct descendants of an objective developed for portrait work by Petzval, for Voigtländer, in 1840. This lens, shown in Fig. 97, gives very good imagery in the center of the field. It is still used to some extent for portrait work. It can be made very

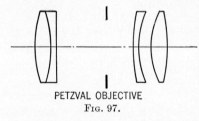

PETZVAL OBJECTIVE
FIG. 97.

fast (up to about $f/2$) and has thus been adopted for projection purposes almost to the exclusion of other types. The second doublet is often cemented and is sometimes reversed from the position shown in the illustration. Because the negative elements are located very close to the positive ones, it is not possible to flatten the field with the glasses used in this design. Thus these objectives usually have strongly curved fields. This causes the poor extra-axial imagery. By placing a negative lens very near the plane of the film it is possible to overcome this defect. This extra negative lens, called a *field flattener*, is so close to the film plane that it affects the power of the system only to a negligible extent. Yet it results in a marked flattening of the field. Lenses equipped with these field flatteners are

made with speeds up to $f/1.4$.   A typical Petzval lens equipped
with a field flattener is shown in Fig. 98.

**Expected Developments.**—The most significant recent development that promises to affect the subject of lens design is the
appearance of a series of glasses of very high index.   These glasses

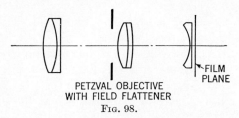

PETZVAL OBJECTIVE
WITH FIELD FLATTENER
FIG. 98.

will permit the designer to double the speeds of present designs
and will undoubtedly lead to the development of important new
designs.

Another field offering great promise is that of the exploitation
of the Schmidt principle.   This principle is exemplified in the
*Schmidt camera,* which consists of a spherical reflecting surface
for forming an image on a photographic film, and a glass plate
having an aspheric surface which
is inserted in the incident parallel beam at the center of curvature of the reflector (Fig. 99).[1]
Because the reflector is spherical
it is not afflicted with coma
(which gives bad imagery at
points off the axis), as is a
paraboloid.   However, it has
a large amount of spherical aberration.   This is eliminated by the plate which is so computed
as to correct each zone of the reflector for spherical aberration.
The amount of figuring (*i.e.,* modification of flat surface) that is
required for correction is very small and is greatly exaggerated in
the illustration.   Because the glass plate is at the center of
curvature of the reflector and is the aperture stop of the system,
all beams coming into the system at various field angles are

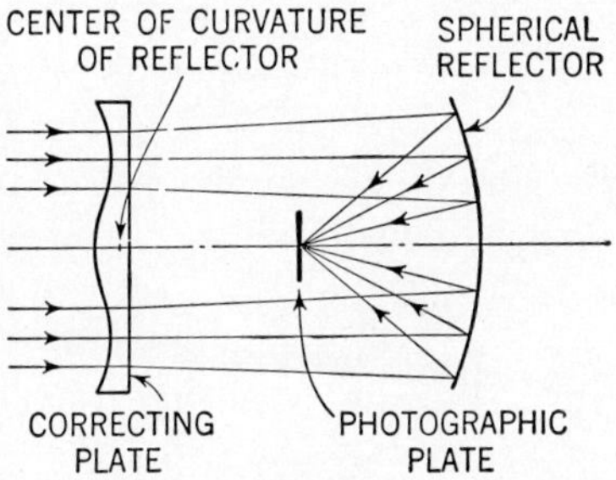

FIG. 99.—The Schmidt camera.

[1] SYNGE, *J. Optical Soc. Am.,* Vol. 33, p. 129, 1943.   This reference has
a good bibliography of the subject.

treated essentially alike and thus astigmatism and coma are not introduced.   The only aberration that is troublesome is curvature of field, and by properly curving the photographic plate the image can be kept in focus to the edge of surprisingly large fields (12° or more).   By filling the space between the correcting plate and the reflector with a block of glass *solid Schmidt cameras* of very high speed are attainable.   These must either be split to permit insertion of the photographic plate or used off-axis as shown in Fig. 100.[1]   In the design shown in Fig. 100 the space between the photographic plate and the glass should be filled with oil of the same index as the glass, so that the rays from the edge of the reflecting surface, which arrive at the photographic

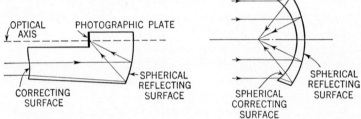

Fig. 100.—The solid-glass off-axis Schmidt camera.

Fig. 101.—The Mangin mirror.

plate at very large incidence angles because of the large possible aperture ratios, will not be directed back into the glass by total reflection.

The Schmidt camera was originally developed for astronomical work, but its application to other fields is receiving serious consideration.   An $f/0.7$ Schmidt system for use in television projection work has been designed, and other devices successfully employing this principle have been constructed.

Another interesting optical system that may receive further development is that of the *Mangin mirror*.   This consists of a negative meniscus lens, one surface of which is silvered to act as a spherical mirror and the other surface of which corrects for the spherical aberration of the reflecting surface (Fig. 101).   The radius of the first or correcting surface, which is spherical, may be so chosen that the marginal rays are brought to the same focus

---

[1] HENDRIX and CHRISTIE, *Sci. Amer.*, Vol. 161, p. 118, 1939.
  BAKER, *Proc. Am. Phil. Soc.*, Vol. 82, p. 323, 1940.

as the paraxial rays.  The state of correction obtained is thus similar to that of an ordinary telescope objective of the same aperture ratio, but the residual zonal spherical aberration is much less.  This type of optical system may therefore be used at high aperture ratios.  If a source is placed at the focus, this device may be used as a wide-aperture projection system for headlamps, signaling devices, etc.[1]

## REFERENCES

"Dictionary of Applied Physics," Vol. IV, Macmillan & Company, Ltd., London, 1923.   Article on Photographic Lenses.

BEREK: "Grundlagen der praktischen Optik," Walter de Gruyter & Company, Berlin, 1930.

GLEICHEN: "Theory of Modern Optical Instruments," (trans. by Emsley and Swaine), His Majesty's Stationery Office, London, 1921.

KINGSLAKE: Lenses for Aerial Photography, *J. Optical Soc. Am.*, Vol. 32, p. 129, 1942.

MARTIN: "An Introduction to Applied Optics," Vol. II, Sir Isaac Pitman & Sons, Ltd., London, 1932.

MERTÉ, RICHTER, and VON ROHR: "Das photographische Objektiv," Julius Springer, Vienna, 1932.

NEBLETTE: "Photography, Its Principles and Practice," D. Van Nostrand Company, Inc., New York, 1938.

TURRIÈRE: "Optique industrielle," Librairie Delagrave, Paris, 1920.

[1] "Dictionary of Applied Physics," Vol. IV, p. 524, Macmillan & Co., Ltd., London, 1923.

# CHAPTER X

## PHOTOGRAPHIC SHUTTERS

In Fig. 102$a$ is shown a schematic view of a representative modern photographic shutter. This is not necessarily to be taken as representing some specific shutter; it is intended merely to show the basic principles of such devices. It is not to scale.

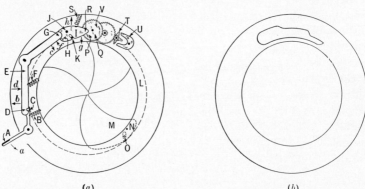

(a)                                             (b)

FIG. 102.—Schematic view of a photographic shutter.

The shutter is snapped open by depressing the thumb lever $A$ against the action of spring $B$, in the direction $a$. Because the hook-shaped projection $C$ on the thumb lever is engaged with the nose $D$ of the main lever $E$, $E$ is forced in the direction of arrow $b$ against the action of the spring $F$. The other end of $E$ travels in direction $c$. Thus nose $G$ travels over ramp $H$ on the time lever $I$. This ramp is shown in detail in Fig. 103. When $G$ moves in direction $c$, it slides up, over, and down behind the ramp. When traveling in the reverse direction $f$, it evidently engages on the ramp's vertical face. $G$ travels over the ramp in direction $c$ without affecting $I$. The motion of $A$ and $G$ continues until the thumb lever $A$ has been moved sufficiently far so that nose $D$ of the main lever slides out of engagement with

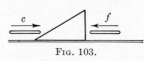

FIG. 103.

144

hook $C$. When thus freed, the main lever $E$ is thrown sharply back in direction $d$ under the action of the strong mainspring $F$. Nose $G$, now traveling in direction $f$, engages the vertical face of ramp $H$ and thus causes time lever $I$ to rotate rapidly in direction $g$ about the pivot $J$. The shutter pin $K$, fastened to the shutter ring $L$, is forced to the left by this movement, causing $L$ to rotate counterclockwise. In order to see how this motion affects the shutter blades consider the typical blade $M$. This is pivoted at $N$. When the ring $L$ is moved counterclockwise, the pin $O$, fastened to $L$, which projects through the slot in the blade, pulls the blade to the open position.

After lever $I$ has opened the shutter, it continues to rotate and its nose $R$ slides over ramp $P$ on gear $Q$. At about the nstant the shutter reaches the fully open position, nose $G$ has slid sufficiently far to the left to disengage from ramp $H$ on the time lever. Under the action of spring $S$, which is now in a state of tension, $I$ would tend to rotate in direction $h$ and close the shutter. However, when so moving, nose $R$ becomes engaged against the vertical face of ramp $P$ on gear $Q$, this vertical face being at the lower edge of the ramp. Thus, in order to close the shutter, the time lever must force gear $Q$ to rotate clockwise. Through a train of intermediate gears this motion is imparted to star wheel $T$, which is caused to rotate very rapidly. This motion is slowed down appreciably by the escapement lever $U$, which is forced to move back and forth as each tooth of the star wheel passes it. The natural inertia of this escapement lever, which may be enhanced by the addition of weights, prevents the mechanism from turning rapidly. Thus nose $R$ can only proceed toward the closed position slowly, and a time delay is thereby obtained. At the end of the delay action, $R$ has moved upward far enough to disengage from ramp $P$ and thus snaps in the direction $h$ under the action of $S$. At this instant the shutter blades start to close and are snapped shut quickly by spring $S$ and another spring connected directly to $L$ because the time lever is no longer retarded. This technique is used to obtain the longest exposure time for which a shutter is designed.

Shorter exposure times are obtained by making the time lever move a shorter distance before it disengages from ramp $P$. This is accomplished through the use of the vertical lever $V$ cn gear $Q$. This projects vertically upward from the plane of the paper through a slot in the time ring shown in Fig. 102$b$. By means of the cam-shaped surface on one side of this slot, lever $V$, and thus gear $Q$, can be held in various positions. Obviously, when $V$ is locked down toward the bottom of the page, $P$ will be held up near the top; thus nose $R$ on the time lever will not engage with $P$. Therefore, as soon as the time lever becomes disengaged from the main lever, it starts to close the shutter, *i.e.*, the shutter starts to close as soon as it has come to the fully open position. Thus with the escapement mechanism locked out the shutter gives its highest speed, and this speed is determined by the inertia and friction of the blade system and the strength of spring $S$. Let us assume that we have a shutter with exposure times from $\frac{1}{500}$ second to 1 second. It is evident that with the escapement fully locked out we shall get $\frac{1}{500}$. Now, if we wish to get $\frac{1}{300}$, we must position lever $P$ so that $R$ touches it for only an instant before the shutter closes; thus the closing mechanism is only very briefly retarded. This means that lever $V$ should be positioned with great precision; this is done with the cam-shaped ramp on the time ring. Unfortunately in many shutters the time rings are made of brass, this material being used so that the various cam surfaces can be easily changed to calibrate it. If the cam surface projects too far, a few strokes of a file dress it down; if it projects insufficiently far, a few blows of a hammer and punch can spread it. This calibration treatment leaves the edge of the cam rather rough, and minute irregularities on this surface can cause very large percentage errors in the timing of the shutter. Furthermore the fact that the time ring is made of brass, which is rather soft, is sufficient to insure that the delicately adjusted cam surface will wear quite rapidly, and the precision of calibration is lost. Generally speaking, only methods of the crudest sort are used in the calibration of many shutters. This results in a rather low standard of precision. However, the wide latitude of modern film enables the user to obtain fairly good results. It is strongly recommended that before any shutter is used for precision work it be carefully calibrated on accurate equipment.

The foregoing description of shutter performance covered only the opening cycle of shutter operation. From this the motions of the various parts in assuming the original orientation shown in the illustration may be easily inferred. After being driven forward to the release position, the escapement mechanism is returned to the starting position under the action of a spring that is not shown.

Various shutters differ in some details from the one described here. Flat springs are often used instead of the coil springs employed schematically in the drawing. Various other engagement devices besides the ramp illustrated in Fig. 103 are used. In some shutters, in order to cover a wide range of speeds, two escapement mechanisms are employed. One escapement has high inertia and is used at low speeds. The other has low inertia and is used to get increased precision at high speeds. The fact

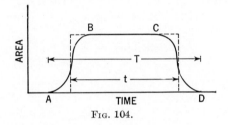

FIG. 104.

that a low inertia escapement is used at high speeds contributes to precision because it results in irregularities in the face of the time cam having a greatly reduced effect on timing.

Figure 104 shows the characteristic curve to be obtained for an average shutter when the area of the opening is plotted against time. The shutter begins to open at point $A$ on the solid curve and is fully open at $B$. At about this instant the escapement mechanism comes into use and holds the shutter open during the time interval $BC$. At $C$ the escapement has released the time lever and the shutter has closed at $D$. By the use of the time control cam the section $BC$ may be shortened, thus reducing the total exposure time. When the escapement is entirely locked out, points $B$ and $C$ coincide, the flat section of the curve having been eliminated. The characteristic curve then becomes $A\overline{BC}D$, $\overline{BC}$ representing the combined points $B$ and $C$.

The area under the curve $ABCD$ represents the total amount of light striking the film. If the shutter had opened instantaneously to its maximum opening when the exposure began and had closed instantaneously but had remained open only long enough to transmit the same amount of light as it did under actual operating conditions, the dotted curve would represent the shutter action.

As far as the ability of the shutter to stop motion (photographically) is concerned, the time $T$ between points $A$ and $D$ gives a fairly valid indication of exposure time. However, as far as the ability of the shutter to build up a photographic image (*i.e.*, to transmit light) is concerned, the effective exposure time is $t$. It is evident that the dotted curve represents the most perfect condition of operation, for when operating in this fashion the shutter has the shortest possible exposure time for the passage of a given amount of light. Thus the efficiency of a shutter if generally measured in the following way:

$$\text{Efficiency} = \frac{t}{T} \tag{62}$$

It is evident from the figure that as the interval $BC$ is shortened the efficiency decreases and reaches a minimum when the escapement is entirely locked out. As the sections $AB$ and $CD$ depend on the opening and closing characteristics, respectively, of the shutter, it can be seen that the efficiency of the shutter, particularly at the higher speeds, is dependent on these characteristics. When the efficiency of a shutter is stated, the speed at which it was measured must also be given. Shutter efficiency increases when the relative aperture of the lens used with the shutter is decreased. (Why?)

In order to get fast opening and closing characteristics, strong springs and light blades should be used. Rubber is commonly used in the fabrication of blades because of its lightness. Its chief disadvantage is its rather low durability. Many attempts have been made to use metal blades in place of rubber ones, but the weight of the metal materially slows down the opening and closing characteristics, lowers the efficiency, and limits the highest speed obtainable under a given set of conditions. However some modern shutters have blades made of steel only 0.0015 in. thick.

Note should be taken of the fact that rubber shutter blades are not resistant to heat and should never be used in any apparatus in which heat might be encountered.

Numerous techniques have been developed to study the exposure speeds of shutters. It is theoretically possible merely to expose a photographic plate to a standard light source through the shutter and evaluate the exposure time in terms of the blackening produced, but so many difficulties in controlling developing conditions, etc., are involved that the method is of little practical value.

It is also possible to take photographs of rapidly moving brightly illuminated objects of many types (falling balls, etc.) and then evaluate the exposure time in terms of the finite length of the recorded image. Another similar technique involves the photographing, through the shutter, of a series of stroboscopic tubes being illuminated one after the other. These methods have the objection that after making the test exposure one must wait for a film to be developed before the result of the test is obtainable. When one is trying to adjust a shutter by means of test apparatus, it is necessary to have the result of the measurement instantly available.

In recent years several reasonably satisfactory photoelectric devices for the measurement of shutter speed have been developed. These usually involve a condenser on which a standard charge is placed. This charge is leaked off the condenser through a phototube, the amount of charge being so removed depending upon the total amount of light incident on this cell during a test exposure. The amount of charge left on the condenser after the test exposure is used to bias the grid of an amplifying tube, and the effect on the plate current of the tube is noted on a milliammeter. This milliammeter may be calibrated directly in terms of shutter speed. Bridge circuits involving the same fundamental principles have also been developed.

The writer was once faced with the problem of studying characteristic shutter curves of the type shown in Fig. 104. A method of instantaneously obtaining the curve was desired. A phototube and amplifier circuit was obtained and the output of the amplifier was fed directly to the plates controlling the vertical deflection of a cathode ray beam in an oscilloscope. A saw-tooth wave from a relaxation oscillator was applied to the plates controlling the horizontal component, thus giving an adjustable time base. Since the saw-tooth oscillator swept the beam horizontally at a constant rate and since the vertical deflection was proportional to the illumination on the phototube at any given instant, the characteristic curve of the shutter was given instantaneously on the oscilloscope screen. Through control of the oscillator frequency it was possible to measure the exposure times $t$ and $T$; thus efficiency could be easily determined. The device was easily calibrated by the use of Lissajous figures obtained from the 60-cycle alternating current of the power line.

## PROBLEM

When set at $\frac{1}{100}$ second a shutter is wide open for 0.0060 second and consumes 0.0024 second in opening and 0.0016 second in closing. What is its efficiency at this speed? When set at $\frac{1}{50}$, it is wide open for 0.016 second. What is its efficiency at this speed? What is the shortest exposure for which the shutter may be used? Assume sections $AB$ and $CD$ of the characteristic curve are linear.

# CHAPTER XI

## REFRACTING AND REFLECTING PRISMS

**Refracting Prisms.**—In an optical instrument it is often necessary to deviate a beam of light. This may be done with an ordinary refracting prism of the type shown in Fig. 105a. However, the angular deviation $D$ caused by the prism is a function of wavelength; thus, if the beam being deviated is composed of white light, the prism will spread the beam into a spectrum.

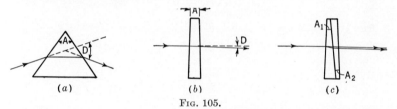

(a)     (b)     (c)

Fig. 105.

An image formed through a prism as strong as that illustrated would be so strongly colored as to be utterly worthless. However, if only a very small deviation in the beam is desired (as in a rangefinder) and if the image being formed through the prism is not to be viewed under high magnification, it is possible to use a very weak prism of the type shown in Fig. 105b without excessive trouble with color. This is done with some small rangefinders. Such a weak prism is called a *wedge*.

With prisms of the type shown in Fig. 105b, the angles of incidence and refraction are so small that it is possible to replace the sines of the angle in Snell's law by the angles themselves. Through such a simplification, the angular deviation $D$ produced by a prism of refracting angle $A$ and index $n$ may be approximately expressed in this manner:

$$D = (n - 1)A \qquad (63)$$

In large rangefinders, the images are viewed at fairly high magnification. Under such conditions the chromatic aberration resulting from the use of even a prism of very small deviation is

151

of too great a magnitude to be permissible.   Thus it is necessary
to eliminate this difficulty by the use of an achromatic prism in
the same way that ordinary chromatic aberration is overcome
by the use of an achromatic doublet.   Two prisms of different
glasses are employed   If two prisms are combined as shown in
Fig. 105c to form an achromatic prism, the total deviation of the
combination is given by

$$D = (n_1 - 1)A_1 - (n_2 - 1)A_2 \qquad (64)$$

(QUESTION: Why is there a minus sign between the two terms in
this expression?)   The condition that the combination shall be
achromatic is expressed by

$$\frac{(n_1 - 1)A_1}{\nu_1} - \frac{(n_2 - 1)A_2}{\nu_2} = 0 \qquad (65)$$

These two equations can be solved simultaneously in any given
case.   However, the solution will be exact only to the extent to
which the approximation to Snell's law that was assumed in
deriving these equations holds.   In practice, these equations
would be used roughly to design a prism and select the best
glasses; then the final results would be obtained by ray tracing.
It is of importance to note that these equations make only
the deviations of the $C$ and $F$ wavelengths equal; other wavelengths still show slightly different deviations.   Thus there is a
residual color aberration similar to secondary spectrum as mani-
fested in any achromat.   This residual aberration is generally of
too small a magnitude to cause any trouble, but its presence
should not be forgotten.

   **Reflecting Prisms.**—It is often necessary to obtain in optical
instruments larger deviations than can be satisfactorily obtained
with refracting prisms.   First surface plane mirrors could be
used for the purpose, but the surfaces would gradually tarnish
and would thus cause a loss of light that would increase as the
instrument aged.   If second surface mirrors were used, reflection
losses and other difficulties would result.   It is thus found
necessary to use reflecting prisms.   As the deviation produced
in these prisms is obtained by internal specular reflection[1] and as

---

[1] *Specular reflection* is mirrorlike reflection in which the angle of reflection
is equal to the angle of incidence.   Its antithesis is *diffuse reflection*, in
which there is a random distribution of angles of reflection for a series of

a deviation so produced is independent of wavelength, it is evident that such prisms may be used without encountering chromatic difficulties provided that the rays enter and leave the prism normal to its faces (as in Fig. 110). However, if the rays enter or leave in some direction other than perpendicularly, refraction will of course occur, and this could cause chromatic aberration.

The only case in which a beam can undergo two refractions at plane surfaces without having its various wavelengths dispersed is that of oblique incidence on a plane parallel plate, as shown in

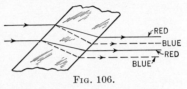

FIG. 106.

Fig. 106. At the first refraction the beam is split into colored components, as it would be by a similar refraction in a prism. However at the second refraction, which is the exact reverse of the first, the rays are again rendered parallel. It will be seen that the various components of a given incident ray will be parallel to each other after the second refraction but will not coincide. After this refraction the red component of one such ray will be combined with the blue component of another, and the beam will be uncolored. If the various colors had emerged in different *directions*, chromatic aberration would have resulted.

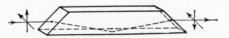

FIG. 107.—Dove, or rotating, prism.

The test of whether a reflecting prism in which the arriving and/or departing rays undergo refraction (*i.e.*, do not arrive perpendicularly) is really achromatic is to determine whether it can be replaced by a plane parallel plate. Thus consider the prism shown in Fig. 107. This is redrawn, as *ABCD*, in Fig. 108. Instead of being reflected at *O*, the ray may be considered as passing through a solid block of glass *ABCDFE*. Thus the real branch *OL* may be replaced by an equivalent fictitious branch *OM*. Face *FD*, which is the reflection of *CD*, is parallel to face

rays all having equal angles of incidence. Specular reflection is a characteristic of highly polished surfaces, while diffuse reflection is a characteristic of rough surfaces like those of mat paper or newly fallen snow. It is the irregular surface of these materials that is directly responsible for the scattering of the reflected light.

*AB*. Thus, in effect, the prism is a plane parallel plate of glass, and the beam will not be dispersed in spite of the refraction. This technique of replacing a reflected ray by a fictitious transmitted ray in a prism will be illustrated further in Chap. XIII.

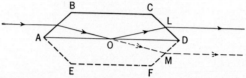

Fig. 108.—Construction showing that a Dove prism is optically equivalent to a plane-parallel plate of glass. *ADFE* may be considered to be the reflection, at *AD*, of the prism *ABCD*. Thus the imaginary transmitted ray *OM* is optically equivalent to the actual reflected ray *OL*.

Consider the ray of light shown in Fig. 109*a*. This is passing from glass into air. The ray is refracted in the amount given by Snell's law,

$$n \sin I = n' \sin I' \qquad (66)$$

Now if we gradually increase the angle of incidence $I$, the angle of refraction $I'$ will also increase and will always be greater than $I$ because $n/n'$ is greater than unity. Thus, eventually, $I'$ will

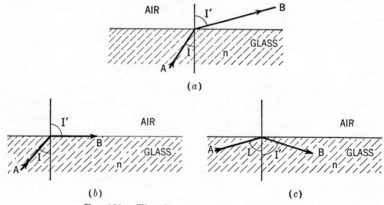

Fig. 109.—The phenomenon of total reflection.

reach the value of 90°. The angle $I$ will be less than 90°. This situation is shown in Fig. 109*b*. For this case

$$n \sin I = n' \sin 90° = n' \qquad (67)$$

Because the ray is traveling into air, $n' = 1$, and thus

$$n \sin I = 1 \tag{68}$$

and

$$\sin I = \frac{1}{n} \tag{69}$$

If the angle of incidence is now increased slightly, the ray will no longer pass through the glass-air interface but will be reflected back into the glass as shown in Fig. 109c. This phenomenon is known as *total reflection*. It occurs for any incidence angle greater than the value given by Eq. (69). This angle, at which total reflection begins, is called the *critical angle*. It is defined as the angle of incidence for which the angle of refraction is 90° when a ray is passing from any medium to one of lower index of refraction, and it may be computed for any pair of media by use of Snell's law. For a ray traveling from glass of index 1.5 to air, the critical angle is about 42°. Thus, if a prism is to reflect light because of total reflection, the rays must all strike the glass-air reflecting surface at angles greater than this. If the rays strike the surface at lesser angles, the surface must be silvered to permit reflection to occur; otherwise the light would pass through the surface and be refracted, as in Fig. 109a.

Because borosilicate crown glass has high abrasion resistance, high resistance to attack by atmospheric constituents, and is relatively easy to manufacture, it is used extensively in the fabrication of reflecting prisms. However, its critical angle is just a trifle too large for use in some prisms (such as right-angle prisms used in instruments covering large fields), and in these cases glass of a higher index, such as barium crown, is used. The critical angle of borosilicate crown ($n_D = 1.5170$) is $41\frac{1}{3}°$, while that of barium crown ($n_D = 1.5725$) is $39\frac{1}{2}°$. Because of the 45° reflection occurring in a right-angle prism, the difference between these two critical angles is very important. This is particularly true because this type of prism is commonly used in a convergent beam of light, and the convergence angle, as well as the field angle, must be taken into account.

It should be borne in mind that prisms may be used for various purposes. Thus, they may be used to deviate, or bend, a ray through a large angle. They may also be used to displace a beam laterally without introducing any deviation. They may be used to rotate an image in its own plane.   They may be used to erect the inverted image produced by the objective or to erect a reverted image.   Finally, they may be used to produce several of these effects simultaneously.   Because of the many functions they are called upon to perform, reflecting prisms have been developed in great variety.   Limitations of space require us to limit our attention to a few typical examples.

The simplest of the reflecting prisms is the *right-angle prism* shown in Fig. 110.   It is used frequently when a deviation of 90°

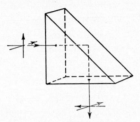

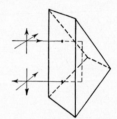

Fig. 110.—Right-angle prism.

Fig. 111.—Porro prism.

is desired.   This prism has one property worthy of further study.   Because of the peculiar character of the reflections that occur, this prism will interchange the right and left sides of an image without altering the relative positions of the top and bottom of the image, or, if the prism is rotated through 90°, the reverse effect occurs.   Thus, one dimension of an image is reversed and the other is left unchanged.   This phenomenon is known as *reversion,* and the image is said to be *reverted.*   The little arrows in this and other figures show the effect of the prism on the orientation of the image.

Another very important reflecting prism is the *Porro prism* shown in Fig. 111.   This may be regarded as two right-angle prisms fused together.   The image is reversed in the plane in which the reflection takes place.   Porro prisms are commonly used in the erecting systems of binoculars.   The most common arrangement is that shown in Fig. 112, which consists of two Porro prisms located perpendicular to one another.   It is known as a *Porro prism system of the first type.*   This system reverses *both* axes of the image, the process being known as *inversion.*   Another form of erecting system that uses two right-angle prisms in conjunction with a Porro prism is shown in Fig. 113.   This is called a *Porro prism system of the second type.* It can also be used in binoculars, but is much less popular than the first type of system because it consists of three elements instead of two, thus increasing the cost. It can also be made of two rather complicated elements, symmetrical about the center. It, too, produces a true inversion rather than a reversion of the image.

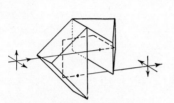 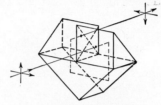

Fig. 112.—Porro prism system of the first type.   Fig. 113.—Porro prism system of the second type.

Both Porro prism systems are obviously achromatic.

The prism shown in Fig. 114 produces a 90° deviation and simultaneously inverts the image. It is called an *Amici prism.* The reflection is produced at two surfaces inclined at 90° to one another to form a little roof. The rays striking the right-hand side of the roof are reflected over to the left-hand side and then out, while those striking the left-hand side follow the reverse course (see Fig. 115). Thus the final image is formed with rays that have crossed over from one side to the other, causing reversion. If the two reflecting surfaces do not intersect within a few seconds of 90°, the beams reflected from them will not match, and a double image will be formed. For this reason this type of prism is very difficult to manufacture. In practice these prisms receive their final adjustment in the optical shop through a laborious

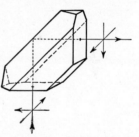

Fig. 114.—Amici prism.

cut-and-try method. As they are widely used in military instruments, they present a real manufacturing problem. The fact that these prisms have inverting roofs results in their frequently being called *roof prisms*, which is somewhat misleading, for several other types of prisms also have roofs. Correctly speaking a roof prism is any type of reflecting prism in which reversion is performed with a roof. In effect the Amici is merely a right-angle prism with a roof. It is pointed out that by making the roof twice as big as that shown in Fig. 115 the difficulties of making a perfect roof are eliminated. This is shown in Fig. 116. No doubling of image can occur with this form of prism (Why?).

The prism shown in Figure 107 is known as a *rotating* or *Dove* prism. It does not deviate the beam nor does it displace the

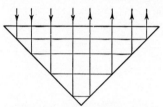

Fig. 115.—Action of a "roof" in reverting an image.

Fig. 116.—Showing how, by doubling the size of the roof, it is possible to avoid the necessity of keeping the roof angle 90° within a few seconds. Compare with Fig. 115.

axis. However, it reverts the image, and is used for this reason. This prism may only be used in a parallel beam of light. In a convergent beam it introduces a prohibitive amount of aberration because the glass plate that may be considered its equivalent is inclined to the beam at a large angle. It must therefore be placed in front at the objective in any telescopic instrument in which it may be used.

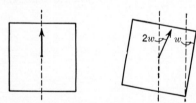

Fig. 117.—Rotation of image by a Dove prism.

This prism has an interesting and unusual property, which is illustrated in Fig. 117. Here we are looking through the prism at an object represented by the arrow. Now as we rotate the prism about a longitudinal axis (perpendicular to the plane of the illustration) through an angle $w$, the image rotates through an angle $2w$, *i.e.*, twice as much as the prism itself. This phenomenon is occasionally used to advantage in devices such as camera view finders, where it is desired to keep the camera horizontal. If the camera is accidentally tilted through a small angle about the axis of the objective, the image seen through the finder, which contains a Dove prism, rotates through *twice* as great an angle, and the error is thus twice as perceptible as with the ordinary view finder and twice as easily detected.   As will be seen in subsequent chapters, this property of the Dove prism is also used in devices of a periscopic nature, such as panoramic sights, to keep a rotating image erect.   The Dove prism, when equipped with a roof at the reflecting surface, is known as a *Wirth prism*. It causes inversion rather than reversion.

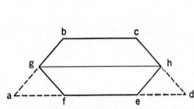

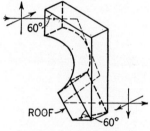

FIG. 118.—Showing how, to conserve space, the Dove prism *abcd* may be replaced by *fghe* and *gbch*.

FIG. 119.—Leman, or Sprenger, prism.   The roof angle is 90°.

When a Dove prism is made of any considerable aperture, it becomes rather long.   If space is at a premium, special means must be adopted to overcome this difficulty.   Consider the Dove prism *abcd* in Fig. 118.   This can be replaced by the two Dove prisms *fghe* and *gbch* cemented together along the face *gh*.   This new prism has the same aperture as the original Dove, yet it is shorter.   It has the same property of reverting an image.   The face *gh* of each prism must be silvered.   The two halves of this prism must be made rather precisely; otherwise a double image will be seen.

The *Leman, or Sprenger, prism*, shown in Fig. 119, laterally displaces the beam and, at the same time, inverts the image by means of a roof.   It is widely used in gunsights of various sorts. Because of the roof angle it is of course difficult to manufacture. The peculiar shape of this prism makes it easy to fasten rigidly in an instrument; in fire control devices this is an important characteristic.

The *Brashear-Hastings prism,* illustrated in Fig. 120, has the desirable property of being able to invert an image without producing deviation or displacement of the beam. It can thus be used to advantage in various telescopic gunsights. Unfortunately, two manufacturing difficulties were experienced in its production: the two upper prisms had to be manufactured separately and cemented on the lower one, this being an expensive

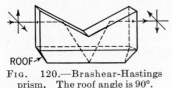

and mechanically unsatisfactory process, and the above-mentioned trouble in properly shaping the roof was encountered. For these reasons this prism is no longer used to any extent.

Fig. 120.—Brashear-Hastings prism. The roof angle is 90°.

When it is desired merely to displace the axis of a beam without introducing deviation and without reverting or inverting the image, the *rhomboidal prism,* shown in Fig. 121, is employed. This finds application in various eyepieces where it is desired to provide means for adjusting to the interocular distance of various observers.

The *penta prism,* shown in Fig. 122, makes possible the modern high-precision rangefinder. This prism has the unique property

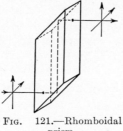

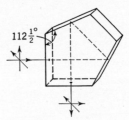

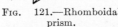

Fig. 121.—Rhomboidal prism.

Fig. 122.—Penta prism.

of deviating a beam exactly 90° in the plane of the rays shown in the figure (known as the *principal plane*) even if the beam should not strike the end faces exactly normal. This does not hold for rays in any other plane. Such prisms are mounted in the two ends of rangefinders. The angles measured by rangefinders are so small that, if such prisms were not used, the normal bending of the tube of the instrument would produce such errors as to render the device worthless. By the use of penta prisms the effect of the bending of the tube is minimized.

In large rangefinders such large penta prisms are required that it is difficult to find large blocks of glass sufficiently homogeneous for the purpose. Thus in such instruments *penta reflectors* consisting of two mirrors oriented by spacers in the same fashion as the reflecting surfaces of the prism are used. Since these mirrors must remain in exact alignment, great care should be taken to see that their alignment is not disturbed by temperature differences across the spacers.

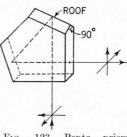

Fig. 123.—Penta prism with roof.

Although the reflections that occurred in the previously considered prisms took place through total reflection, in the penta prism the rays do not strike the reflecting faces at an angle sufficiently large to insure their being totally reflected. It is therefore necessary to silver the two reflecting faces.

The penta prism is sometimes equipped with a roof on one of the reflecting faces for the purpose of reverting the image. This form is shown in Fig. 123. It is used in combination with a

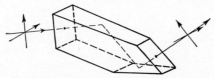

Fig. 124.—D-40, or 40° deviation, prism.

right-angle prism to form the inverting system of some Hensoldt binoculars and is then called a *Daubresse prism* (see page 215).

In many fire-control devices, such as antiaircraft equipment, it is desirable to deviate the beam in order to make possible a more comfortable position for the observer. For example, he might have to view a target above him without bending his head back. A number of prisms that deviate a beam without affecting the orientation of the image have been developed for this purpose. A typical prism of this sort is that shown in Fig. 124. It deviates the axis through 40° without otherwise altering the image. By slightly changing the angles of this prism, it is possible to obtain deviations of 45 and 50°. A modification of this prism that gives a 60° deviation is shown in

Fig. 125. The 40 to 50° prisms deviate the beam by total reflection but, since the rays strike the lower surface of the 60° at too great an angle for this to be accomplished, the surface must be silvered. A still different modification of the same basic prism is shown in Fig. 126. This gives a 90° deviation. Its

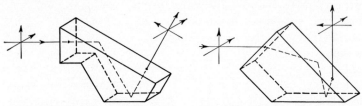

FIG. 125.—D-60-a, or 60° deviation, prism.

FIG. 126.—D-90, or 90° deviation, prism.

lower surface of course must be silvered. This differs from the other prisms of the same category in that the beam neither enters nor leaves the prism normal to the bounding surfaces but is refracted at a large angle. Thus this prism should be restricted to parallel beams of light and not used in a convergent beam. If such a prism were to be used to deviate a beam in a periscopic

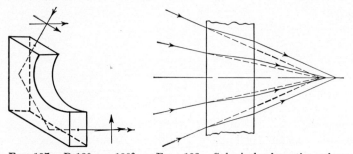

FIG. 127.—D-120, or 120° deviation, prism.

FIG. 128.—Spherical aberration of a thick glass plate.

instrument, the prism would have to be placed ahead of the objective (in a parallel beam) rather than behind the objective (in a converging beam) to avoid excessive aberration.

A prism that gives a 120° deviation without inverting or reverting the image is shown in Fig. 127. This can be used in a parallel or convergent beam. No surfaces on it must be silvered.

It will be realized by now that each of these various prisms may be represented in any optical system by a thick plate of glass with plane parallel faces. In the case of the Dove, Wirth, and 90° deviation prisms the plate is tilted in the beam; with the other prisms it is perpendicular to the beam. It should be remembered that even a plane parallel plate normal to the beam possesses definite aberration characteristics and is not aberration-free as is sometimes assumed. Figure 128 shows how such a plate causes spherical aberration, for example. The spherical aberration introduced by the plate shown is of the same character as the spherical aberration that would be caused by a negative lens; as a general rule, this holds for the other aberrations introduced by such plates, *i.e.*, such aberrations are negative in sign. It will be appreciated that the aberration characteristics of

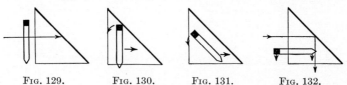

Fig. 129.    Fig. 130.    Fig. 131.    Fig. 132.

Figs. 129–132 —Showing how the orientation of an image formed by light passing through a prism may be determined.

prisms should thus be taken into account in designing any optical system in which they are employed. It is often possible to use the aberration characteristics of such plates to good advantage. In this way lateral color, introduced by the Kellner eyepiece used in binoculars, can be compensated by the aberration characteristics of the erecting prisms.

In the various illustrations shown in this chapter the inverting or reverting characteristics of the prisms are illustrated by arrows showing the orientation of two components of the image before and after passage through the prism. It is possible (and quite easy) to predict how any prism system will affect the image by taking a pencil and orienting it perpendicular to the direction of propagation of the light beam. The pencil is moved over a drawing of the prism in a direction parallel to that taken by the light. The two ends of the pencil are permitted to undergo "reflection" as though they were two segments of a wave front. In Figs. 129 to 132 this method of analyzing the reflection in a right-angle prism is shown. For analyzing the component perpendicular to the plane of the paper the same technique would be used, with the pencil held normal to the paper. In this case it is evident that both ends of the pencil would be "reflected" at once and no reversion would occur in this plane. Whenever a roof is encountered, the pencil should be reversed because the rays themselves reverse in the roof. After a few minutes of practice it is possible to trace reflections through quite complicated systems without difficulty by the use of this technique.

Another factor that should be kept in mind in analyzing these reflections is the position of the observer. Let us return for a moment to the Porro prism of Fig. 111. It is evident that the prism has reversed the vertical component of the image without changing the horizontal component. We might thus assume that the image has been reverted instead of inverted. However, we should keep in mind the fact that the observer who saw the image before the prism was placed in the beam, *i.e.*, an observer to the right of the prism and facing to the left, would have seen one arrowhead to his right and one pointing upward. In order to see the image after the prism had been placed in the beam, he would have to place himself to its left, facing to the right. He would now see one arrowhead to his left and the other pointing downward. Thus, as far as he is concerned, the image has been completely inverted. Considerations of this character should be kept in mind whenever an instrument involving a prism system is being designed.

In coincidence rangefinders it is necessary to present to the observer's eye an image of which one half comes from the optical system on one side of the instrument, the other half of the image coming from the optical elements on the other side. The two images formed by the two objectives are fused into one by means of a complex arrangement known as a *coincidence prism* or *ocular prism*. One of these is illustrated and described in Chap. XVI (Fig. 204). At some place in such a prism is located a surface, usually silvered, which reflects light into the eyepiece from one objective. An appropriate hole is left in the silvering, and light from the other objective is transmitted through this aperture to form the other part of the image. The common focal plane of the two objectives should be at the plane of this surface in order that the two fields may be separated by a sharp line, as is necessary for accurate coincidence setting. Thus the eyepiece must also have this dividing surface in its focal plane, and the dividing line between the two fields will then be imaged sharply. The exact design of the coincidence prisms it employs in its rangefinders is a subject that each nation attempts to keep secret.

## REFERENCES

Czapski and Eppenstein: "Grundzuge der Theorie der optischen Instrumente," J. A. Barth, Leipzig, 1924.

Gardner: "Elementary Optics and Applications to Fire Control Instruments," Government Printing Office, Washington, 1924.

Gleichen: "Theory of Modern Optical Instruments" (trans. by Emsley and Swaine), His Majesty's Stationery Office, London, 1921.

König: "Die Fernrohre und Entfernungsmesser," Julius Springer, Berlin, 1937.

Martin: "An Introduction to Applied Optics," Vol. II, Sir Isaac Pitman & Sons, Ltd., London, 1932.

## PROBLEM

Given the glasses 1.5170/64.5 and 1.6170/36.6, compute the components of an achromatic prism that will give a total deviation of 17'. Solve the same problem with the glasses 1.5170/64.5 and 1.6490/33.8. (In this system of notation for optical glass the first number gives the $D$ index, the second gives the reciprocal dispersion.) Which of the foregoing pairs of glasses appears preferable for this application?

# PART II
*Representative Instruments*

# CHAPTER XII

## TELESCOPES

Inasmuch as the basis of practically all military instruments (binoculars, gun sights, periscopes, rangefinders, etc.) is the telescope, it is of the greatest importance that the fundamentals of the telescope be completely understood before consideration is given the other devices.

**Galilean Telescope.**—The earliest known telescopes date back to about 1600. They were apparently invented in Holland,

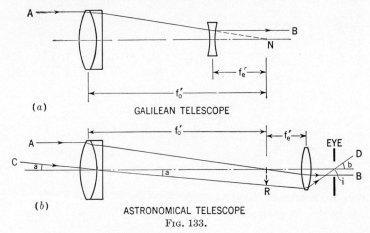

(a)

GALILEAN TELESCOPE

(b)

ASTRONOMICAL TELESCOPE

FIG. 133.

although considerable doubt exists as to who the discoverer was. In 1609 Galileo heard of the invention and immediately applied himself to the task of duplicating it. Although he knew nothing of the details of such an instrument, he constructed one in the space of a day. This device was fundamentally the same as the instrument we know today as the Galilean telescope, which is shown in Fig. 133a. It will be seen to consist of a positive objective and a negative eyepiece with their focal points in coincidence. The line $AB$ represents a ray of light from an infinitely distant object on the axis of the system. This is refracted by the objective toward its focus at $N$. If no eyepiece

169

were present, a real inverted image would be formed at $N$.  However, the rays are intercepted at the eyepiece (which has its focus at $N$), and, as they are converging toward the focus of the eyepiece, they emerge parallel, thus entering the eye.  If the individual using the instrument is near- or far-sighted, he may compensate for his visual defect by adjusting the distance between the two lenses so as to move the focal points of objective and eyepiece out of coincidence.  This will cause the emergent rays to diverge or converge sufficiently to compensate for his eye.  The final image is of course virtual and, for a normal eye, is usually formed at infinity, although it may be formed as close as 10 in., this depending on how the individual adjusts the eyepiece.

The Galilean system is shown again in Fig. 134.  The ray $AB$ striking the objective is the principal ray from the edge of the

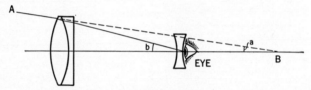

FIG. 134.—Galilean telescope.

field, the angle $a$ being the half angle of the field.  With such a system the eye is the aperture stop and the principal ray must of course pass through its center.  It will be noted that the aperture that limits the angle at which principal rays can arrive is the objective.  Thus, because of this aperture, no principal ray can arrive at an angle greater than $a$.  It is evident, then, that the objective is the field stop and entrance window of the system; thus the extent of the field of this instrument is determined by the diameter of the objective.  This is an important characteristic of Galilean systems.

Let $f'_o$ be the focal length of the objective and $f'_e$ be that of the eyepiece.  Inasmuch as $f'_e$ is negative, it is evident that the objective and the eyepiece are separated by a distance $f'_o + f'_e$.  The apparent field is approximately measured by angle $b$.  It is evident that if $d_o$ is the diameter of the objective

$$\tan b = \frac{d_o}{2(f'_o + f'_e)} \qquad (70)$$

In the event that the user of the telescope forms the final virtual image at infinity, as is usually done, the magnification is given by

$$M = -\frac{f_o'}{f_e'} \tag{71}$$

As $f_e'$ is always negative with a Galilean instrument, $M$ is always positive, meaning that the instrument always gives an erect image. From Eq. (70) and (71), it can be seen that for large magnifications

$$\tan b = \frac{d_o}{2f_o'} \tag{72}$$

Thus the apparent field is determined by the relative aperture. It normally has a value of about 16°. The apparent field and true field are related by

$$\tan \text{ half apparent field} = M \times \tan \text{ half true field} \tag{73}$$

Thus, as the magnification increases, the true field decreases. The Galilean glass is therefore limited to small fields and low magnifications. If an attempt is made to increase the field by

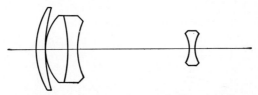

Fig. 135.—An elaborate form of Galilean telescope.

increasing the aperture ratio of the objective, it becomes difficult to correct the system for color, distortion, and astigmatism. If, by using a three-element objective, these aberrations are given a higher state of correction, it becomes possible to use a larger aperture ratio and thus cover a wider field. This was accomplished by Zeiss, who produced a telescope of the type shown in Fig. 135.

The Galilean telescope is very short and compact and gives a bright image because of the few glass-air surfaces involved. It gives an erect image without the aid of an erecting system. It is thus widely used with magnifications of two or three in field glasses, opera glasses, etc. It has two serious defects that closely limit its use for military purposes. In the first place no real image is formed in the instrument.   If a reticle is to be used, it must be in the plane of a real image, for it can then be seen in the same plane.   As no real image is formed, there is no place in the instrument for a reticle, and it thus cannot be used for most military purposes.

Second, because the field of view is fixed by the diameter of the objective, it is not possible to combine a useful field of view with a reasonable amount of magnification.   Most of the commercial Galilean glasses work at two or three power and thus give fair fields of view.   However, a magnification of six is about the least generally used in military binoculars; with such a magnification, a Galilean instrument gives a hopelessly small field.   Occasionally a few field glasses of this type do find their way into military channels, and a few were used during the last war, out of sheer necessity, by the U.S. Navy and the German army. They are sometimes used in sextants and stadimeters but are generally avoided whenever possible.

**Astronomical Telescope.**—The basis of the telescopic systems used in present military instruments is the astronomical telescope shown in Fig. 133b.   This consists of a positive objective and a positive eyepiece with their focal points coinciding.   The ray $AB$ represents light coming from a distant object on the axis. This crosses the axis at the focal point of the objective, where a real inverted image of the object is formed.   As this is at the focus of the eyepiece, light diverging from this point emerges as parallel rays.   The eyepiece is a magnifier through which the real image at $R$ is examined.   If the entrance pupil of the eye is represented by the hole in the stop marked "Eye," it is evident that the telescope will get more light into it than it would receive unaided, for most of the light incident on the objective will enter the eye.   However, we shall see that this does not mean that an increase in brightness results.

Inasmuch as light from the axial object entered the instrument parallel and left it parallel, it would appear that no magnification was introduced.   In order to understand the mechanism of magnification, it is necessary to consider a principal ray (*i.e.*, one through the center of the stop) from some point on the object removed from the axis.   Let us consider the ray from the point of the object at the extreme edge of the field.   This is the ray *CRD. In all astronomical telescopes and in most terrestrial telescopes derived from them, the aperture stop is the objective itself.* Thus the principal ray is drawn through the center of the objective. As it comes from the edge of the field, the angle at which it arrives, $a$, is the half field covered by the instrument. As a ray passing through the center of a lens is not refracted, the ray leaves the objective still making an angle $a$ with the axis. Inasmuch as the ray originated at the edge of the object, it passes through the edge of the real image at $R$. Upon being refracted by the eyepiece, it strikes the axis at $i$. As this ray crossed the axis at the objective, it can be considered as emanating from the objective, and the fact that it again crossed the axis at $i$ indicates that a real image of the objective is formed at $i$. The image of a stop formed by the lenses to its right is defined as the exit pupil. As the objective is the stop, it is immediately evident that the exit pupil of the instrument is located at $i$. This is the narrowest point in the emergent beam; consequently, the entrance pupil of the eye is located here. It is usually preferable to locate the center of rotation of the eye here instead but this is usually not practicable. During the designing of a telescope, the location of the exit pupil should be given careful consideration. If it is placed too far back, the eyepiece will become unnecessarily bulky; if it is placed too close, the user of the instrument will suffer discomfort. The distance from the eye lens to the exit pupil is called the *eye relief*, and this should be about 8 mm. For gun sights it is often made much longer so that the sight will not strike the user when recoil occurs.

The principal ray entered the telescope at an angle $a$ with the axis. It enters the eye at an angle $b$, which is much larger than $a$. Thus the image subtends a much larger angle at the eye than does the object, and the instrument has caused angular magnification. The *true field* of the instrument is, by definition, the angle $2a$, while the *apparent field* is the angle $2b$. It is evident that the angular magnification is $b/a$, but for ease in computation we use the following defining equation:

$$M = \text{angular magnification} = \frac{\text{tan half apparent field}}{\text{tan half true field}}$$

$$= \frac{\tan b}{\tan a} \quad (74)$$

The tangents are used because they appear in certain other

magnification formulas, and the magnification defined in this fashion is of great practical value. It is very nearly equal to the magnification obtained from $b/a$.

From the geometry of Fig. 133$b$, it is easily demonstrated that

$$M = \text{angular magnification} = -\frac{f_o'}{f_e'} \tag{75}$$

where $f_o'$ is the focal length of the objective and $f_e'$ is the focal length of the eyepiece. The minus sign shows that the image formed by the instrument is inverted. It is of interest to note that this same equation applies to the Galilean telescope. In that case $f_e'$ is always negative, thus giving a positive value for

PLATE I.—Telescope in use aboard an aircraft carrier. (*Official U.S. Navy Photograph.*)

the magnification and indicating that an erect image is formed. It is evident that, to get high magnification in both types of telescopes, it is necessary to have either an objective of long focal length or an eyepiece of short focal length.

Although we use Eq. (74) as a rigid definition of magnification, we often use the ratio $b/a$ as a close approximation, particularly when estimating the apparent field of an instrument when given the true field and the magnification. It will be noted that Eq. (75) gives the magnification only when the instrument is so focused that the virtual image is at infinity, *i.e.*, the focal planes of objective and eyepiece are coincident and the rays emerging from the eyepiece are in parallel bundles. It will be remembered that objects can be seen distinctly if they are as close as 10 in. to the eye. As the image is moved closer to the observer (by focusing the instrument so as to throw the focal points of objective and eyepiece out of coincidence), it increases somewhat in size. Many observers try to get as much magnification as possible out of an instrument and thus bring the image to within 10 in. of the eye to get maximum results. The eye is more strained while viewing an image here than it is in seeing one formed at infinity; thus, it is not recommended that this procedure be followed. When an instrument is focused, the observer does not know where he is placing the image; he merely locates it in the position of best seeing, or of maximum magnification.

When the image is formed 10 in. from the observer rather than at infinity, the magnification is given by

$$M = -\left(\frac{f_o'}{f_e'} + \frac{f_o'}{D}\right) \tag{76}$$

$D$ is the closest distance for distinct vision (10 in.).

When the focal points of the eyepiece and the objective are placed in coincidence, *i.e.*, when the instrument is focused for infinity, the telescope is capable of forming images of objects located at finite distances. Regardless of the location of object and image, the magnification of such a system is constant, being unchanged by a shift of object position.

If $d_o$ is the diameter of the objective, and $d_i$ is the diameter of the exit pupil, then the absolute value of $M$ is given by

$$|M| = \frac{d_o}{d_i} \tag{77}$$

This equation is useful in that it gives an easy method of measuring the magnifying power of a telescope. By illuminating the objective with a diffuse source of light and measuring the resulting exit pupil with a scale or traveling microscope, the magnification is easily computed. It is also possible to place the open points of a pair of dividers before the objective. Their images will be located just in front of the exit pupil. By taking the ratio of the distance between the points to the distance between their images the magnifying power is determined.

Telescopic systems are unique in that their principal points and focal points are located at infinity.

**Resolving Power.**—The next point to be considered is that of *resolving power*. This is of the utmost importance, and to consider it we shall leave the subject of telescopes briefly. It will be remembered that a perfect optical system cannot form a point image of a point object because of diffraction phenomena.

Instead, the image takes the form of a system of concentric light and dark rings, the pattern being known as an Airy disk (see Fig. 136). The whole problem of resolving power merely reduces to determining the conditions under which the images of two point sources can be distinguished from one another. Usually, the condition for resolution is taken to be the situation

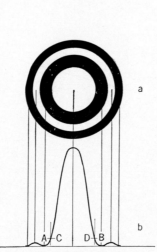

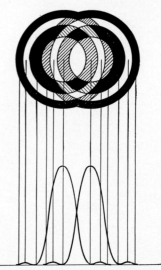

Fig. 136.—The central rings of an Airy disk. A diffraction pattern contains many more rings than are shown in the illustration, but the outer ones are too faint to be of importance in the design of most instruments. The curve in the lower portion of the figure gives the relative intensities of the various parts of the pattern.

Fig. 137.—The overlapping diffraction patterns of two adjacent point sources that may just be resolved. The curves at the bottom of the illustration show the relative intensities in the two patterns. The outer rings of each pattern have been omitted because they are not important.

where the center of the Airy disk of one image approaches the center of the Airy disk of the other image no closer than the first dark ring. This condition is shown in Fig. 137.

Consider an objective of diameter $d_o$, as shown in Fig. 138. With a point object this objective will form an image consisting of an Airy disk diffraction pattern. In measuring the diameter of this pattern we shall consider only the central bright disk and shall take the effective diameter of the whole pattern as the diameter of the first dark ring. We are justified in doing this because about 84 per cent of the total energy in the diffraction pattern appears in the central bright disk. The angular size of this pattern, as measured by the diameter of the first minimum, depends only on the diameter of the objective and the wavelength of the light being used. For the objective of diameter $d_o$, the

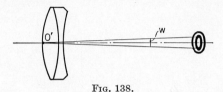

FIG. 138.

angle that the first minimum will subtend at the second nodal point of the objective is

$$w = \frac{2.44\lambda}{d_o} \tag{78}$$

$\lambda$ can of course be taken as 555 m$\mu$; $d_o$ must then be measured in the same units. The actual diameter $x'$ of the first minimum is then given by

$$x' = 2.44\lambda \frac{f_o'}{d_o} \tag{79}$$

and it is seen to be proportional to the focal ratio (ratio of focal length to aperture). Thus, if we were attempting to photograph a small object and found that an $f/3.5$ objective did not have sufficient resolving power to give a sharp image, we should have to use a faster objective, say an $f/2$, of the same focal length and try again. Of course what we are trying to do is to make $x'$ as small as possible, for we wish as nearly as possible to obtain a point image of a point object. In practice, we should find that the decrease in image size that we would obtain in going from an $f/3.5$ to an $f/2$ objective would not be so great as had been anticipated because of other factors, particularly the graininess of the photographic emulsion. For the same reason we should probably find that in practice we would obtain better resolution if we increased the focal length of the objective, keeping the focal ratio constant, although our equations state that resolving power is only a function of focal ratio, and not focal length. Theoretically, in aerial photography, one should be able to obtain the same resolution whether he uses a short focal length objective of a certain focal ratio and then enlarges the negative, or uses a long focal length lens (to get a large negative) of the same focal ratio and makes a contact print. Experience shows that the contact print will be superior to the enlargement, probably because of the graininess of the emulsion, aberrations of the lenses, etc. This fact is responsible for the present interest in long focus objectives for use in aerial photography.

If one wishes to know whether a telescope objective will resolve two specific point sources, it is necessary to determine whether the objective will make their diffraction patterns, formed in the plane of the real image, sufficiently small so that they will not overlap more than is shown in Fig. 137. If an objective can *just* resolve two points that subtend a certain angle at the objective, that angle is called the *angular resolving power*. This may be computed, for an objective, by the following equation, which has been derived from those given above:

$$\text{Angular resolving power} = \frac{5.5}{d_o} \quad \text{(seconds)} \quad (80)$$

In this expression the diameter $d_o$ must be expressed in inches. It is derived on the assumption that the eye can just distinguish $AB$ as being the effective diameter of the diffraction disk shown in Fig. 136. Many experiments on the eye, using both microscopes and telescopes, indicate that the eye cannot discern the faint light near the bottom of the central peak, and they suggest that the visually effective diameter of the pattern is $CD$. The astronomer Dawes investigated this point. He investigated the ability of telescope objectives to resolve double stars. For two stars of approximately equal brightnesses he found that Eq. (80) should have the form

$$\text{Angular resolving power} = \frac{4.5}{d_o} \quad \text{(seconds)} \quad (81)$$

On the basis of these data it can be shown that the constant in the classic equations of resolving power [Eqs. (78) and (79)] should be 2.0 instead of 2.44.

Equation (81) applies only to the case of two equally bright point sources and might require modification for other types of objects. It is useful in that it gives, in a general way, a basis of comparison of various telescope objectives and an approximation to their probable performance. It will of course be appreciated that these various equations of resolving power all assume that the objectives under consideration are aberrationless, and the limit of resolution is determined by diffraction. With properly designed and constructed telescopes it is often possible to fill this condition. The equations given thus can be used. This also applies to microscope objectives. With photographic objectives, however, the resolving power is usually limited by aberrations because of the comparatively large fields they cover. Telescopes usually cover true fields of from 1 to 15°, averaging about 3°. Photographic objectives cover fields of 40° to about 150°!

In attempting to resolve two point objects with a telescope, it is not only necessary that they be resolved in the plane of the real image by the objective; after this has been accomplished, they must be distinguished by the eye. Their angular separation should be greater than the minimum that can be resolved by the eye. The limit of visual resolution (minimum separabile), as we saw in Chap. V, is usually taken as 1′, and in general this figure is useful as a criterion of resolving power.

It has been shown that the angle subtended by a single Airy disk at the second nodal point of the objective was $w$. For a telescope of angular magnifying power $M$ the angle this disk will subtend at the eye will be approximately $Mw$.

If a point source is being viewed by a telescope, the Airy disk will be formed at $R$ in Fig. 133$b$. It is then viewed by the eyepiece, which magnifies it. If the eyepiece is of low magnification, this disk will still appear as a point; as the power is increased, the details of the disk will become evident. Thus when the telescope is being used to view a target, if the magnification is too high, the details of the target will be lost because of the fuzziness of the diffraction patterns. Consequently there is a definite limitation upon the permissible magnification that may be associated with a given resolving power. For an objective of diameter $d_o$ in. the magnification that will just bring out all the detail (*i. e.*, give a diffraction pattern that subtends an angle at the eye of 1′) is given by

$$M = 13d_o \tag{82}$$

Therefore, if we are designing a telescope with a 2 in. objective, a magnification of 26 will bring out all the detail of the image formed in the focal plane of the objective. However, some of this detail might be too small to be easily seen, so it is permissible to increase the magnification from two to four times to make the resolved detail in the final virtual image more easily visible. This additional magnification does not add to the resolving power and is therefore known as *empty magnification*. If further magnification were employed, detail would become somewhat blurred by the increasing size of the diffraction pattern, and this is definitely objectionable. Eq. (82) has been derived from Eq. (81) rather than from Eq. (80). Strictly speaking, the constant in Eq. (82) should be replaced by a variable that is a function of exit pupil diameter (see page 74).

Suppose we were designing a telescope having an objective of focal length $f'_o$. We should like to known the focal length of the eyepiece we should use with this objective to give the maximum resolving power. As we increase the focal length of the eyepiece, we produce two effects: we decrease the magnification and thus reduce the size of the diffraction image, and we increase the size of the exit pupil. The classical view of this question is to consider only the first of these effects. If Eq. (78) is accepted as stated, it can be easily shown that in order to make the image of the diffraction pattern of a single point source formed in the objective's focal plane subtend an angle of 1' at the eye when viewed through the eyepiece, the focal length of the eyepiece must be given by

$$f'_e = 2.44 \frac{f'_o}{d_o} \quad \text{(millimeters)} \tag{83}$$

where $d_o$ is the diameter of the objective. By comparison with Eqs. (75) and (77) it will be seen that this is equivalent to stating that the exit pupil must have a diameter of 2.44 mm. However, investigation of the variation of visual acuity with pupil diameter (see Chap. V)[1] has shown that with an exit pupil of 2.44-mm diameter the eye cannot resolve 1'. Therefore we see that Eq. (83) would be valid provided that visual acuity were con-

---

[1] The data in Chap. V relate visual acuity to the entrance pupil diameter of the eye. However, if the exit pupil of an instrument is smaller than the entrance pupil of the eye, it sets the limit to the zones of the eye through which light will pass (see Fig. 139). Therefore, instead of the iris, the exit pupil of a telescope may be the limiting aperture of the eye.

stant at all pupil diameters. The fact that this is not true eliminates from consideration equations of this sort, and we must conclude that the most satisfactory value of $f'_e$ is that which gives us an exit pupil diameter of 4 mm (which is the diameter of maximal acuity) or

$$f'_e = 4.0 \frac{f'_o}{d_o} \tag{84}$$

If we, instead of accepting Eq. (78) as stated, used as a constant in it the value 2.0 instead of 2.44, for the reasons previously outlined, we would have arrived at a value of 2.0 mm for the optimum exit pupil diameter. Actually the eye has very poor visual acuity at such a pupil diameter, and it would appear that an eyepiece designed in accordance with Eq. (84) would give the best resolving power. In practice the designer usually has the opportunity of controlling exit pupil diameter by varying both objective diameter and magnification.

We shall see below that, in order to make use of the full resolving power *of the objective*, the exit pupil must be a certain size. It should be borne in mind that the ultimate limit on resolving power is set by visual acuity, and this is a maximum with a 4-mm pupil.

**Stops.**—Reference is again made to Fig. 133*b*. It will be noted that the extreme principal ray from an object at the very edge of the field can be determined by a stop in the plane of the real image *R*. A stop of this sort that limits the field is the field stop. It is put in the plane of *R* in order that it might be sharply defined in the field of view and thus give a sharp image. It cuts out the parts of the image that might suffer too greatly because of extra-axial aberrations, keeping visible only the sharp part of the image. The image of this stop seen by the eye is the exit window. It will be noted that the brightness of the image is controlled by the stop formed by the objective (aperture stop), while the field of view is controlled by the field stop. Thus these two variables may be controlled independently. If *r* is the radius of the field stop (and this is the height of the image at *R*), it will be noted in Fig. 133*b* that this relationship holds:

$$a = \tan^{-1} \frac{r}{f'_o} \tag{85}$$

In a telescope or other instrument in which the resolving power that one expects on the basis of diffraction is realized, a diaphragm placed over the periphery of the lens to reduce illumination also reduces resolving power because of the decreased aperture.   However, if the illumination is reduced by placing an opaque disk over the center of the lens, leaving the diameter at its original value, the resolving power will not only be retained, but will actually be somewhat improved.   The diameter of the first dark ring in the diffraction pattern will be reduced.   Photographic objectives are normally too afflicted with aberration to approach the theoretical resolving power, and therefore considerations of this character do not apply to them.

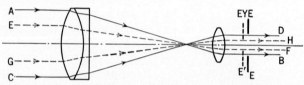

Fig. 139.—Effect of size of entrance pupil of the eye on effective diameter of the objective of a telescope.

**Size of Exit Pupil.**—In the design of a telescope the selection of the proper exit pupil size is of some importance, as has been indicated previously.   We have seen that the exit pupil is the image of the aperture stop, which for the astronomical and terrestrial telescope is the objective.   The diameter of the exit pupil is the diameter of the aperture stop (objective) divided by the magnification [Eq. (77)].

Consider the telescope shown in Fig. 139.   The edge rays $AB$ and $CD$ are able to enter the eye because its entrance pupil $E$ is larger than the exit pupil of the telescope, the diameter of this pupil being equal to $DB$.   In this case the resolving power of the objective is given by Eq. (81), with $a_o$ equal to $AC$.   Thus, when the entrance pupil of the eye is larger than the exit pupil of the instrument, we make use of the full resolving power of the objective because the objective is the limiting aperture of the system.   Now, suppose that the entrance pupil of the eye is smaller than the exit pupil of the telescope.   In this case let the entrance pupil of the eye be represented by $E'$ in Fig. 139. Note that rays $AB$ and $CD$ now no longer enter the eye, being stopped by its iris.   Instead, $EF$ and $GH$ are the extreme rays.

No rays between *EF* and *AB*, and *GH* and *CD*, enter the eye. Thus the marginal rays are now *EF* and *GH*, and the effective diameter of the objective is *EG*. The resolving power of the objective is now obtained by using *EG* for $d_o$ in Eq. (81), and the resultant resolving power is less than when we used the whole diameter of the objective. We thus see that, in order to make full use of all the resolving power inherent in a given objective, (and this *does not* mean to attain maximum visual acuity) it is necessary that the entrance pupil of the eye be at least as large as the exit pupil of the telescope.

In order to appreciate the relationship of pupil size to illumination, let us consider an actual case. Suppose we were comparing 8 × 30 and 8 × 40 binoculars. (The first number in these designations refers to angular magnification; the second gives the diameter of the objective in millimeters.) Assume the instruments are to be used for daytime vision, in which case the diameter of the entrance pupil of the average eye is about 5 mm. Because the amount of light passing through a circular aperture is proportional to its area and thus to the square of its diameter, it is evident that the 30-mm objective picks up $(30/5)^2$ or 36 times as much light as the unaided eye with its 5-mm pupil. Because the magnification is 8, the area of the retinal image formed with the binocular is $8^2$ or 64 times as large as that formed with the unaided eye. Thus with the binocular we have 36 times as much light, but it is distributed over an area 64 times as large as with the eye alone. The illumination on the retina when using the instrument is therefore only 36/64, or 56.3 per cent, of that without it. These calculations have neglected reflection and absorption losses in the lenses, and such losses would reduce the illumination still more. With the 8 × 40 binocular it is seen that the amount of light entering the eye is $(40/5)^2$ or 64 times that entering the unaided eye. Because the magnification is 8, the retinal image is again 64 times the original size. The illumination is now 64/64 or equal to that on the unaided eye (again neglecting reflection and absorption losses). If we were to use an 8 × 50 binocular, we should find that because of the considerations illustrated in Fig. 139 the effective diameter of the objective would still be 40 mm, and the light coming through the extra 10 mm of diameter would strike the iris of the eye and be lost. This is easily seen when we consider that the size of the exit pupil of an 8 × 50 binocular is 50/8 or 6.25 mm. As its exit pupil is larger than the entrance pupil of the eye, it is evident that all the light passing through the exit pupil of the telescope cannot enter the eye. Thus we see that for maximum illumination the exit pupil of the instrument should be at least as large as the entrance pupil of the eye. We have seen that to make full use of all the resolving power of the objective the entrance pupil of the eye has to be at least as large as the exit pupil. Therefore, to obtain maximum illumination and use all the resolving power of the objective, it is necessary that the exit pupil of the telescope should be equal in size to the entrance pupil of the eye. As has been mentioned, the average size of the eye's entrance pupil in the daytime is 5 mm. Thus for an objective 40 mm in diameter a magnification of 40/5 or 8 is required to achieve this end. The magnification that does make the exit pupil diameter of an instrument equal to the entrance pupil diameter of the eye is called *normal magnification*. For night vision the entrance pupil of the eye is about 7 mm in diameter. Therefore for night work the normal magnification should be such as to make the exit pupil 7 mm in diameter. A 7 × 50 binocular is thus a good night glass, but its 7.15-mm exit pupil is larger than necessary for day use. In the daytime a 7 × 35 binocular would be just as effective.

We have seen that when designed for normal magnification an instrument makes full use of the inherent resolving power of the objective. However, nothing has been said about making use of the resolving power of the eye. The resolving power of the objective controls the quality of the real image formed at $R$ in Fig. 133b, and the resolving power of the eye limits the quality of the image formed on the retina. We have already seen in Chap. V that the eye shows maximum resolving power for a pupil diameter of about 3 to 5 mm. If, instead of working at normal magnification, we slightly increase this magnification, the diameter of the exit pupil of the telescope will be reduced and will thus be 4.0 mm, an efficient value for good vision. This increase in magnification, which may be obtained by reducing the focal length of the eyepiece, introduces some "empty magnification" which has been shown to be desirable.

Thus, although instruments with large exit pupils have well-illuminated images, they generally fall slightly short of giving all the resolving power inherent in them. By increasing the magnification and therefore reducing the exit pupil size, an improvement in resolving power can be effected but only at the cost of illumination.

There are a number of annoying discrepancies in the various experimental data and equations relating visual acuity to pupil size, and it would seem desirable that some time be devoted to rectifying this situation.

PLATE II.—Army field observation, or spotting, telescope with prismatic erector. The instrument is of 3 power. (*Official War Department Photograph.*)

**Night Glasses.**—We have seen that, even with an instrument in which no reflection losses take place, the illumination on the retina is never greater than that obtained with the unaided eye, and with any real instrument it is always less. How, then, does a so-called night glass work? The answer to this is not clearly understood. It is known that, when we consider objects of various sizes and measure the brightness of each that can just be seen under standardized conditions (threshold brightness), it is found that the minimum visible brightness is approximately inversely proportional (for objects subtending angles of 1 to 4° at the eye) to the size of the object.[1] In other words, the larger the

[1] MARTIN, *Bull. No.* 3, Department of Scientific and Industrial Research, His Majesty's Stationery Office, London.

object, the more easily it is seen in dim light. Magnification increases the apparent size of an object, and it is this magnification, then, rather than any increase in brightness, that is responsible for the success of night glasses.

We saw previously that a star that could not be seen when imaged on the fovea became visible when imaged closer to the periphery of the retina. This suggests that the extra-foveal portions of the retina are more sensitive to low levels of illumination than the fovea, and is in accord with the theory of rod and cone vision. In a night glass the magnification extends the area of stimulation of the retina into the outer regions, and this extension is apparently associated with some increase in the sensitivity of the central portions because the center of the image appears as bright as the edge. Can stimulation of the extra-foveal portions of the retina increase the sensitivity of the fovea? This point has been investigated on several occasions, and the answer appears to be in the affirmative,[1] the phenomenon being called *spatial induction*. Jones found that a motion picture could be seen more clearly if the extra-foveal portions of the retina were stimulated. Cobb, Martin, and Emerson and Martin[2] investigated contrast sensitivity, and found that the fovea of the eye showed an improvement in this respect if the extra-foveal portions of the retina were stimulated by a field of approximately the same brightness as that used in stimulating the fovea. The effect was less marked for less bright extra-foveal stimulation, and a decided decrease in contrast sensitivity was obtained when the extra-foveal portions were stimulated by too bright a field. Emerson and Martin also tried an experiment in which a photometric matching field, used to measure contrast sensitivity, of $3\frac{1}{2}°$ was surrounded by a dark field of $16°$ on the retina, and then the retinal region between this field and $45°$ was stimulated. Again an increase in contrast sensitivity of the retina was noted. This last experiment, particularly, suggests that the fovea is sensitized by extra-foveal stimulation, and this may well be the explanation of the functioning of the night glass.

[1] JONES, *Comm.* 135, Research Lab., Eastman Kodak Co., Rochester, N.Y.

[2] COBB, *J. Exp. Psychol.*, Vol. 1, pp. 419, 540, 1916.

MARTIN, *Proc. Roy. Soc.*, Vol. A 104, p. 302, 1923.

EMERSON and MARTIN, *Proc. Roy. Soc.*, Vol. A 108, p. 483, 1925.

Martin and Richards[1] reasoned that if excessive stimulation of the extra-foveal portions of the retina reduced the contrast sensitivity, field glasses that were being used to study small dark objects surrounded by brightly illuminated fields might function better if the field were markedly reduced to decrease the excessive extra-foveal illumination. This is particularly the case with glasses intended for marine use, where one might wish to view a small dark object, such as a vessel, surrounded by a bright field consisting of light from the sky and water. They experimented with binoculars having fields of 20 and 50°, under such conditions, and found that fewer discrimination errors were made with the instrument having the smaller field. They conclude that it might be desirable to provide marine binoculars with an adjustable diaphragm so that the apparent field may be temporarily reduced when studying objects of this sort.

Martin found that a photometric brightness match could be made with greater precision if the extra-foveal portions of the retina were stimulated by a field of brightness approximately equal to that of the photometric field. For the same reason, with night glasses and other instruments intended for night use it would appear desirable to stimulate artificially the extra-foveal portions of the retina. This could be done presumably with electric lights, but that would not generally be a practical solution. However, we usually limit the field of a visual instrument with a field stop, this stop serving to cut out the edge of the image which would appear of poor quality because of bad eyepiece performance at 20 to 25° from the axis. Instead of using an opaque object for a field stop it might be possible to use a diffusing medium, such as ground glass. This would be illuminated by the bad peripheral portions of the image that we do not wish to see, and would, for normal targets, automatically fill the requirement that the extra-foveal retinal stimulation be of approximately the same level as the foveal stimulation. The use of phosphorescent paint might also prove of some value. Not enough data have been accumulated concerning the effects of stimulating portions of the retina more than 25° removed from the eye's optical axis to tell whether these techniques might prove of marked value, and it would appear desirable to clear these points up experimentally.

[1] MARTIN and RICHARDS, *Trans. Opt. Soc.*, Vol. 30, p. 22, 1928–1929.

**Objectives.**—Most telescope objectives are of the type shown in Fig. 140. The first element is made of crown glass, the second of flint. The designer first decides what focal length he wishes. This determines the total power of the objective. He next determines the ratio of the powers of the crown and flint elements that will achromatize the system. He then bends the lens as a whole to remove spherical aberration. If he has chosen his glasses properly, he will be able to achromatize the system without introducing excessively steep curves, which are objectionable

Fig. 140.—Ordinary cemented doublet type of telescope objective.

from the viewpoint of both performance and manufacture. Again, if the glasses have been properly chosen, the final shape of the system that will remove spherical aberration will be similar to that shown in the illustration. If the glasses were not correctly chosen, either an extreme shape will result or no solution will be found. The form shown in Fig. 140 (with the last surface plane) is desired for manufacturing convenience and may be obtained through proper selection of glass. An equi-convex shape for the crown element is also highly desirable. It will be noted that the only aberrations that can be corrected are spherical aberration and longitudinal chromatic aberration. Correction of these usually suffices to give a good system. If the instrument is to be used at points well removed from the axis, *i.e.*, at large field angles, coma will have to be given consideration. With a cemented doublet no degree of freedom is left for the correction of this aberration but, if the proper glasses are chosen, rather good correction can be obtained automatically. The cementing of the contact surface is generally considered desirable for it helps to maintain the two elements in alignment under sharp blows and also decreases the light loss through reflection at the two surfaces in contact. In addition, it aids in cleanliness. Lenses of large diameter cannot be cemented because of the difference in the thermal expansion coefficients of crown and flint glasses.

Occasionally an objective with the flint element in front is encountered. This is called a *Steinheil* or *flint-in-front objective* (Fig. 141). It is far less popular than the standard type because the flint element, which is more sensitive to attack by atmospheric constituents than crown, is exposed. Another objection is that flint glass is softer than crown and resists abrasion to a lesser extent. This type gives a more curved field than the standard crown-in-front type, but less zonal spherical aberration. It is used for some military purposes.

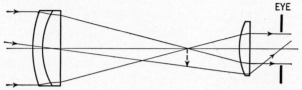

EYE

Fig. 141.—Astronomical telescope with flint-in-front objective.

If particularly good correction for coma is desired, an additional degree of freedom is required. This is obtained by bending the two elements independently. This means that they cannot be cemented, and a lens of the type shown in Fig. 142 results. This is often called a *broken-contact objective*. The additional degree of freedom may be used to correct spherical aberration at two

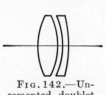

Fig. 142.—Un-cemented doublet (broken-contact) telescope objective.

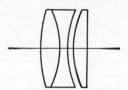

Fig. 143.—Photo-visual, or Cooke, telescope objective.

different wavelengths (*Gauss objective*); if this is done, coma correction must be sacrificed.

Ordinarily two different types of glass are combined to achromatize an objective at two different wavelengths. Objectives so achromatized commonly suffer from large chromatic residuals known as secondary spectrum, this being caused by a distance between the $D$ focus and the combined $CF$ focus of about $1/2,500$ of the focal length for most glasses. This aberration may be greatly reduced by using three different glasses to achromatize at three different wavelengths. An objective of the shape shown in Fig. 143 results. This type of lens was developed by H. Dennis Taylor and is known as a *photo-visual* or *Cooke objective*. It is rarely encountered in practice for the curves required are generally quite steep. It cannot be used at speeds much above $f/15$.

Occasionally it becomes desirable to have a very highly corrected objective. In this case Cooke Triplets and Tessars (see Figs. 87 and 84) are used. These are used for astrographic work and for some military purposes.

**Eyepieces.** *General Considerations.*—An objective forms a real image at its focus. This image is rather small and is generally too close to the eye to be easily seen. If it is moved far enough from the eye to be visible, it subtends too small an angle at the eye. Thus extra lenses are added to magnify this image and form an image of it sufficiently far away (usually at infinity) to be clearly seen. These lenses are the eyepiece of the instrument. The eyepiece works satisfactorily if it forms an image (virtual) anywhere between the point of most distinct vision of the eye (about 10 in. distant) and infinity.

Eyepieces usually cover apparent fields of 40 to 50°. These figures place a definite limitation on the true field that can be covered with a given magnification, or vice versa.

The simplest basic forms of eyepieces in general use consist of two simple lenses. The lens nearest the eye does the actual magnifying of the image and can affect the quality of the image. This is known as the *eye lens*. The other element, called the *field lens*, is usually located near the plane of the real image and has less effect on it. The purpose of this lens can be seen by a study of Fig. 145. The marginal rays *AB* and *CD* pass through the system and emerge parallel without obstruction. The principal ray from the edge of the field (*EF*) presents a different picture. Note that, if it were not for the presence of the field lens, this ray would miss the eye lens completely, and the edge of the field would thus be dark. Thus the function of the field lens is to collect the rays from the outer part of the field and divert them into the eye lens, giving a reasonably uniformly illuminated image. This lens does not greatly affect the size of the image. Theoretically, the field lens should be exactly in the plane of the real image, in which case it would have no effect whatever on magnification. In this case it would move the exit pupil in closer to the instrument without changing its size. In the eyepiece shown, the field lens has been moved away from the real image. This is done partly to keep any dust that might be on the field lens out of the field of view, for if the lens were in the plane of the image any dirt on it could be clearly seen. By moving the field lens away from the image plane it is caused to exert some effect on magnification and the quality of the image; it being generally used to correct coma.

The general function of the eyepiece can be seen by reference to Fig. 141. It receives the rays that enter the objective parallel and directs them as a parallel beam into the eye. It forms an image of the objective at the point at which the eye is placed, this image of course being the exit pupil.

The axial rays passing through the eyepiece are so close to the axis, and so nearly parallel, that spherical aberration and longitudinal chromatic aberration in the eyepiece are usually not serious. One of the aberrations given the deepest consideration in eyepiece design is transverse chromatic aberration, or lateral color. The simple basic eyepieces consist of two simple lenses (eye and field lenses) of focal lengths $f_a'$ and $f_b'$ respectively made of the same type of glass. It can be shown that for such a system the condition for freedom from lateral color is that the spacing $d$ between these elements should be

$$d = \frac{f_a' + f_b'}{2} \tag{86}$$

This formula is not exact, but it is good enough for the preliminary design of an eyepiece. More exact formulas have been derived but are not widely used.

It is also necessary to have a reasonably flat tangential field; it is equally important to have the eyepiece corrected for coma. There are not enough degrees of freedom to secure all these corrections, but fortunately it so happens that by correcting an eyepiece for coma, sufficient negative astigmatism is obtained from the convex surface of the field lens to give a flat tangential field, as shown in Fig. 29.

It will be noted that the simple basic forms of eyepieces use only plano-convex lenses. Considerable experience has shown lens designers that essentially nothing is to be gained by using other forms in most eyepieces, and as the plano-convex form is desirable from a manufacturing viewpoint it is used almost exclusively. The question of whether the convex surface shall be on the right or left in these various components is decided upon the basis of correction for oblique aberrations, particularly astigmatism and curvature of field.

*Huygenian Eyepiece.*—In eyepieces of this form (Fig. 144) the real image formed at the focus of the objective is at *I*. However, because the rays strike the field lens before arriving at this image, they are diverted, and the image appears at *I'*. The chief point in favor of this eyepiece is that it can be completely freed of lateral color and so is preferred to other types for observational purposes. However it has one serious drawback: it cannot be satisfactorily used with a reticle. A reticle would have to be placed inside the eyepiece, in the plane of *I'*, and this offers considerable mechanical difficulty. Furthermore, although the eyepiece as a whole is corrected, its individual components are not. A reticle located at *I'* would be viewed solely by means of the eye

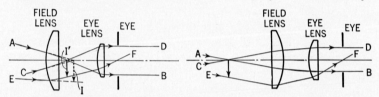

Fig. 144.—Huygenian eyepiece.          Fig. 145.—Ramsden eyepiece.

lens. This would introduce a large amount of aberration, particularly distortion and lateral color. Huygenian eyepieces with reticles are used with microscopes, but in this case the reticle is kept small so that it is seen only at the center of the field.

This eyepiece normally has both elements made of the same type of crown glass.

In Fig. 144, *AB* and *CD* are marginal rays from a distant axial object point and *EF* is the principal ray from the edge of the field (see Fig. 150).

With regard to the residual aberrations of this type of eyepiece it may be mentioned that it has a rather considerable amount of longitudinal color, more even than a simple thin lens of the same glass and focal length. Spherical aberration is present to a certain extent. If an attempt is made to use such an eyepiece at $f/7$ or better, it will be necessary to overcorrect the objective to balance out this aberration. The Petzval surface is curved toward the objective, but this is compensated by negative astigmatism that gives a fairly flat tangential field. A rather large amount of pincushion distortion ($-3$ per cent at $15°$) is usually present, but it is not often noticed. Coma and lateral color can be eliminated.

It should be noted that with Huygenian eyepieces having focal lengths of less than 1 in. the eye relief is usually too short for comfort.

*Ramsden Eyepiece.*—This type of eyepiece is illustrated in Fig. 145. A real image is formed in front of the eyepiece and is examined by it. Since a reticle may be placed in the plane of the real image, this general type of eyepiece is widely used with reticles. The only serious drawback to the Ramsden is the fact that it has a very considerable amount of lateral color. With regard to all the other aberrations it is better, if properly designed, than the Huygenian. The only possible way to achromatize the Ramsden is to bring the plane of the real image inside the eyepiece, and thus a reticle could not be used.

The lettering in Fig. 145 is similar to that in Fig. 144.

With regard to residual aberrations it may be said that the Ramsden has about one-fifth the spherical aberration of the Huygenian and about one-half the longitudinal color. The distortion is less than half that of the Huygenian. The tangential field of the Ramsden curves back, away from the objective, and in about the proper amount to compensate for the forward curvature caused by the normal objective. It is thus superior in this respect to the Huygenian. Coma is essentially zero.

The eye relief of the Ramsden is about 1.5 times that of the Huygenian—another important point in its favor. In addition its aberration characteristics are much less sensitive to slight changes in the focal length of the objective for which it was calculated.

*Kellner or Achromatized Ramsden Eyepiece.*—It has been pointed out that the Ramsden is a very desirable eyepiece and has only the disadvantage of a large amount of lateral color. This aberration can be reduced to a small quantity by making the eye lens of the Ramsden in the form of a cemented doublet. This type of eyepiece is known as a *Kellner* or *achromatized Ramsden*. To correct it for lateral color the real image must be formed in the plane of the field lens, and this cannot be done if a reticle is to be used. Consequently a certain amount of color correction is usually sacrificed, and the image is placed as shown in Fig. 146. In order that this eyepiece might not have bad aberration characteristics, it is important that the proper glasses be chosen for the eye lens, these being a dense barium crown (such as 1.5744/57.7) and a light flint (such as 1.6041/37.8).

The rays shown in Fig. 146 are the same as those shown in Figs. 144 and 145.

Residual aberrations are as follows: Spherical aberration is a little worse than with the unachromatized form but longitudinal color is much better. Distortion is much smaller and of reversed sign. The field is backward curving (*i.e.*, it bends toward the eye at the edge), and this compensates for the forward curving field (which bends away from the eye at the edge) of the objective. Coma is essentially zero.

These eyepieces are commonly used in prism binoculars. It is possible to remove the lateral color through the aberration charac-

FIG. 146.—Kellner, or achro-    FIG. 147.—Orthoscopic    FIG. 148.—Sym-
matized Ramsden, eyepiece.            eyepiece.                   metrical, or two-
                                                                  doublet, eyepiece.

teristics of the prisms, and the spherical aberration can be simultaneously reduced.

*Orthoscopic Eyepiece.*—This eyepiece gives a wide field and high magnification while giving a satisfactory eye relief. It is used on high-power telescopes and rangefinders. It is free of distortion, hence its name. It is shown in Fig. 147.

*Symmetrical Eyepiece.*—This eyepiece, shown in Fig. 148, is second in popularity to the Kellner for use in fire control instruments. Telescopic sights mounted on a member of a gun that recoils must have considerable eye relief in order that contact may be avoided between the eye of the gunner and the eyepiece, and the symmetrical eyepiece is used for this purpose. It may be noted that a very large exit pupil and low magnification are always associated with large eye relief. This eyepiece has a much larger aperture (diameter of eye lens) than a Kellner of the same focal length and is therefore used where a fairly sizable field must be combined with long eye relief.

The reason that an eyepiece of large clear aperture (*clear aperture* is the diameter of the section of the lens through which rays actually pass, *i.e.*, the useful or effective diameter) must be used when a long eye relief is to be combined with a large apparent field is easily seen in Fig. 149. A principal ray, from the edge of the field, is shown passing through an eyepiece of clear aperture $d_e$ and eye relief $r$. The half apparent field angle is $w$. Obviously, if the designer wishes to combine an apparent field $2w$ with an eye relief $r$, he must make the clear aperture of the eyepiece equal to $2r \tan w$. If he wishes to cover an apparent field of 50° and have an eye relief of 1 in., he must use an eyepiece of 0.932 in., clear aperture.

The point in Fig. 149 marked *eye point* gives the location of the exit pupil of the instrument, and the entrance pupil of the eye should be located here. On layout drawings of instruments one often finds the vertex of the cornea shown at this point. With the short eye reliefs encountered with binoculars

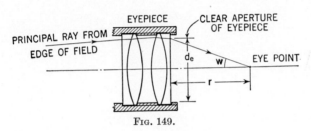

FIG. 149.

and some telescopes, the percentage error thus introduced is large. The eye should actually be shown about $2\frac{1}{4}$ mm closer to the eye lens. Another serious error usually encountered on optical layout drawings is the indication of the position of the exit pupil as located by paraxial rays. If the exit pupil is located by means of trigonometrically tracing a principal ray from the edge of the field, it is often found to be 25 to 30 per cent closer to the eyepiece than is indicated in the drawing. If the eye is placed at the paraxially located exit pupil, it will not receive the principal rays from the edge of the field. Fundamentally, this error is caused by spherical aberration of the pupil points. This error and the one mentioned at the beginning of the paragraph are usually additive.

**Erecting Systems.**—The astronomical refracting telescope gives an inverted final virtual image because the real image is inverted. A positive system of lenses may be used to form an erect real image of the inverted real image. Such a system is termed an *erector*. The eyepiece is used to examine the erect real image and thus forms an erect virtual image. An astronomical telescope equipped with an erector is called a *terrestrial telescope.*

1. *Terrestrial Eyepiece.*—This is illustrated in Fig. 150. *AB* and *CD* are marginal rays and *EF* is a principal ray from the edge of the field. The first two plano-convex lenses form the erector, and these will be recognized as being essentially a Ramsden eyepiece. Note, however, that the principal ray crosses the axis inside the erector. Thus, if it is considered an eyepiece, it has its exit pupil inside. As it is not being used as an eyepiece, no harm comes of this. For this particular con-

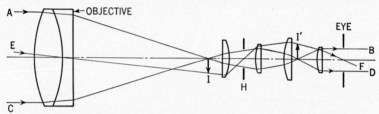

Fig. 150.—Telescope equipped with terrestrial (erecting) eyepiece.

dition it is possible to correct a Ramsden for lateral color. As the eyepiece end of this system is a true Huygenian, the entire system can be corrected for lateral color. The principal ray crosses the axis at *H*, and an image of the objective is thus formed at this point. A stop (called an erector stop) is commonly placed here to eliminate stray light. If a reticle is used with this eyepiece, it should be located at the first real image *I* rather than at the second real image *I'*, for an object at *I'* would be viewed only by the eye lens, and its image would suffer from a large amount of distortion and lateral color. This type of eyepiece was once very popular but has now been replaced by more efficient forms.

2. *Two-doublet Erecting System.*—This is illustrated in Fig. 151. The symmetrical construction of the erector gives it freedom from lateral color, coma, and distortion, for it usually works at or near unit magnification. The reticle may be placed in the plane of either *I* or *I'*, the choice being made for mechanical reasons. It is often placed at *I*, for the reticle, erector, and eyepiece then form a unit and may be mounted in a single tube and any lateral shift of the erecting system will not disturb the line of collimation.

In determining the magnification of a system of this sort the magnification of the erecting system should be taken into account. The equation of magnification takes the form

$$M = -\frac{f'_o}{f'_e}\frac{b}{a} \tag{87}$$

The focal length of the objective is $f'_o$; that of the eyepiece is $f'_e$. $a$ and $b$ are as shown in the illustration. As $a$ is negative and $b$ is positive, $M$ will come out positive. It is also possible to design

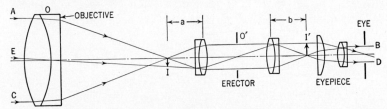

Fig. 151.—Telescope with a two-doublet, or symmetrical, erector, with real images at focal points of erector lenses and with objective image in center of erector.

the erectors so that the real images are not at their focal points; then the magnification cannot be computed by Eq. (87) but must be obtained in the fashion described on pages 14 or 27.

Systems of this sort can be made in various ways. When the erectors are close together, the image of the objective $O$ might not be formed inside the erector as in Fig. 151, but outside it as

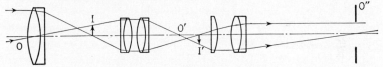

Fig. 152.—Telescope with two-doublet erector, with objective image outside erector.

in Fig. 152 at $O'$. The exit pupil is of course the image of $O'$, which itself is the image of $O$. Inasmuch as $O'$ is well to the right of $O$, it is evident that the exit pupil $O''$ (image of $O'$ formed by the eyepiece) will be well to the right of its location in an astronomical (non-erecting) telescope. Thus the exit pupil might be too far back, away from the instrument. This difficulty is sometimes encountered in the design of low-power gun sights. At times when this happens some physical object in the telescope, such as the eyepiece barrel, is apt to limit the field and thus act as field stop. This situation is shown in Fig. 153, in which

*AB* is the exit window and *CD* is the exit pupil. The extreme principal rays through the system must pass through the edge of the exit window, and they must also pass through the exit pupil. For this reason rays *AD* and *BC* are the extreme principal rays that get through the system. If the eye is placed at the exit pupil, which may be much larger than the entrance pupil of the eye, rays *AG* and *BG* will limit the field seen for *AD* and *BC* may well miss the eye. However, if the eye is placed at *E*, the wider field between *AD* and *BC* will be covered. It is evident, then, that *E* is the proper location for the eye.

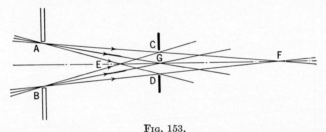

Fig. 153.

If the eye is to the right of *F*, the field is obviously limited by the exit pupil rather than the exit window. This situation is encountered infrequently with normal erecting telescopes, but it does occur with low-power gun sights of long eye relief. In this case it may be said that the eye rather than the objective is the aperture stop of the system, and the image of the eye formed by the telescope is the entrance pupil. The entrance pupil may then be located several inches in front of the objective.

By referring to Fig. 152 it will be seen that the erectors have had to be made sufficiently large to intercept the extreme principal ray through the edge of the real image formed at *I*. If the erectors had been made smaller to conserve space, the extreme principal rays would have missed them. This is shown in Fig. 154, where ray *AB* has missed the small erectors. The result would be that, although the center of the field was well illuminated, the edge would be quite dark. However by placing lens *F*, known as a *field lens*, in the plane of the real image the extreme rays are diverted sufficiently to enter the erector. As this field lens is in the plane of an image, it contributes nothing to the power of the system or to the aberrations, except Petzval curvature, but it does give uniform illumination. Generally, no field lens is placed in the plane of the second real image because the field lens of the eyepiece performs the same function, and it is located near the image. This matter of field lenses will be discussed further in Chap. XV.

The location of the exit pupil will depend on the location of the image $O'$ of the aperture stop (Fig. 154). The farther this is located to the right, the greater the eye relief. When erector lenses are used, the eye relief sometimes gets too large and can be decreased by placing a field lens at $F$. The stronger this lens, the farther to the left will be the exit pupil. By eliminating the field lens the eye relief can be made large, as is desirable for gun sights.

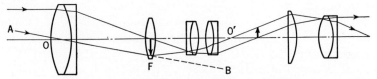

FIG. 154.—Terrestrial telescope with field lens.

3. *Triplet Erector.*—A triplet cemented combination (usually symmetrical) of the form shown in Fig. 335 may be used as an erector and is employed for this purpose by the British. It has an advantage over the symmetrical erector that is so popular in this country in that it contains one less element; in addition, it has less light loss. It is also simpler to mount. The symmetrical erector is favored in the United States because slight adjustments in power may be made during assembly by changing the spacing of the two doublets. The British claim, however, that a similar adjustment may be made with the triplet erector by varying the distance between the erector and the eyepiece.

For design purposes the triplet erector may be assumed to consist of two similar doublets placed in contact. These are achromatized by third-order equations and then placed in contact to form a single triplet which is trigonometrically (*i.e.*, by ray tracing) corrected for longitudinal color. The British used such an erector, of 1.5-in. focal length, very successfully during the First World War.[1] When combined with an objective of 19.3-in. focal length it was found to give good definition over an extended field.

[1] GIFFORD, "Lens Computing," Macmillan & Company, Ltd., London. 1927.

This type of erector may be combined with any type of eyepiece.

4. *Anastigmat Erectors.*—Erectors always contribute to a system a large amount of positive Petzval curvature which is difficult to overcome. It may be possible to get around this difficulty through the use of anastigmat erectors, perhaps of the Cooke Triplet (Fig. 87) or Celor (Fig. 83) form of construction.

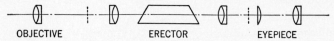

OBJECTIVE          ERECTOR          EYEPIECE

Fig. 155.—Terrestrial telescope with Dove prism between erector lenses.

**Unusual Forms of Construction.**—The various forms of construction of telescopes shown in this chapter are conventional and satisfy most requirements. However, special requirements must occasionally be satisfied, and then unusual forms of construction are employed.

It has been indicated in Chap. XI that Dove prisms, because of their aberration characteristics, should be used in a beam of parallel light. Thus these prisms are normally placed in front of the objective in the instrument in which they are used (see, for example, Fig. 177). This tends to make the instrument very

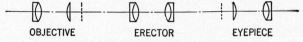

OBJECTIVE          ERECTOR          EYEPIECE

Fig. 156.—Wide-angle telescope.

long, because the whole of the telescopic system must thus be placed behind the prism. A way of getting around this difficulty is shown in Fig. 155 in which the Dove prism is placed between the erectors. In this position, it is again in a beam of parallel light and so will not introduce excessive aberration as it would in a converging beam. With this scheme the designer can get a larger angular field through the prism than is possible using the conventional location.

In some telescopes, such as are used in tanks as gun sights and observational devices, it is necessary to cover wide fields. As the ordinary telescope objectives cannot be used with wide fields, some other form of objective must be found. In this case one can use an eyepiece, which of course can cover a very wide field, as an objective in the way shown in Fig. 156. The same form of eyepiece is used both as eyepiece and objective. Both have the same focal length. Thus such magnification as is desired must be obtained in the erector. This may be accomplished by making the two components of different focal lengths or by using two similar components at unequal conjugates. The scheme of using the same elements for objective and eyepiece has the advantage of simplified manufacture. True fields of 75° may be covered.

Wide fields may also be covered by using anastigmat types of photographic objectives—as the Cooke Triplet (Fig. 87) or Tessar (Fig. 84)—for telescope objectives.

**Collimation of Telescopes.**—When lenses are assembled in a tube to form a telescope, the optical axis of the telescope system will usually not coincide with the mechanical axis of the tube. This can be seen by rotating the telescope about its longitudinal axis in a pair of bearings: the image will be seen to move as the telescope is rotated. If a cross-hair reticle is used, the cross hair will move over the image during rotation. In some military sights the telescopic sight is mounted in rings and might be located in a new way each time it is inserted in the rings. It is evident that, if the optical and mechanical axes are not aligned, the gun will sight differently every time the telescope assumes a new rotational orientation. When the optical and mechanical axes of a telescope have been brought into alignment to eliminate this source of trouble, the telescope is said to be *collimated*. In order to collimate a telescope, provision must be made to move the reticle laterally. The telescope is set up in Y-shaped rings facing a collimator, which consists of an illuminated reticle in the focal plane of a telescope objective. The objective renders the light from the reticle parallel, and this parallel light enters the telescope being adjusted. By looking through this telescope, one sees the image of the illuminated reticle at infinity. The collimator is now adjusted (or the adjustment may be made on the Y-rings) so that the telescope reticle and the collimator reticle appear to intersect. The telescope is now rotated in its mount. If its cross hairs move away from those of the collimator, the instrument is out of adjustment. The reticle is adjusted in a systematic manner until rotation of the telescope produces no shift of the cross hairs, in which case collimation has been completed. It is obviously preferable to design telescope mounts so that the telescope can be fastened in only one position rather than employ the costly and time-consuming collimation procedure.

**Reticles.**—The subject of reticles (or *graticules* as they are called by the British) appears fairly simple; in actuality, it is very complex, and much research has been, and is being, done in this field. The subject is not of sufficiently general interest to warrant more than a very cursory treatment here, however.

In the early days of optics, reticles were made of fine hairs, fibers, spider web, etc. Such devices have been largely supplanted by glass reticles except where extremely fine sharp lines are required. Spider web and platinum wires are still used in theodolites and other high-power instruments.

The types of reticles used in fire-control instruments are often quite simple in character, consisting of a pair of intersecting lines, a grid of parallel lines, or a circle with a dot at its center, etc. Simple reticles, particularly those with only a few straight lines, may be made mechanically on glass. They can be ruled with a diamond point and then left either in that state or filled with an opaque material. Fine sharp lines may be obtained in this fashion. Alternately, the glass can be coated with wax, and the reticle pattern is scratched through the coating. The sample is then exposed to hydrofluoric acid fumes, and the pattern is thus etched into the glass. This gives less sharp lines than the scratching process. If the pattern is filled with an opaque material, it will appear black against an illuminated background in the daytime and will appear luminous when illuminated by suitable apparatus at night. Many fire-control instruments have to be used at night and thus have special illuminators for the reticles. Barium flint glass etches nicely and is thus generally used for etched reticles.

Many photographic techniques for producing reticles have been developed. When suitable precautions are taken, nice results may be obtained by their use. In producing very small and fine patterns, the limit of fineness is often set by the resolving power of the lens used to photograph the original pattern. Usually an attempt is made to draw the pattern on a large scale and then reduce it photographically but this practice has definite limitations.

**REFERENCES**

DANJON and COUDER: "Lunettes et télescopes," Revue d'Optique théorique et instrumentale, Paris (XV<sup>e</sup>), 1935.

"Dictionary of Applied Physics," Vol. IV. Macmillan & Company, Ltd., London, 1923. Article on Telescopes.

"Handbuch der Physik," Band XVIII, Julius Springer, Berlin, 1927.

HARDY and PERRIN: "The Principles of Optics," McGraw-Hill Book Company, Inc., New York, 1932.

KÖNIG: "Die Fernrohre und Entfernungsmesser," Julius Springer, Berlin, 1937.

MARTIN: "An Introduction to Applied Optics," Vol. II, Sir Isaac Pitman & Sons, Ltd., London, 1932.

## PROBLEMS

**1.** Two objects are located 1 yd apart at a distance of 5,000 yd. Can they be resolved by a telescope objective of 1 in. clear aperture? If the telescope were of unit magnification, could they be resolved by the eye? Could they be resolved if a telescope of 2 power were used? Explain.

**2.** In designing a telescope you use an objective of 3 in. clear aperture and 20 in. focal length. What focal length eyepiece would you select (*a*) to just resolve all detail? (*b*) to make all detail clearly visible? What would be the minimum magnification you could employ to make use of the inherent resolving power of the objective? In this case how large would the exit pupil be?

**3.** You are given an objective of 3 in. focal length and a Huygens eyepiece of 1 in. focal length. You combine these to make a telescope. Would the instrument give an erect or inverted image? If the final virtual image were formed at infinity what would be the magnification? If the final virtual image were formed 10 in. from the eye what would be the magnification? You know the eyepiece will cover satisfactorily a total apparent field of 40°. How large a field stop would you employ to give the instrument this field and where would you place it? How large would you make the objective to obtain a 5-mm exit pupil?

**4.** Repeat Prob. 3 with an objective of 20-in. focal length and an eyepiece of 1 in. focal length.

**5.** A designer wishes to develop a telescope covering an apparent field of 15°, and having an eye relief of 4 in. What is the clear aperture of the eyepiece he must employ?

# CHAPTER XIII

## BINOCULARS AND BATTERY COMMANDER'S TELESCOPES

**Binocular Vision.**—The ability of an observer to appreciate distance and the three-dimensional properties of objects depends upon a phenomenon known as *stereoscopic vision*. This is psychological or physiological in origin and depends on the ability of the brain to fuse the two images formed on the individual retinas. The two eyes view any object from slightly different angles, and the two different retinal images are combined to give a sensation of shape or form. Stereoscopic vision cannot be accomplished with a single unaided eye.

In Fig. 157 let $A$ and $B$ represent the two eyes of an observer who wishes to view point $P$ which is at a distance $r$. The images

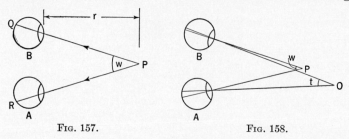

Fig. 157.          Fig. 158.

of $P$ are formed on the two retinas at points $Q$ and $R$, which will generally not coincide with the fovea centralis of either eye. Subconsciously the observer will rotate both eyes to bring the images onto the foveas; at the same time he will automatically accommodate to bring $P$ into focus on the retina. This situation is shown in Fig. 158. Now suppose that the observer is trying to tell which of the two points, $O$ or $P$, is nearer to him. As he cannot see both distinctly at once, he shifts his eyes back and forth from one to the other to bring the images of each alternately on his foveas. When viewing $P$, the convergence angle of the axes of his eyes is $w$; when viewing $O$, the convergence angle is $t$. He appreciates the distance of each object because of the con-

vergence required to image it on both foveas. It is thus evident
that he appreciates the difference in the ranges of $O$ and $P$ because
of the difference in the convergence required to view each. If the
difference $w - t$ (known as the *binocular parallax difference*) is
sufficiently large, he realizes the two objects are different distances away. However, as they come closer together, the
difference $w - t$ becomes smaller until a limiting value is reached
at which the difference is too small to be appreciated. For
normal conditions of viewing this limiting value is about 30″.
If the difference in the convergence angles of two objects is
greater than 30″, the fact that one object is farther away than the
other is appreciated, and the objects are said to be *stereoscopically
resolved*. Under special conditions of observation, with trained
observers, this limiting angle can become as low as 2″. Returning to Fig. 157, it will be seen that $w$ decreases as $r$ increases.
Eventually $r$ will reach a point at which $w$ becomes 30″. This is
the limiting range of stereoscopic vision. It is evident that, when
two objects are being viewed, if both objects are farther away
than the limiting range, neither can give a convergence angle of
30″; thus the difference of their convergence angles cannot be 30″.
It is therefore evident that objects beyond the limiting range cannot be stereoscopically resolved. Using as the interocular
distance the average value of 65 mm and using 30″ as the limiting
value of the binocular parallax difference, calculation shows the
limiting range for the average eye to be about 500 yd. Thus, a
light located at a distance greater than 500 yd cannot be stereoscopically resolved from a distant star.

If the object is viewed under a magnification $M$ with a pair of
field glasses, it is evident that the rays striking the instrument
with a convergence angle $w$ will arrive at the eyes at a convergence
angle of approximately $Mw$ because of the magnification.
Under these circumstances the limiting angle of stereoscopic
resolution is 30″/$M$ and more distant objects can be stereoscopically resolved than was the case with the unaided eye.

Consider Fig. 159, which is exaggerated and not to scale. Here
an angle $w$ is subtended at an object $P$ by the eyes, which are
spaced by a distance $I$. Now suppose the object be viewed
through the mirror system of base length $L$. The angle subtended by the end mirrors at $P$ is $r$, which is the angle at which
the rays arrive at the eyes. In this case the limiting angle

becomes 30″ $I/L$, and again the limiting range is correspondingly increased.   When both magnification and an artificially increased base length are used, as with a rangefinder or binocular, the range of stereoscopic resolution is given by

$$R = \frac{500 \times M \times \text{base length}}{\text{normal interocular distance}} \qquad (88)$$

This is of course measured in yards.   With a pair of standard 6 × 30 military binoculars the range $R$ is about 5,000 yd.

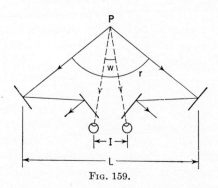

Fig. 159.

However the difference in the ranges of objects at greater distances may be estimated on the basis of other factors, such as the angles subtended by the objects at the eye, light and shade, perspective, and color.   Some optical engineers claim that these factors play a much greater part than stereoscopic vision in the determination of range differences.

The importance of stereoscopic resolution in military work is of course associated with the need of spotting the location of shell bursts relative to targets, etc.

**Military Binoculars.**—Although some field and opera glasses are made on the style of Galilean telescopes, all military binoculars employ as their basis the astronomical telescope with a prismatic erecting system.   A representative system is shown in Fig. 160.   The objective $O$ is a cemented doublet.   The focal plane of the doublet is at $R$, where a reticle is often placed, usually in only one of the two eyepieces.   The image is erected by the two Porro prisms $P_1$ and $P_2$ arranged in a Porro prism system of the first type.   The real image formed by the objective at $R$ is viewed by a Kellner eyepiece having a field lens $F$ and an eye lens (doublet) $E$.

*Constructional Data.*—The main body of each side of a binocular is usually made of a single die casting of an aluminum alloy.

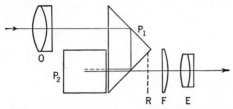

FIG. 160.—Optical system of a typical prism binocular.

In this are assembled the prisms. To it are fastened the tubes in which the objective and the eyepiece are mounted.

The question of the method of mounting the prisms in the main body is of considerable importance. In the first place their faces

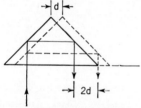

FIG. 161.—Effect of a displacement $d$ of a Porro prism on the path of the light rays traveling through the prism.

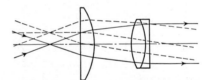

FIG. 162.—Result of the prism shift shown in Fig. 161.

must be kept perpendicular to the optical axis. Second, because rotation of one prism with respect to the other through a certain angle causes a rotation of the image through twice as large an angle, it is important that they be positioned rigidly. Third, a lateral displacement $d$ of a Porro prism causes a shift in the light path of $2d$, as is shown in Fig. 161. What happens then is shown in Fig. 162, in which will be found the eyepiece of a binocular. The solid lines show the path of rays through the eyepiece when the prisms are properly adjusted. If the prisms are improperly located in the fashion shown in Fig. 161, the rays that were on the axis of the eyepiece now arrive displaced from the axis. The dotted lines in Fig. 162 represent these rays. It is seen that they emerge from the eyepiece inclined to the axis. Thus the image will not be seen on the axis but will rather be displaced from it through an angle. If the other tube of the instrument is in proper adjustment, the eye looking through that tube will be looking along the optical axis, while the eye looking through the tube illustrated will be looking (at an image of the same object) along a line inclined to the axis. If the error is not large, the observer will fuse the two images in his brain, and vision will appear normal. However the subconscious effort he must make to fuse the images will cause severe headache without his being aware of the cause. If the

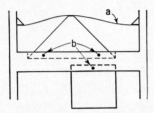

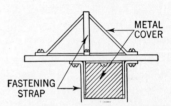

Fig. 163.—Method of mounting Porro prisms in a binocular body.

Fig. 164.—Method of mounting Porro prisms.

error is large, he will be totally unable to fuse the images but will see two of them, the effect being called *diplopia*. Under these circumstances the instrument is unusable. Adjustment for this defect is made through lateral displacement of the objective, as is described on page 209.

To avoid rotation of the image it is evident that considerable care must be taken in mounting the prisms in the instrument. Indeed, this is one of the most important features of binocular construction.

In binoculars of the type manufactured during the First World War the prisms were dropped into shallow depressions in the body and were held in position by means of a leaf spring (*a* in Fig. 163), caught under lugs that were part of the main casting. The prisms were aligned by means of adjusting screws (*b* in the illustration). This method was none too good, for the adjusting screws were frequently tightened excessively. This placed the glass of the prism in a state of strain and thus increased the possibility of breakage by a sudden blow. In addition, the strain caused a local change of index (and also birefringence) that could result in poor imagery, and it sometimes altered the shape of the prism surface.

A second method of mounting the prisms in high-quality binoculars involved careful machining of the face in the main body against which the prisms were positioned, and then peening the prism in position by upsetting the metal around the prism's base at several points  This practice resulted in considerable breakage of prisms during assembly.

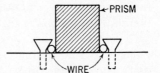

Fig. 165.—Method of adjusting Porro prisms.

Present practice, as illustrated in Fig. 164, involves the assembly of the prisms outside the binocular.  The prisms are placed against opposite sides of an aluminum plate and are held in position by metal straps fastened to the plate.  This assembly is then dropped into position and fastened inside the main body.  This method eliminates some of the difficulties involved in the preceding schemes.

Fig. 166.—Method of laterally adjusting objectives in prism binoculars. This adjustment is made to bring the optical axes of the two binocular tubes into parallelism.

A modern method of adjustment is based upon the use of a piece of wire about the hypotenuse of the prism, as shown in Fig. 165.  The wire is held in position by the conical screw heads.  If it is desired to move the prism to one side, one of the screws is loosened and the other tightened, thus cramping the wire and prism toward the loosened screw.  By placing several such screws about the prism base, the prism may be rotated.

Provision is usually made to align the axis of the objective with that of the main body.  An arrangement of the type shown in Fig. 166 (which is exaggerated) may be employed.  The center of the objective may be placed anywhere desired within a certain area by appropriate manipulation of the eccentric rings.  The rings may then be locked in position.  A certain amount of skill is required for ease in operation of these positioning rings.  This adjustment is used to obtain parallelism of the optical axes when the mechanical axes of the two tubes are not parallel.  The purpose of this function is described on pages 208 and 213.

In binoculars intended for sporting use it is customary to have both eyepiece tubes joined by a transverse bar so that they may be focused by a central focusing screw.   This arrangement makes it possible to accomplish focusing rapidly, but it is not used for military purposes because a blow that damages one tube of the instrument and jams it in position thereby also locks the undamaged tube and makes it unusable.   American military binoculars have eyepieces that are individually focused.   If one tube is destroyed, the other can still be used as a monocular.   Another important consideration is the fact that the central focusing type often has large apertures through which moisture may gain

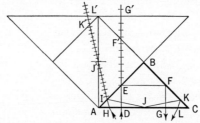

Fig. 167.—The location of a ghost image in a Porro prism.

access to the interior of the instrument.   The individual focusing type is usually less susceptible.   Once moisture penetrates an instrument it presents a formidable problem, for on cold days the moisture condenses on the lenses and often renders the instrument useless.   It of course cannot be removed without disassembling the instrument.   All screw holes and other apertures are sealed to resist penetration by moisture.

*Prisms.*—The characteristics of the individual prisms to be used in the instrument will next be given consideration.

It will be recalled from Chap. XI that in tracing the path of a ray through a prism it is possible to consider, trigonometrically, each mirror reflection as the passage of a ray through a surface. This can be seen by reference to Fig. 167 in which $ABC$ represents a Porro prism.   The reflection $EF$ of ray $DE$ at surface $AB$ may be represented by the hatched line $EF'$ in the mirror reflection $ABL'$ of $ABC$.   Thus the ray $DEFG$ may be represented by $DEF'G'$.   This technique is very useful in tracing down the cause of various ghost images that arise from multiple reflections in prism systems.   Any straight line drawn through a figure of this sort represents a possible ray.   In Porro prisms, the ray $HIJKL$, represented by the straight line $HIJ'K'L'$, is of considerable importance. The bundle of which it is a part undergoes one more reflection than does $DEFG$, and the image formed by it is thus reverted with respect to the normal image. It is important that this so-called ghost image be eliminated. The way in which this is accomplished is shown by a study of the illustration. It is evident that, if the troublesome bundle could be stopped at $J'$ (the image of $J$), the difficulty would be overcome. This is normally accomplished by cutting a groove across the prism at $J$. This eliminates the undesired reflection. The base $AC$ must be lengthened by the width of this groove (a very small quantity) to restore the clear aperture to its initial value.

The size of the prism controls the path length of a ray through it, and consequently must be controlled rather closely during manufacture. If the 45° base angles deviate from the correct value the truncated base can act as a stop and reduce illumination. Even when very poor manufacturing technique is employed, it is unusual for these angles to be off by more than 10′. If the 90° angle is not correct a certain amount of prismatic error can be introduced, *i.e.*, the prism acts as a wedge rather than a plate of glass. The effects of small errors in these angles are not serious, and close tolerances need not be held. Tolerances of 3′ for the right angle and 5′ for the 45° angles will give reasonably satisfactory results.

*Alignment of Individual Tubes.*—The halves of a binocular are generally joined along an axis parallel to the optical axes, and provision is made to control the distance between the eyepieces by rotation of the halves about this common axis. The interocular distance varies from about 55 to 70 mm among individuals, which is the normal range of adjustment provided on most binoculars.

The axes of the two tubes must be parallel to within a small amount, otherwise the observer will encounter severe discomfort, for his eyes will automatically attempt to fuse the two abnormally separated images into one. If the angular displacement is not too large, the eyes will accomplish this fusion, and the observer will not realize that the axes and images are misaligned. However, after a short period of use he will experience headaches, etc.

Figure 168 represents a pair of binoculars in which axial misalignment has occurred. $A$ and $B$ are the entrance pupils of the two tubes and $C$ and $D$ are the corresponding exit pupils. The tubes are inclined to one another at an angle $a$. If $BD$ is directed toward a distant object, the rays from this object (such as $EA$) that enter tube $AC$ will arrive at an angle $a$ to the axis of the tube. If the angular magnification is $M$, the emergent rays, as $CF$, will leave at an angle $Ma$ to $CG$, which is the prolongation of $AC$.[1] It is immediately seen from the illustration that these rays will enter the eye at an angle $(M-1)a$ from the desired line of sight. Note that, if the binocular tubes are so misaligned

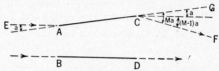

FIG. 168.—The effect of lack of parallelism between the optical axes of two binocular tubes.

that the two tubes diverge toward the eyes, the rays emerging from these tubes converge toward the eyes, and vice versa. Furthermore, when the rays themselves converge toward the eyes, the axes of the eyes become divergent. Therefore, if the binocular axes diverge toward the eyes, the eyes themselves become divergent.

The eyes are more accustomed to functioning while convergent than divergent; thus a greater misalignment error can be tolerated in this direction. If the tubes diverge toward the eyes (requiring divergence of the eyes), the axes must not be misaligned by more than

$$D = \frac{7.5}{M - 1} \quad \text{(minutes)} \tag{89}$$

If the binocular tubes converge toward the eyes (requiring convergence of the axes of the eyes), the tolerance for misalignment becomes

$$C = \frac{22.5}{M - 1} \quad \text{(minutes)} \tag{90}$$

These two equations hold only for the horizontal component of alignment errors. The tolerance for the vertical component is

$$V = \frac{8}{M - 1} \quad \text{(minutes)} \tag{91}$$

[1] For angles as small as those involved here, $\tan a = a$.

If the optical axes are not parallel to the hinge axes, the inclination of the axes may vary with the interocular setting, and thus alignment must be checked at several (usually three) settings.

The parallelism of the axes may be determined by the methods that follow. If adjustment must be made to eliminate the effects of lack of parallelism described above, the optical axis of either tube may be appropriately inclined by laterally displacing the objective through the use of the concentric ring arrangement shown in Fig. 166. This laterally displaces the objective, which is the aperture stop, and thus results in an angular deflection of the optical axis.

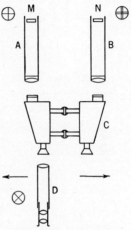

The magnifications produced in the two tubes must be equal. If they are slightly different, the observer will be able to fuse the two images but only at the cost of suffering discomfort from the use of the instrument. In addition, the stereoscopic effect produced by the instrument will suffer. If the two magnifications are greatly different, the observer will be unable to fuse the images, and the device will be useless.

Fig. 169.—Method of testing binoculars for parallelism of axes.

Another error that can have the same result is the rotation of one image with respect to the other as might be caused by rotational misalignment of the Porro prisms, *i.e.*, by their major axes not being inclined at 90° to each other.

The general method of testing binoculars can be understood from a consideration of Fig. 169. The two tubes *A* and *B* are collimators, consisting of objectives with reticles *M* and *N* located in the focal planes of the objectives. The reticle patterns are shown next to the collimators. When the reticles are illuminated, they are seen at infinity because of their location in the focal planes of the objectives. The instrument is initially adjusted without the binoculars *C* in position. Telescope *D*, which contains a reticle as shown to its left, can be moved in the direction of the arrows, and it is aligned with the left-hand collimator *A*. This collimator is adjusted until its cross hairs bisect those of the telescope. The telescope is then slid over in front of collimator *B*, and this collimator is similarly adjusted into parallelism with the observing telescope. The collimator axes are now parallel. The binocular to be tested is now placed on a stand at *C* so that light from the collimators goes through it. The telescope is slid in front of the left eyepiece and the binocular is adjusted on its stand until the patterns of the reticles of collimator *A* and telescope *D* intersect at their mid-points. The telescope is now slid in front of the right-hand eyepiece. The adjustment process has put the axes of the collimators and observing telescope into parallelism, so, if the binoculars tubes are parallel, the pattern of the reticle of collimator *B* will now coincide with that of telescope *D*. If the patterns are found to be out of coincidence, the binocular tubes are not parallel.

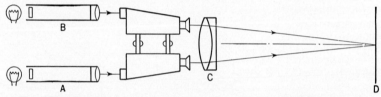

Fɪɢ. 170.—Simplified method of testing binoculars for parallelism of axes.

Another way of making this test is shown in Fig. 170. The axes of the two collimators *A* and *B* are parallel. The lens *C* is located symmetrically with respect to the two collimator tubes, and the screen *D* is placed at its focal plane. If the axes of the two tubes of the binocular are parallel, the images of their two reticles will be superposed on the screen by lens *C*. If they are out of parallelism, the screen images will be out of position by an amount depending on the angle between the tubes of the binocular. Thus the lack of parallelism is easily detected and measured.

Many other simplifications of the above-described basic procedure have also been developed.

*Performance Data.*—Data on a few typical modern glasses are as shown in Table III.

*Unusual Erecting Systems.*—Although the vast majority of existing binoculars use the erecting system described herein, several other types are also in use. Thus, in the Schütz instrument, a Porro prism system of the second type is used (see Fig. 113). In Fig. 171 is shown a Daubresse prism in use by Hensoldt. This consists of a right-angle prism in conjunction with a penta prism equipped with a "roof" angle for reverting purposes.

Another Hensoldt instrument employs the *König prism* shown in Fig. 172. This erects the image without introducing lateral deviation of the beam. The Zeiss firm puts out binoculars, under the name Teleplaste, with an unusually large distance between the objectives in order to increase the stereoscopic effect. The necessary lateral deviation and erection of the light beams is produced with a pair of Sprenger prisms.

TABLE III

| Erecting system | Power | Objective diameter, mm | True field, ° | Exit pupil, mm | Purpose |
|---|---|---|---|---|---|
| Porro, first type.... | 6 | 15 | 8.3 | 2.5 | Day use |
| Porro, first type.... | 6 | 30 | 8.3 | 5.0 | Day and twilight |
| Porro, first type.... | 8 | 40 | 8.75 | 5.0 | Day and twilight |
| Porro, first type.... | 7 | 50 | 8.5 | 7.1 | Night |
| Galilean.......... | 4 | 50 | 4.0 | ... | Theater |

*Binoculars vs. Monoculars.*—A study of binoculars as military instruments should not be concluded without considering their relative advantages or disadvantages when compared to monoculars. This question was studied at some length under the auspices of the National Research Council[1] in 1920. In the resulting report it is pointed out that a blow is liable to introduce

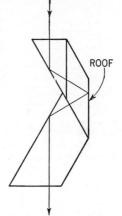

misalignment into binocular axes, rendering the instrument unfit for further use. Furthermore, focusing of a binocular is much

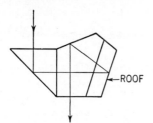

FIG. 171.—Daubresse erecting prism, used in some Hensoldt binoculars.

FIG. 172.—König erecting prism used in some Hensoldt binoculars and Zeiss telescopes (*cf.* Fig. 120).

[1] See HYDE, COBB, JOHNSON, and WENINGER, *J. Franklin Inst.*, Vol. 189, p. 185, 1920.

less convenient and much slower than that of a monocular. Again, military binoculars cannot be cleaned in the field because of difficulty in reestablishing parallelism of the axes upon assembling the device; this trouble is not encountered with the monocular. The binocular is bulkier and heavier and requires a very uncomfortable leather carrying case with shoulder strap; the monocular can be carried in a shirt pocket ready for instant use.

PLATE III.—A modern high-quality prism binocular. The eyepiece in this 8 X 30 instrument is much more complex than the Kellner ocular usually employed, and thus this instrument covers a 68° apparent field rather than the 50° field covered by the more common construction. Note eccentric ring mounting of objective. (*Courtesy of Bausch & Lomb Optical Company.*)

The speed of production of the binocular is slower, and its cost is about three times that of the monocular.

Various possible advantages of the binocular over the monocular were considered during this investigation. The fact that they offer the advantage of stereoscopic vision was not denied, but it was pointed out that for 6 power binoculars this advantage disappears at ranges over 5,000 yd. Then again, as has been pointed out before, the ability of an observer to distinguish between the relative positions of two objects depends on various other factors besides stereoscopic vision.

Experiment showed that under certain conditions of observation it was possible to obtain better resolving power with monoculars than with binoculars, for the monocular is normally used by an individual with his better eye, while he obtains only an average of the two eyes with binoculars. This result varied with the type of test object employed; under field conditions, slightly better results were obtained with binoculars.

It was found that small brightness differences, which play an important part in the detection of objects under field conditions, could be more readily detected with binoculars than with monoculars.

It was learned that a delay of 1.5 to 2.0 seconds occurred in getting the binoculars to the eye from their carrying case as compared to monoculars. However, once at the eye, the binocular enabled the observer to report on an object in from 0.32 to 0.44 seconds less time. The total time consumed in getting the instruments into action were 3.6 seconds for the binocular and 2.7 seconds for the monocular, a distinct advantage for the latter.

In general, more comfort was found in using the binocular than the monocular, this being associated with freedom from eye strain.

As far as the ability to distinguish indistinct objects is concerned, a 6 power binocular was found to be not more than 12 per cent better than a 6 power monocular. If the power of the monocular had been increased to 6.27 power, it would be expected that they would perform equally well in this respect.

On the basis of this work it seems definitely feasible to replace binoculars with monoculars for many applications with a great saving of time and money and without loss of efficiency.

**Battery Commander's Telescope.**—One of the principal advantages of a binocular instrument in which the interobjective distance is made greater than the normal interocular distance is the increased stereoscopic effect. Another advantage is that the objective, being normally much larger than the eye, can receive more principal rays from different locations and give an increased power of penetration when objects are to be discerned in underbrush, etc. Both of these properties are highly desirable in an instrument intended for fire-control purposes. The commander of a battery of field artillery must be able to spot the point of impact of the shells from his guns and determine whether they have burst short of, or beyond, the chosen target.   Since, in the absence of other reference objects, he may have to do this by purely stereoscopic means, it is desired to give him an observing instrument with greatly enhanced stereoscopic capabilities.

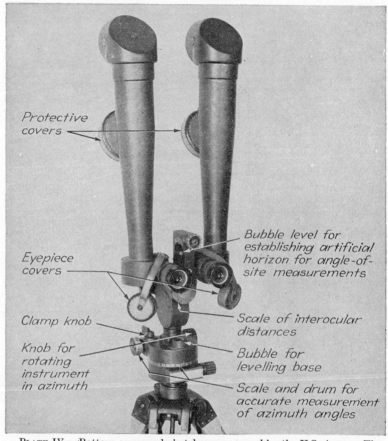

PLATE IV.—Battery commander's telescope as used by the U.S. Army.   The instrument covers a 4°15′ true field and operates at 10 power.   It uses a Kellner eyepiece and has a 4.3-mm exit pupil.   (*Official War Department photograph.*)

Such an instrument is the *battery commander's telescope*, otherwise known as a *B. C. telescope* or a *scissors telescope*.   It consists of two short periscopes fastened together with the eyepiece axes parallel, and so hinged that they may be rotated about axes parallel to, and adjacent to, the eyepiece axes.   With the two

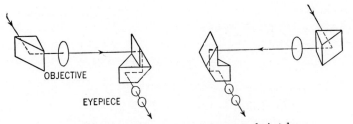

Fɪɢ. 173.—Optical system of a battery commander's telescope.

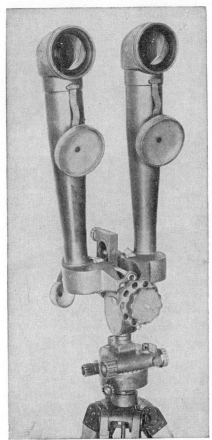

Pʟᴀᴛᴇ V.—Another view of the battery commander's telescope shown in Plate IV
*(Official War Department Photograph.)*

tubes in the vertical position, the device functions as a binocular periscope and permits of observation from behind cover. When the tubes are swung into a horizontal position, the objectives are separated by a distance of 27 in., giving the maximum stereoscopic effect.

The optical system of one of the devices is shown in Fig. 173. The erecting (and deviating) system will be seen to consist of a Porro prism system of the second type with one of the right-angle prisms merely removed some distance from the others. The eyepiece is often of the Kellner type. The instrument normally contains a reticle in one eyepiece and is mounted with divided circles so that it may be used to measure both vertical and horizontal angles. It is mounted on a portable tripod.

A typical instrument has an objective of about 45 mm in diameter and covers a field of view of 4°15′. Its magnification is 10×, and the exit pupil is thus about 4.5 mm in diameter. The stereoscopic power of this instrument is about 100 times that of the unaided eye.

Stereoscopic instruments of this general type are used by the Navy to observe gunfire; they are known as *spotting glasses* or *spotters*.

### REFERENCES

"Dictionary of Applied Physics," Vol. IV, Macmillan & Company, Ltd., London, 1923. Article on Telescopes, Small.

GLEICHEN: "Theory of Modern Optical Instruments" (trans. by Emsley and Swaine), His Majesty's Stationery Office, London, 1921.

KÖNIG: "Die Fernrohre und Entfernungsmesser," Julius Springer, Berlin, 1937.

MARTIN: "An Introduction to Applied Optics," Vol. 2, Sir Isaac Pitman & Sons, Ltd., London, 1932.

VON ROHR: "Die binokularen Instrumente," Julius Springer, Berlin, 1920.

### PROBLEMS

**1.** An antiaircraft shell bursts 100 ft over an airplane flying at an altitude of 25,000 ft above the ground. Can an observer on the ground directly below the airplane tell whether the burst was high by use of stereoscopic vision, if he is equipped with 7 × 35 binoculars having the centers of the objectives separated by a distance of 4½ in.? The observer has an inter-pupillary distance of 70 mm.

**2.** What are the tolerances for parallelism of axes of the tubes of the binoculars mentioned in Prob. 1?

# CHAPTER XIV

## PERISCOPES

Inasmuch as a periscope is an instrument intended for viewing a displaced beam of light, with perhaps some magnification, it would appear that the design of such an instrument would be not appreciably more complicated than the design of a telescope. Such a belief is wholly in error, for a periscope is an instrument of vastly great complexity and warrants considerable study. In the limited space available it will be possible to suggest only some of the problems in periscope design.

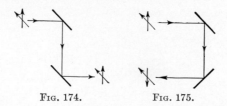

Fig. 174.    Fig. 175.

The simplest form of reflecting system for deviating a beam is that shown in Fig. 174. The character of the reflections are such as to give an erect image of the original object. If, now, an attempt is made to use a system of the type shown in Fig. 175, trouble will be experienced. With this arrange-ment no lateral reorientation of the beam occurs, but the vertical component of the image is re-versed; in other words, the image is apparently reverted. With this arrangement, an effect of considerable interest is present. It will be noted that light from the right side of the object arrives at the right side of the image. Yet,

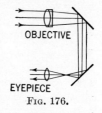

OBJECTIVE

EYEPIECE

Fig. 176.

because the observer has his back to the original object, right and left have interchanged for him; so as far as he is concerned, right and left, as well as up and down, have reversed and the image is completely inverted. If, now, an astronomical telescope were added, the device would be as shown in Fig. 176. As it has been shown that an astronomical telescope completely inverts the image, the inversions caused by the mirrors and telescope with this system would cancel one another, and the image would appear erect.    If a telescope were to be used in conjunction with the system illustrated in Fig. 174, an erecting (terrestrial) instrument would of course be required.

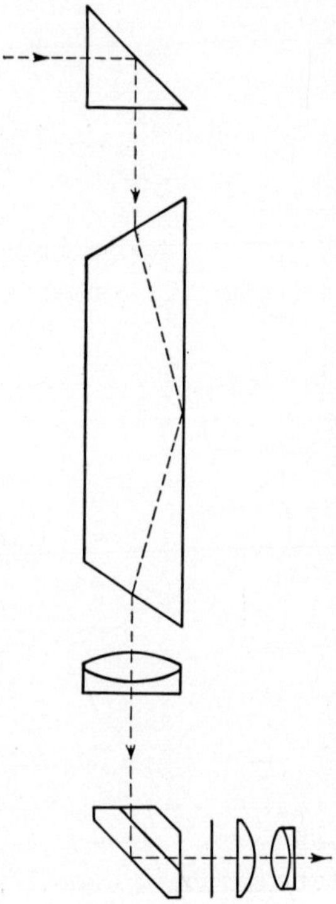

It is evident that, if we start with a periscope of the type illustrated in Fig. 174, an attempt to scan the horizon by rotation of the upper mirror, the image will rotate and become completely inverted by the time the upper mirror has rotated through 180°.    In certain types of fire-control instruments a periscope with the ability to present an erect image to the observer for any azimuthal setting of the upper tube is required.    For this purpose the device shown in Fig. 177 is used.    As the figure shows, light, upon entering the instrument, is deviated through 90° by a right-angle prism.    It then passes through a Dove, or rotating, prism; thence through the telescope objective to an Amici prism from which it emerges to pass through the eyepiece. When used as shown, the vertical component of the image is reverted by the Dove prism, and the lateral component

Fig. 177.—Optical system of a panoramic sight.

by the Amici prism.    Thus these prisms completely invert the image, and the astronomical telescope then inverts it again, bringing it out erect.    As the right-angle prism revolves about an axis normal to its lower base, *i.e.*, about a vertical axis, the image seen in the eyepiece rotates.    This is compensated for by having the Dove prism rotate about its long axis at one-half the angular velocity of the right-angle prism; the final image then remains erect.    This rotation of the Dove prism is of course caused by a simple differential gear linkage existing between it and the right-angle prism.    It should be noted that the Dove prism is placed in *front* of the objective.    This is done because when used in a convergent beam of light (as emerges from a telescope objective) a prism of this type introduces terrific aberration, while if used in a parallel beam (as shown) no trouble will occur. This optical arrangement is commonly used in panoramic sights.

In submarine periscopes the directions of sight and orientation are usually kept identical, so an elaboration of the system shown in Fig. 174, together with an erecting telescopic system, is generally used—and the whole instrument is rotated when the direction at viewing is changed.

As far as the question of deviating a beam of light is concerned, the periscope follows simple principles. Its special optical characteristics arise out of the necessity of designing a telescope with a very large field of view and a uniformly illuminated field, to fit into a long narrow tube. Special features of construction are required to achieve these objectives.

Fig. 178.

Consider a periscope tube of average dimensions, about 30 ft long and 6 in. wide. If one were to look through this tube, the natural field of view would be about 1°. If one were to use two lenses in this tube and sought the optimum location and powers to increase the field of view as much as possible, he would find that for a tube of length $L$, the lenses should have a focal length of $L/5$, the first lens should be located a distance $2L/5$ from the object end of the tube, and the second lens should be placed a distance $2L/5$ from the first. With this arrangement the field of view would be about 5°, an impossibly small figure for practical purposes. In addition, the image would be inverted.

If three equal lenses were to be used, it would be found that an optimum condition would be attained when the first lens was a distance of $2L/7$ from the object end of the tube, the second lens in the middle, and the last lens $2L/7$ from the eye end. The focal lengths would be $L/14$. The field covered would be about 7°, and the image would be erect. This system is shown in Fig. 178.

As the number of lenses was increased, the field of view would generally increase. For a given number of lenses a number of possible arrangements of varying effectiveness, with respect to

field of view covered, would be found.   It would be found that
with different arrangements different numbers of inversions would
occur, and that, generally speaking, the system with the greatest
number of inversions would cover the largest field.   The reason
for this can be seen qualitatively from a consideration of Figs.
179 and 180, which represent periscope systems with different
numbers of lenses.   The paths of the principal ray from the edge
of the field are shown in both systems, the lenses being omitted
for the sake of simplicity.   It is seen that the system exhibiting

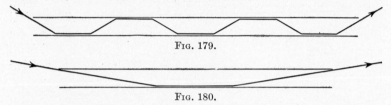

Fig. 179.

Fig. 180.

a large number of inversions covers a larger field than that with
but a single inversion.

It will be of course realized that considerations of illumination
throughout the field would also play a part in the choice of a
system.   This too would have to be computed.   The whole
question is very complex and has to be evaluated on the basis of
protracted mathematical analysis.

The foregoing remarks apply to comparison of various arrangements of lenses in tubes of the same diameter.   The diameter of
the tube itself is also of primary importance, for it is desired to
fill the entrance pupil of the eye with light; thus the ratio of the
diameters of the tube and this entrance pupil must be considered.
Generally speaking, the wider the tube the easier it becomes to
obtain uniform illumination throughout the field; thus, from the
optical design point of view a wide tube is preferable.   During
the First World War submarines operated with their periscopes
above water a good deal of the time, and, as large periscope tubes
were considered objectionable because they were more easily
detected by hostile vessels, emphasis from the military point of
view was placed on tubes of narrow diameter.   The usual compromise involved the use of a wide main tube with a narrow top
tube to project above the surface.

In most optical systems it is necessary to consider the location
and size of the entrance pupil and window to determine the field of

view to be obtained with a given number of elements.  With periscopes this does not hold, and it is possible to determine in advance what may be accomplished with a given number of

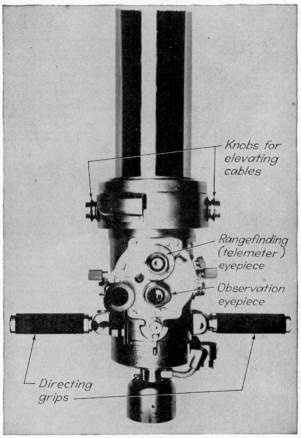

Knobs for
elevating
cables

Rangefinding
(telemeter)
eyepiece

Observation
eyepiece

Directing
grips

PLATE VI.—Eyepiece end of a periscope used by the U.S. Navy.  With a magnification of 6 this instrument covers a true field of 8.7°.  The upper eyepiece is used for range finding by the method illustrated in Fig. 186; the lower eyepiece is for observation.  The instrument can be used at 1.5 and 6 power.  When used at 6 power, the instrument has an exit pupil of 4 mm diameter.  The eye relief is 20 mm.  The total amount of light transmitted by the optical elements is 24 per cent.  (*Official U.S. Navy photograph.*)

lenses in a certain tube without computation of the system.  In comparing two systems, the following formula may be used:

$$L = k \, \frac{d^2 n}{a V^2} \qquad (92)$$

$L$ is the distance between the extreme lenses of the system, $k$ is a constant of proportionality, $d$ is the diameter of the tube, $n$ is the number of lenses employed, $a$ is the aperture (external) of the system, and $V$ is the diameter of the field of view. When a large number of lenses is used, numerous solutions are possible; other factors being equal, the best solution is that of employing the weakest lenses. This is of course desirable to reduce residual aberrations and Petzval curvature. In most practical cases the lenses are uniformly spaced. For this condition the weakest lenses are obtained for a solution in which a lens is located in the plane of each image of the aperture stop. A slight reduction in residual aberration may be obtained by the use of non-uniform spacing, but the gain is so small that it is practically always neglected.

When a periscope of a single magnifying power is being designed, the arrangement of the lenses for the main part of the tube is first studied according to the foregoing principles, then an objective is computed to fit in with this system, and an eyepiece is then designed to match the objective. If a periscope with two powers is desired, the problem becomes much more complex. It is possible to vary the power by the use of a variable power eyepiece, but this results in corresponding changes in the size of the exit pupil so that at high power a very small exit pupil is obtained. This of course results in a loss of brightness in the retinal image, and such a loss cannot be tolerated. It can be shown that, if a variable power objective is used instead of a variable power eyepiece, the illumination of the image remains much more constant under changes in magnification. Thus variable power objectives are used.

Inasmuch as changes from high to low magnification, or vice versa, under operating conditions must be made instantly, it is necessary that the change be made without the need of re-focusing the eyepiece. This is equivalent to stating that the objective should always form its image in the same plane regardless of its power. It is possible to design various two-lens combinations that give a continuous variation of power, through variation in spacing, without changing the image position. Such devices are not used in practice because the mechanism required to change the spacing is generally sufficiently bulky to require the enlargement of the upper end of the periscope tube beyond desirable limits; in addition they are rather sensitive to slight mechanical shock and are liable to fail at inappropriate times.

Although the two-lens combination of continuously variable power must be eliminated because of its complexity, it is possible

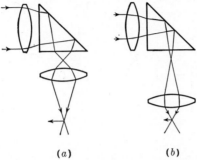

(*a*)                    (*b*)

Fig. 181.—Periscope objective system with two powers.

to use an arrangement that gives only two different powers. The required movement of a single lens is much more easily obtained than the complex motion of both lenses necessary in an

arrangement of continuously variable power. The field will be momentarily obscured while the change from one power to another is occurring, but this is considered a relatively slight disadvantage compared to the advantage of reasonably reliable mechanical performance. The arrangement shown in Fig. 181 has been used by Zeiss for this purpose. The chief objection to this system arises from the difficulty of getting satisfactory correction for aberrations at both settings of the lower lens.

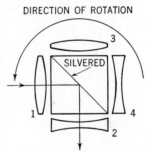

Fig. 182.—Periscope head assembly by which either objective 1-2 or objective 3-4 may be selected.

A popular scheme for changing power is that shown in Fig. 182. This was developed by Goerz. Lenses 1 and 2 form one objective, and 3 and 4 form another. These both form their images in the same plane, but, because the principal surfaces of the two are differently located, the images are of different size. The cube is rotated through 180° to bring objective 4-3 into the beam. It will be noted that with this latter objective the entering beam strikes the negative lens first, while the reverse was true in the situation shown in the illustration. Each of the two objective systems is corrected independently for aberration.

Periscopes with two magnifications are commonly constructed with $1\frac{1}{2}$ and 6 powers, the former figure giving the sensation of viewing with the naked eye. A figure in excess of 1 should be

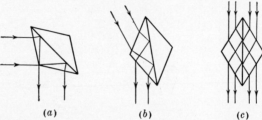

(a)                    (b)                    (c)

FIG. 183.—Double isosceles prism for scanning through a wide angle in a single plane. A 90° rotation of the prism scans through 180°.

used to compensate for the psychological effect of looking through a narrow tube. The apparent field covered is of the order of 60°. In a 25-ft periscope the wide portion might be 6 in. in diameter and 21 ft in length, and the narrow portion $2\frac{1}{2}$ in. in diameter and 4 ft in length.

The periscopes just discussed are limited in use solely to horizontal viewing. With the advent of the airplane it became desirable to make available to the submarine commander means for vertical viewing. A good solution was found to be the use, in the upper end of the tube, of a prism of the type shown in Fig. 183. This consists of two isosceles prisms (forms of Dove prisms), silvered on their bases, which are cemented together. The action of this arrangement at different elevations is shown in the figure. It will be realized that a single prism could be used, but the arrangement shown gives more uniform illumination at large angles of elevation although uniform illumination could be obtained if the single prism were made very large (see Fig. 118).

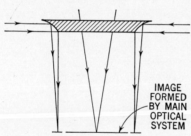

IMAGE FORMED BY MAIN OPTICAL SYSTEM

FIG. 184.—Optical system for forming an image of the entire horizon. This annular distorted image surrounds a distortion-free image of any desired point on the horizon.

It often becomes desirable for a submarine commander to be able to scan the entire horizon at once while directing the bulk of his attention in a single direction. For this purpose there have been developed periscopes (see Fig. 184) containing an annular mirror of circular section located at the upper end of the tube, the plane of the annulus being perpendicular to the axis of the tube. This toroidal surface acts as a spherical reflector and forms images from all directions at once. This gives an annular field, which is viewed by an eyepiece. The radii involved in this toroidal surface can be selected so as to eliminate astigmatism, but coma and spherical aberration will still be present together with a large amount of distortion. Through the center of the annulus may be placed a normal periscopic optical system that will give a large distortion-free image from any desired direction. This image will be seen in the center of the annular image formed

Fig. 185.—Another optical system for the same purpose as that shown in Fig. 184.

by the reflector. It is also possible to replace the spherical reflecting arrangement with a combination refracting and reflecting device using spherical refracting and parabolic reflecting surfaces (Fig. 185).

For fire-control purposes in submarines it is necessary to know the range, speed, and direction of motion of a hostile vessel. These can be determined by means of appropriate attachments to the periscope. Periscopes are usually fitted with an etched reticle in the plane of one of the real images. This contains an angular scale, by use of which much of this requisite data can be estimated. If a dimension, such as length, of the target vessel is known and if this length is perpendicular to the line of sight, measurement of the angle subtended at the submarine by the known length gives sufficient data to calculate the range. Submarines usually carry as complete data as possible concerning the linear dimensions of all types of vessels for this purpose. A method of estimating range based on this principle is suggested by Fig. 186. Two ring-shaped wedges are located near the periscope objective. Two images are formed by this system, one (a) by the light passing through the wedges and the other (b) by the light passing undeviated through the aperture in their centers.  By rotating one of these rings relative to the other about the optical axis the separation of the two images, which will be seen superposed, will vary.  If the wedges are of equal refracting angles, the deviation they produce will be zero when the thickest part of one is opposite the thinnest portion of the other.  By rotating one wedge relative to the other, the separation of the images may be controlled; by rotating the two wedges as a unit, one image may be caused to rotate about the other.  By means of these wedges it is possible to form two images of an enemy vessel and then bring the prow of one image into contact with the stern of the other.  If the length of the enemy vessel and its inclination to the line of sight are known, its range may be

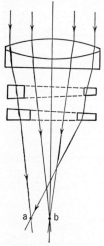

Fig. 186.—Telemeter for estimating range.

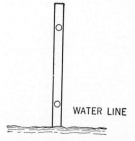

WATER LINE

Fig. 187.—Vertical base rangefinder built into submarine periscope.

calculated.  As a check the two images may be aligned vertically with the water line of the vessel in one image touching the top of the smokestack or mast in the other.  If this height is known, the range may again be calculated from the setting of the wedges. This is preferable to the horizontal method because the orientation (*i.e.*, direction of motion) of the vessel relative to the line of sight need not be known.  The submarine commander might find it very difficult to determine that orientation because of camouflage.  The vertical measurement might be in error because the enemy vessel could be using a false or altered smokestack or topmast.  This type of rangefinder is called a *telemeter*.

Because the above methods are open to error, it is preferable to use conventional rangefinders.  It is possible to use a vertical base rangefinder with one objective arranged above the other as shown in Fig. 187. Coincidence can be obtained with this type of device in spite of some rolling of the submarine. However, it has certain flaws, and a T-shaped horizontal device (Fig. 188)

WATER LINE

Fig. 188.—Horizontal-base rangefinder built into submarine periscope.

is sometimes used in preference. A typical instrument has a base length of 2.7 meters and a vertical length of 6 meters. It works at 20 power and is capable of measuring to 1 meter at 1,000 meters and 25 meters at 5,000 meters. This instrument is of the coincidence type, but stereoscopic rangefinders have also been employed in submarines.

### REFERENCES

Czapski and Eppenstein: "Grundzuge der Theorie der optischen Instrumente," p. 611, J. A. Barth, Leipzig, 1924.

"Dictionary of Applied Physics," Vol. IV, p. 350, Macmillan & Company, Ltd., London, 1923.

Gleichen: "Die Theorie der modernen optischen Instrumente," p. 173, F. Enke, Stuttgart, 1923.

König: "Die Fernrohre und Entfernungsmesser," p. 101, Julius Springer, Berlin, 1937.

# CHAPTER XV

## GUN SIGHTS

**Rifle and Machine-gun Sights.**—The early history of the use of optical sights is quite obscure. As far as is known now, the earliest use of telescopic rifle sights occurred during the Revolutionary War, when they were used by American riflemen.

*Galilean Type Sights.*—This simple optical sight (see Fig. 189) is used extensively in England but is rarely seen in this country. It consists, essentially, of the same simple Galilean telescope system that was discussed previously. The objective and eyepiece are contained in separate mounts. The objective is mounted near the muzzle of the rifle and is usually hooded to protect it from rain. The rear sight consists of a very small aperture, to position the eye properly, behind which is located the usual negative eye

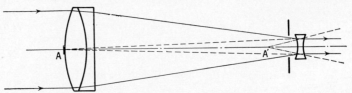

Fig. 189.—Galilean-type rifle sight.

lens. The aiming mark *A* is mounted on, or ground into, the front surface of the objective.

If the eyepiece is to define the target clearly, it should be a negative lens. The aiming mark is then seen at *A'*. However, if it is to define the aiming mark clearly, it should be a positive lens with a focal length equal to the distance between the two lenses. Often the target is kept in focus. The inevitable blurring of the aiming mark is then reduced to a minimum by keeping the eye aperture very small (about 1 mm). If the aiming mark is to be kept in clear focus, the eye lens is sometimes omitted; this gives a reasonably good compromise between the two extremes. Generally a negative lens of longer focal length than that necessary to keep the distant target perfectly defined is chosen to give an acceptable compromise.

It is obvious that the field of view of this type of sight is very small (see Eq. 72) and the illumination is very poor. Generally with any rifle it is desirable to keep the sight radius (distance between the front and rear sights) as large as possible to improve accuracy. A large sight radius is particularly useful with this type of sight because definition of target or aiming mark, whichever is out of focus, is directly proportional to sight radius. This type of sight has an unusually large sight radius.

This sight was used by the British on snipers' rifles in the First World War, but its imperfect definition, small field of view, and fragility proved to be sufficiently great handicaps to cause its employment for such purposes to be terminated. It has been used extensively for target shooting at Bisley.

*Terrestrial Telescopic Sights.*—This type of sight employs both the terrestrial eyepiece shown in Fig. 150 in Chap. XII and the erecting system shown in Fig. 151 of the same chapter. The theory of these systems has already been explained. Usually a symmetrical eyepiece (Fig. 148) is used in place of the Kellner eyepiece shown in Fig. 151. These telescopes are generally contained in short, more or less cylindrical tubes 8 to 12 in. in length. Because of the large fields and long eye reliefs encountered, the eyepiece is usually at least of the same diameter of the objective and may even be larger. Sometimes a field lens is placed in the plane of the real image as shown at $F$ in Fig. 154. This lens serves the same purpose as the field lens in the eyepiece: it diverts into the erector system rays from the edge of the image that might otherwise miss the erector, thus keeping the field uniformly illuminated. As this lens is in the plane of a real image, it of course has no effect on the size of the image but it shortens eye relief. In some German telescopic sights still another lens (usually a doublet) is placed between the field lens and the erector so that the power of the telescope might be varied.

These sights vary in power from unit magnification up to 12. For general military purposes rather low powers (two to four) are desirable, for with low powers no tremor of the rifleman is magnified by the optical system to an undesirable magnitude. In the high-power sights (8 to 12 power) any slight quiver of the hand holding the gun makes the sight appear to wander over a very large area. Thus these sights are used principally for target shooting.

The field of view of a sight of this type is much greater than for a Galilean device of equal magnification.   The illumination of the image is so good that accurate shooting may be performed under poorer conditions of lighting than is possible with any other type of sight.   The only exception is the case where the rifleman is firing from a spot in the open toward the sun at an object in deep shade.   In this case iron sights are preferable.

In order that the sight might not strike the eye of the user in recoil, it is necessary to locate the eye point (*i.e.,* the exit pupil)

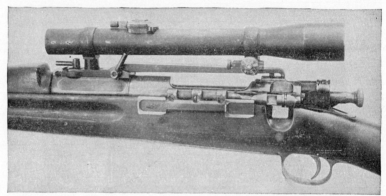

PLATE VII.—Telescopic sight mounted on Springfield rifle.  Adjustment for range is obtained by a movable reticle controlled by the drum on top of the sight.   Windage adjustment is obtained by a rotating screw in the mount.   The windage adjusting knob may be seen beneath the rear mounting ring.   (*Official War Department photograph.*)

about 8 cm behind the eye lens.   This of course results in a rather large exit pupil (7 to 10 mm) which is desirable, in spite of some loss of illumination, because the target may be seen when the iris of the eye is located anywhere within the area of this pupil; thus it is not necessary to line the eye up carefully with a small pupil. This increases the rapidity with which a target may be picked up.

Some years ago telescopic sights as long as the barrel were used, but these were abandoned because of their structural weakness. Present telescopes, as has been noted, are generally mounted in tubes 8 to 12 in. in length.   They are mounted on bases rigidly fastened to the receiver or barrel of the rifle and are usually attached to these bases through dovetail slides in such a fashion that they may readily be dismounted or attached.   It is necessary that the telescope be rigidly fastened to the rifle, and precautions should be taken to see that it does not work loose under recoil. This presents very formidable problems in mechanical design. In some sights the telescope is permitted to slide in its retaining rings under recoil. It is then returned to position either by hand or with springs. This type requires a good deal of care in adjustment and is not particularly popular.

Adjustment for elevation and windage is made by moving the reticle appropriately, by moving the telescope relative to the fixed base, or by moving the fixed base relative to the rifle. In each case special precautions should be taken to keep the adjustment from working loose under recoil. Sometimes combinations of the above systems are used, with the elevation adjustment in the reticle and the lateral adjustment in the base, for example. In one of their service telescopes the British use a wedge-shaped piece of glass in front of the objective to make the initial lateral adjustment. A rotation of 360° of this wedge causes the cross hair to appear to rotate through a circle 15 ft in diameter on a target 500 yd away. It is evident that lateral adjustment cannot be attained with this method without also affecting the elevation.

Telescopic sights are not generally collimated and, particularly with the type with the movable reticle, considerable error can be introduced through rotation of the sight in its mounting rings. The greatest drawback of the telescopic sight is the difficulty of keeping it rigidly fixed relative to the rifle. The sight base is usually very short. This magnifies any linear error of alignment many times compared with a similar error in iron sights.

The great advantage of the telescopic sight arises from the fact that the sight and the target are seen in the same focal plane, and the eye does not have to shift focus back and forth from sight to target. However, it is a special-purpose device and is certainly not generally used. Because of the great advantage of having the target and the sight in one focal plane, the author believes that at some time in the future there will be adopted for general military use a simple unit power telescopic sight of very simple construction to be fastened directly to the iron sight of a service rifle for combat use.

Some of the factors of design will now be briefly considered. It has been mentioned that a field lens is located in the plane of the real image formed by the objective. This may form an image of the objective in the center of the erector. The erector forms an image of the field lens on the erected image, etc. The field lens contributes nothing to the power but illuminates the field fairly uniformly and reduces eye relief. It contributes adversely to Petzval sum, curving the edge of the image plane toward the objective. It does not affect the other aberrations, provided that it is a true thin lens. Actually, of course, it has thickness and does contribute to the other aberrations, particularly distortion. If it is placed before the image, it gives barrel distortion; if behind, it gives pincushion distortion. This adds to the difficulty of the general optical design, as the eyepiece must be corrected to overcome this distortion.

The erecting system generally consists of two doublets of equal focal lengths. The focal plane of the first doublet coincides with the plane of the real image formed by the objective, and that of the second doublet coincides with the focal plane of the eyepiece. In this case the erector works at unit magnification and so does not alter the magnification of the system. The erector is thus said to "work at one to one." If the two erector doublets have different focal lengths, they will introduce a magnification given by the ratio of these focal lengths. If they are kept of the same focal length but are used at unequal conjugates, the magnification they introduce will be given by the ratio of the conjugates measured from the principal points of the erector components.

If the erectors are used in the normal fashion with the images at the focal points, a change in their spacing (keeping their focal lengths constant) will not affect magnification but will play an important part in locating the exit pupil, and thus the eye point. As their spacing is increased, the exit pupil will move to the left, and eye relief thus decreases. It is generally desirable to space the erectors sufficiently far apart so that an image of the objective is formed halfway between them. In this case the stop of the erector system is this image of the objective, and, as the stop is in the center of the erector system (which we shall assume to consist of two doublets of equal focal length), the whole erector is symmetrical. In this case it introduces no distortion, lateral color, or coma because it is symmetrical and working with equal conjugates. However, the erectors will always introduce considerable positive Petzval curvature and thus curve the edge of the field toward the objective. The objective and field lenses also curve the field in the same direction, and the entire burden of correction is thrown on the eyepiece by the introduction of negative astigmatism. It is perhaps possible to overcome the difficulty by using a symmetrical triple erector consisting of a negative lens between two positive elements, the whole system being air spaced. The theory of such a system would be same as that of the Cooke triplet photographic objective, and it may be possible to introduce therein negative curvature in a similar fashion. Although it might be possible to introduce at this point sufficient negative curvature to compensate for the curvature of the objective and field lenses, this would probably in most cases lead to very strong curves and thus excessive high order aberration. Other aberration corrections could also be introduced with this erector.

As has been pointed out, it is possible to control the position of the eye point by varying the power of the field lens. The stronger the field lens, the shorter the eye relief. When very long eye relief is desired, the field lens is omitted. Of course in instruments employing prismatic erecting systems no erecting lenses are present to give a real image of the objective in the middle of the system; thus these systems are normally afflicted with very short eye relief. This is one reason for their unpopularity for use in rifle telescopes.

Rifle telescope systems have as many as 15 or more surfaces and are sometimes tedious to compute when an attempt is made to correct them carefully. However, it is often possible to obtain good results from a rather hastily computed system, for the tolerances involved in visual instruments are fairly large. They have light transmissions of 40 per cent or so, and because of the more-or-less logarithmic functioning of the eye the 60 per cent reduction in illumination caused by the instrument is not particularly significant, the image appearing quite bright. Most of the 60 per cent loss can be eliminated by coating the lenses. This is desirable when the sight is to be used under conditions of poor illumination.

These systems may be designed by starting with an erector consisting of two doublets, giving these doublets powers consistent with the dimensions of the instrument. Next an objective is selected, its power being determined by the magnification desired and its clear aperture from considerations of the desired exit pupil diameter. This objective is computed by methods to

be described in Chap. XXVIII.   Now the spacing of the erector
may be selected on the basis of the desired length, and by means
of the simple equations given in Chap. I the power of the field
lens (located at the focus of the objective) that will give an image
of the objective in the cente  of the erector is determined.   The
aperture of the field lens is taken sufficiently large to permit
passage of all the rays that pass through the real image formed in
its plane.   An eyepiece is computed as described in Chap. XXIX
and added to the system.   The location of the exit pupil is
determined by locating the final image of the objective, which
is the aperture stop.   If the eye relief is too great, the field lens
is strengthened and the erector spacing then readjusted to keep
the first image of the objective in its center.   If the eye relief is
too short, the reverse procedure is followed.   The performance
of the entire system is now checked with ray tracing and a third
order analysis.

Because the eye relief of these instruments is large and it is
necessary to keep the size of the eyepiece within reasonable
limits, the apparent field is normally kept below 25°.

Practically all rifle telescopes in present use have lens erecting
systems of the type just described.   However, it may be noted
that prismatic systems have been used both in this country and
abroad, although without great success.   Lightness is essential
in a rifle telescope, and such prismatic telescopes as have been
made to date have been so heavy as greatly to impair their
usefulness.   Those seen by the writer were in addition afflicted
with atrociously poor mechanical design, and some were even
mounted on the side of the rifle rather than directly above the
barrel so the rifleman had to pull his cheek away from the stock
to see through them.   In addition, the massive casting mounted
off to the side tended to cant the rifle, making good marksman-
ship difficult.   The reticle in these instruments was etched on a
piece of glass, which was usually covered with oil and dirt, a
greatly magnified image of which was commonly seen superposed
on the target.   Finally, as the eye relief was very short, the
rifleman had to keep his eye quite close to the sight.   A rubber
eyecup was provided to exclude stray light, and as the eye had
to be pushed well into this device because of short eye relief, it
was not unusual for the rubber cup to be set back hard against
the face of the user under recoil, where it remained stuck by

vacuum forces. Eventually the manufacturer chanced upon the happy idea of drilling holes in the rubber cup but the resulting improvement in the overall efficiency of the device was not noteworthy.

The rifle telescope is usually mounted over the center of the barrel as close to the bore as possible so that the rifleman can position his cheek firmly against the stock while sighting. Occasionally the sight is mounted slightly higher, and provision is made so that the gunner can use the ordinary iron sights, while the telescope is in position, by looking under the telescope.

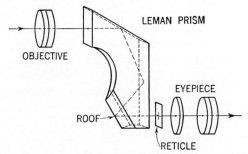

Fig. 190.—Optical system of infantry machine gun sight.

This, however, results in a certain amount of discomfort when the telescope is used because of the impossibility of positioning the cheek. The Zeiss people have shown on theoretical grounds that the best line of sight is that which is tangential to the trajectory at the target. A simple calculation suffices to show that if one were shooting with a military rifle at a range of 800 yd with a sight attached to the gun so as to fulfill this condition, the sight would be 16 yd above the bore of the rifle. This location would appear to be other than ideal, and it would seem that this theorem is of little practical use when applied to military telescopic rifle sights.

*Optical Machine Gun Sights.*—Although optical machine gun sights for ground-service machine guns have not yet come into extensive use in this country, they have been extensively developed by the Zeiss firm and are apparently in wide use by the German army. Small but rugged instruments with both lens and prism erecting systems have been produced. The type with the lens erector is conventional in design. That with the prism is shown in Fig. 190.   The erector is a Leman or Sprenger prism, which erects the image and deviates the beam at the same time, this latter being desirable as some small additional protection is furnished the head of the gunner by allowing him to lower it slightly.   The device is very small, being only some 3 in. high. It is of 2 power and covers a 30° apparent field.   It is provided with a small electric bulb for illuminating the reticle when firing is to be attempted under conditions of poor visibility, or for night use.   Another model is intended solely for use on heavy machine guns.   This has a prismatic erecting system and contains a micrometer so that angles may be laid off very precisely when indirect fire is attempted.   When the gun is to be used for antiaircraft fire, a ring near the objective is rotated, turning the eyepiece so that the line of sight is deviated 60° upward.   Fire may thus be directed at aircraft with the head in a comfortable position.   The device is of 2 power and covers a 35° apparent field.   A third model, intended for use on light machine guns, has a lens erector similar to a rifle telescope.   This has 1.5 power and covers a 20° apparent field.   It also has a precision micrometer for laying off angles and, in addition, has prismatic equipment for use in indirect fire.   An additional prism may be attached to the eyepiece for the purpose of deviating the beam through 60° when antiaircraft fire is attempted.

The objections to the employment of an optical sight for ground machine-gun use are as follows:

1. The reticle of the sight is generally obscured by the recoil while firing is in progress.   However, the optical sight helps to pick up and identify the target and aids in laying the gun quickly.

2. The optical sight is not generally so rugged as the standard iron sight.   Although this is true, it would appear that optical sights would be very valuable when it is difficult to locate targets.

Generally speaking, it would appear that the arguments in favor of using optical machine gun sights as special-purpose devices were very strong.

Simple low-power telescope sights of large exit pupils are used for the fixed guns on some military aircraft and also on tank and anti-tank guns.   The large exit pupil is desirable in that it enables the target to be picked up without the expenditure of too much time in orienting the eye with the optical axis of the sight.

The sight in most general use for the fixed (and some flexible) guns of military aircraft is known as a *reflector sight* and is shown schematically in Fig. 191.   Light from the electric lamp passes through the reticle, illuminating it.   This reticle is located at the focus of the objective lens and is therefore imaged at infinity. This light is reflected from the glass plate into the gunner's eye. Light from the distant target passes through the plate and thus also reaches the gunner's eye.   The reticle is imaged at infinity

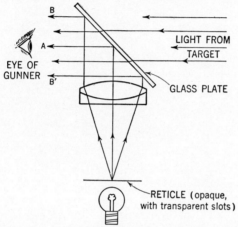

Fig. 191.—-Optical system of reflector sight for aircraft machine guns.

by the objective and is therefore seen in the plane of the target. This sight is simple to construct.   It has a very large exit pupil and the target and reticle can thus be easily located without much movement of the head.   Because the reticle is illuminated, it can easily be seen even under conditions of very poor visibility. There is no particular point (eye point) along the horizontal axis at which the gunner must place his eye.   He can use the sight with his eye in any desired location.   Although the field covered is large, the sight has no means of introducing magnification, and this is one important disadvantage.   The glass plate could be partly silvered but this would only result in the target being seen less clearly because of light reflected and absorbed by the silver.   The reticle image may be made as bright as desired by selecting a suitable electric light to illuminate it.   During the recent revolution in Spain a pilot using the reflector type of sight sometimes experienced the unpleasant sensation of getting onto the tail of an enemy plane and then, when glancing through the sight to open fire, finding that he had forgotten to turn on the electric light.   When the bulb becomes broken or burned out, the sight of course becomes useless.

If, for mechanical convenience, it is desired to have the axis of the reticle-objective system horizontal, this can be accomplished with an additional mirror.

The user's eye is the aperture stop of the reflector sight.   Thus this system has the advantage of a very small aperture stop (to minimize aberration) with a large exit pupil.

When a sight of this type is adjusted on an airplane, the line of sight $A$ (or line of collimation as it is sometimes called) is adjusted to bring the reticle onto the point of impact of the

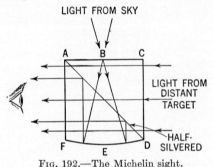

Fig. 192.—The Michelin sight.

machine gun at a known range.   If the objective of this sight is afflicted with spherical aberration so that the rays $B$ and $B'$ are not parallel to the central ray $A$, a false line of sight will be established by an eye placed so as to receive such rays instead of $A$.   If the eye shown in Fig. 191 were either above or below the position shown, it would intercept these rays.   It is evident that an objective intended for use in a sight of this type should have a minimum of zonal spherical aberration.

If the reticle is not placed exactly in the focal plane of the objective, the rays $B$ and $B'$ will not be parallel to $A$ (Why?) and errors of sighting similar to those described in the preceding paragraph will result.

A device developed during the First World War for bombing purposes may prove useful for use in fire-control instruments. This is the Michelin sight, shown in Fig. 192.   It is constructed of two glass components cemented together along the line $AD$.

The unit is approximately cubical in form, the dimension perpendicular to the paper being of length $AC$. Face $FD$ is spherical, the radius of curvature being $2BE$. Face $FD$ is silvered and acts as a spherical reflector. Face $AC$ is covered with an opaque lacquer through which is scratched the pattern of a reticle $B$. Light passes through these scratches and the reticle is imaged at infinity by the reflecting surface $FD$ because $B$ is at the focus of this spherical reflector. This light is reflected at the surface $AD$, which is half silvered, into the eye of the user. Light from the target passes through faces $CD$ and $AF$ to the user's eye. The reticle (magnified) is thus seen superposed on the target, in its plane. These devices can be made quite small—about 1 in. on a face. They are relatively easy to manufacture. They do have, however, several disadvantages. In the first place, it is difficult to make a sufficiently narrow scratch in face $AC$ to give a sharp reticle line. This line, being magnified, is usually seen as being very broad and rather fuzzy. If it be made very fine, so little light gets through it that it is difficult to see. The visibility of the reticle is dependent on the amount of light incident upon face $AC$, and if the device is used indoors where little light strikes this face, the reticle cannot even be seen. The silvering on the face $AD$ greatly reduces the visibility of the target by reflection and absorption of light. This is a serious defect under borderline conditions of illumination. The device might be useful when used with an artificially illuminated reticle.

The image of the reticle is formed by a single reflecting surface, and the imagery obtained is not particularly good because there is no possibility of obtaining correction for aberration. In addition, spherical aberration causes sighting errors similar to those obtained with reflector sights as the eye moves from one side of the exit pupil to the other. These objections might be overcome by application of the Schmidt principle described in Chap. IX.

**Artillery Sights.**—The simplest type of artillery sight is the collimator sight, shown in Fig. 193. It consists solely of an objective $O$ and a reticle plate $R$ mounted in a thin wall tube. The reticle consists of an opaque metal plate with a cross cut through it, as shown at the left of the illustration. As the eye is placed at $A$, it receives light both from the target (off to the left) and the sight. As the reticle is at the focus of the objective, it is imaged on the retina together with the target, and the cross appears superposed on the target or aiming point in use. These devices are light, compact, inexpensive, and simple. They are accurate enough for directing the fire of light artillery and were used during the First World War with 75-mm guns, but they give no optical assistance in locating or identifying a target under conditions of poor visibility. They are used at present as auxiliary aiming devices on telescopes, etc., and are also used as infantry mortar sights.

Regular telescopes with lens or prismatic erecting systems are used with seacoast and railway artillery. As weight is less of a

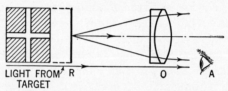

LIGHT FROM R                          O        A
TARGET

Fig. 193.—The collimator sight. The vertical line *R* is the reticle plate, and this, when viewed from the objective, appears as shown at the left of the figure.

consideration than with rifle sights, prismatic telescopes are much more popular for this purpose than they are for use with rifles. Porro prism systems of the first type are commonly used, although a König prism (see Fig. 172) is used in an instrument manufactured by Goerz. A typical sight of this type covers a 3° true field at 15 power and has a 5-mm exit pupil.

Telescopes with Amici erecting prisms are called *elbow telescopes* because the 90° deviation introduced by these prisms causes a right-angle bend in the tube. Such telescopes are used with antiaircraft guns and for pointing other fire-control instruments, such as directors and heightfinders. A typical instrument covers a 6° true field at 8 power.

Gunfire is often controlled by the use of auxiliary aiming points, which may be located anywhere with reference to the gun. To sight on these one must have a sight that can be pointed in any azimuthal direction without motion of the eyepiece. For this purpose *panoramic telescopes* or *panoramic sights* (known to the British as *dial sights*) are used. These are generally based on the system shown in Fig. 177 and described in Chap. XIV. It will be recalled that the function of the Dove prism in that device is to revert one coordinate of the image. This reversion can be accomplished without a Dove prism by the use of two cylindrical lenses with their principal axes parallel, these lenses being located at the same point in the optical system as the Dove prism. They, too, revert only one dimension of the image, and they are rotated

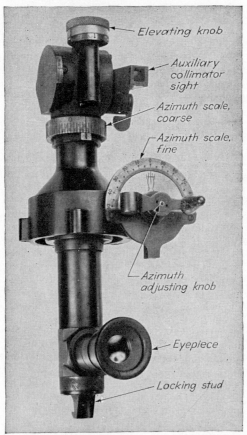

PLATE VIII.—Rear view of French (S.O.M.) panoramic sight. The instrument is of 4 power and covers a 10° true field.

in the same fashion as the Dove. This system is shown in Fig. 194, the cylindrical lenses being $C_1$ and $C_2$. The cylindrical lenses cause far more aberration than the Dove prism.

Another type of panoramic telescope manufactured by Goerz is shown in Fig. 195. As the upper right-angle prism rotates in azimuth, the Porro prism rotates about the axis $CD$, thus keeping the image erect. This prism is fastened in a mount rotating about $CD$ as an axis; the eyepiece is attached rigidly to this mount and rotates with it. The device is somewhat prone to mechanical failure because of the multiplicity of moving parts

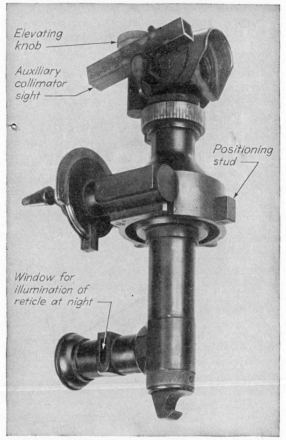

Elevating knob

Auxiliary collimator sight

Positioning stud

Window for illumination of reticle at night

PLATE IX.—Front view of panoramic sight shown in Plate VIII.

and is thus not widely used. Then, too, the eyepiece moves as the Porro prism rotates. This is somewhat disadvantageous.

With these panoramic sights, the distance between the upper prism and the eyepiece is so fixed that the gunner can sight over his own head at aiming points to his rear. A typical instrument is of 4 power and covers a 10° true field. The exit pupil is 4 mm in diameter.

The Zeiss firm has produced some simpler types of aiming devices, which consist of various optical systems so designed that the gunner can sight simultaneously on two points located 180° apart. A typical system of this character is shown in Fig. 196.

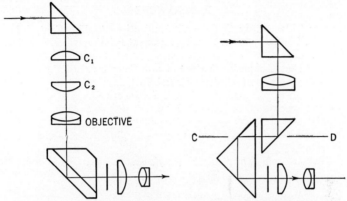

FIG. 194.—Panoramic sight, with Dove prism replaced by cylindrical lenses.

FIG. 195.—Panoramic sight with Porro prism.

Light enters the two objectives and is deviated by the two right-angle prisms into the single eyepiece. In some devices of this sort intended for use by mountain artillery, provision is made to use the sight either as a direct laying device or an indirect sighting instrument for use with auxiliary aiming points.

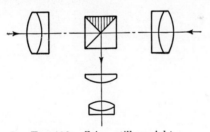

FIG. 196.—Zeiss artillery sight.

Other sighting devices consist of several telescope systems fastened together so that by using one after the other it is possible to sweep the whole horizon, using rotations of less than 90°. These are used as substitutes for panoramic sights for indirect laying. Various types of prism systems are also used to sweep the horizon.

It is pointed out that all these artillery laying devices are precision instruments. They must be mounted on some part of the gun that does not recoil, for the recoil would quickly throw them out of adjustment.

## REFERENCES

GARDNER: "Elementary Optics and Applications to Fire Control Instruments," *Ord. Dept. Doc.* 1065, Government Printing Office, Washington, 1924.

GIFFORD: "Lens Computing," Macmillan & Company, Ltd., London, 1927.

GLEICHEN: "Theory of Modern Optical Instruments" (trans. by Emsley and Swaine), p. 166, His Majesty's Stationery Office, London, 1921.

HAYES: "Elements of Ordnance," John Wiley & Sons, Inc., New York, 1938.

KÖNIG: "Die Fernrohre und Entfernungsmesser," pp. 132 *ff.*, Julius Springer, Berlin, 1937.

"Textbook of Small Arms," His Majesty's Stationery Office, London, 1929.

# CHAPTER XVI

## RANGEFINDERS

For mapping and surveying, as well as for military purposes, man has always desired to determine the distance to inaccessible objects. He has known for many centuries the basis of the proper technique, for he knew that to solve a right triangle it was necessary to know only one side and one acute angle. He was not able to put this knowledge to practical use until he acquired angle-measuring instruments of sufficient precision to give him reliable readings. When the theodolite was developed, it became possible to measure angles sufficiently accurately to make rangefinding possible. With these instruments it was necessary to lay off a base line very accurately and then measure the angle between the base line and the line to the target from each end. This could be done with a single theodolite, setting the instrument up at each of the two observing stations in turn. Since speed is a prime requisite in military work, two theodolites were used simultaneously. This involved the use of two observers, plus additional messengers, etc., to communicate the readings and make the necessary calculations. The method was simplified further by mounting two telescopes, with their axes parallel, on a short base, having the optical axes normal to the base. The base was rotated until the cross hairs in one telescope could be placed on the target. The cross hairs in the other telescope were now off the target, and they were traversed mechanically until they also fell on the target. The required motion of the reticle to accomplish this was a measure of the unknown range. Two observers could operate this device to increase the speed of measurement, but there was no way of insuring that they would both range on the same target or on the same spot on the chosen target. Later the device was constructed of two telescopes connected with a chain. It became evident that it would be necessary to permit one observer to make both observations at the same time; only in this way could speed and accuracy be assured.

Various techniques of employing a single eyepiece for the two parallel telescopes were developed, but none were conspicuously successful until an Englishman named Adie developed the basis of our present coincidence-type rangefinder in 1860. From this time on developments appeared rapidly and culminated in the appearance in 1888 of the Barr and Stroud instrument, the pattern of the present coincidence rangefinder. In 1893, a German, de Grousilliers, took out a patent describing an instrument on which the present stereoscopic rangefinder is based. This type of instrument received most of its subsequent development in Germany. The Germans favor the stereoscopic type of instrument; the British prefer the coincidence type; our own armed forces use both types.

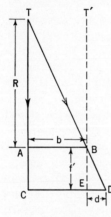

Fig. 197.

**Coincidence Rangefinders.**—The fundamental triangle to be solved with the coincidence rangefinder is shown in Fig. 197. This represents a rangefinder of base length $b$, having objectives of focal length $f'$. If the target were infinitely distant, light from it would arrive along lines $TA$ and $T'B$. However, assume the target $T$ to be a finite distance $R$ away from the instrument. The light rays now arrive along the lines $TA$ and $TB$. Now assume that at $A$ and $B$ are located objectives of focal length $f'$ which form images of $T$ at $C$ and $D$, respectively, the optical axes of the objectives lying along $TA$ and $T'B$. If the target were infinitely distant, its image formed by objective $B$ would be at $E$ rather than at $D$. The displacement $d$, equal to $ED$, is called the *parallactic displacement* and is easily seen to be a measure of the range. From the geometry of this figure it is simple to demonstrate that the following equation holds:

$$R = \frac{bf'}{d} \qquad (93)$$

The symbols in this equation are as shown in the figure. This is the fundamental equation for the coincidence rangefinder and also holds for the stereoscopic instrument.

Now suppose we place prisms at $A$ and $B$ to deviate each arriving beam ($TA$ and $T'B$) through exactly 90°, and suppose we choose the focal length of the objectives so that the two images will be formed in a single plane. The images will be displaced from one another by a distance $CD$, and the instrument will be as shown in Fig. 198. It will now be in the form that is used for military purposes. The basic elements of this device can be seen in Fig. 199. $A$ and $B$ are two penta prisms to deviate the beams exactly 90° in the principal plane regardless of angle of incidence, and the images of the target formed by the two objectives are located in the common plane $I$, from which they are reflected by the two prisms at $P$. The upper half of the image formed by one objective and the lower half of the other

Fig. 198.

are reflected by the prisms into the eyepiece $K$ (Fig. 200). It would be possible, by means of a movable reticle, to measure the parallactic displacement between them. However, this would involve carefully placing the cross hair over one image, then over the other. A quicker setting may be made by bringing the two

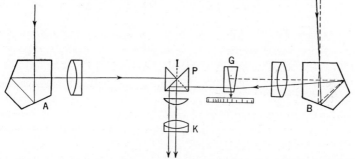

Fig. 199.—Optical system of a coincidence rangefinder (no infinity or halving adjustment shown).

images themselves into coincidence (this giving the instrument the name *coincidence rangefinder*). This is often done by means of a prism as shown at $G$. As the prism is moved along the optical axis, the rays strike it at different heights, and consequently different amounts of deviation are produced. Thus by shifting the prism the deviation may be changed. Therefore this prism is moved along the axis until the two images have been brought into coincidence. The amount the prism has moved is a direct measure of the range, and the scale on which the motion of the prism is measured is usually calibrated directly in units of range. If the prism moves a distance $S$ in causing an angular deviation $h$, the following equation holds quite closely:

$$S = \frac{bf'}{hR} \tag{94}$$

In practice, a number of changes are made to make this device more practical for field use. The dividing line between the two images is not sharp when ocular or coincidence prisms of the type shown at $P$ are used to fuse the two images. A sharp dividing line is necessary for precision in setting; thus more involved prisms that give sharp lines are employed.

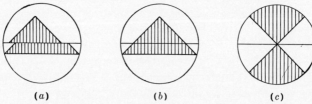

(a)  (b)  (c)

Fig. 200.—Eyepiece field of a coincidence rangefinder. (a) Appearance of field before coincidence has been obtained, (b) appearance of field after coincidence has been obtained, (c) appearance of invert-type field after coincidence has been obtained.

The base length (distance between penta prism centers) in coincidence instruments varies from 66 cm to 100 ft depending on the degree of accuracy desired. A typical instrument is the 1-meter base rangefinder used by our infantry, field artillery, and cavalry. It has 15 power magnification and covers a true field of 3°10′. Its range scale is graduated in yards from 400 to 20,000. The device may be rotated 18° above or below the horizontal and may be traversed through a wide angle.

Generally, erect images are seen in the two fields, this being the case when the device is to be used on well-defined targets (Fig. 200, a and b). Figure 200a shows the appearance of the eyepiece field before coincidence is established; Fig. 200b shows it after. If poorly defined targets are being ranged, one of the fields may be inverted. Thus, if the distance to a tree were being determined, an erect image of the tree would be seen in one field and an inverted image in the other. The two would of course be brought into alignment. This type of instrument (sometimes referred to as the *invert type*) has the additional advantage of making use of the observer's sense of symmetry in making the setting, and this increases the precision setting. The appearance of the eyepiece field is shown in Fig. 200c.

**Stereoscopic Rangefinders.**—As has been pointed out in Chap. XIII, two objects at different distances from the eye can be stereoscopically resolved (*i.e.*, the observer can tell which is nearer) if the angles subtended by the eyes of the observer at the two objects differ by more than a certain limiting value, this being taken as 30″ in ordinary work. If we assume 30″ to be the limiting angle, objects at a distance of more than 500 yd cannot be stereoscopically resolved by the unaided eye unless an instrument to give increased magnification or an artificially increased interocular distance is used. As was revealed in Chap. V, the eye can actually work to 10 or 12″ with considerable precision under controlled conditions, such as are obtained in rangefinders.

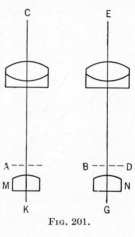

Fig. 201.

Consider an instrument consisting of two telescopes mounted rigidly to a fixed base with their optical axes parallel and with the distance between the telescope axes equal to the interocular distance of an observer. This is shown in Fig. 201. If the target is infinitely distant, light will enter the telescopes along the paths *CK* and *EG*. The images will be formed in the planes *A* and *B* and will be viewed by the two eye pieces *M* and *N*, which we shall assume to be of the erecting type. Now assume that we have placed in the plane of the images at *A* and *B* reticles consisting each of a single dot. One dot is kept fixed, and the other is made movable in the direction of a line joining the two (*i.e.*, along *BD*). Each of these dots will be seen by only one eye, and the two will be fused together stereoscopically so that one dot suspended in space will be seen by the observer in the same way that he sees only one image of the target. This can be seen easily by consideration of Fig. 202. *A* and *B* are the planes of the reticles, the rest of the telescopes being omitted for convenience. If the fixed dot is at *C* and the movable one at *D*, the observer will fuse these two images and will see a dot suspended in space at *E*. Of course, if there were a physical dot at *E*, its image would be seen by the two eyes at *C* and *D* along the lines *EC* and *ED*. Thus the eyes see the same thing whether there is a physical dot at *E* or two dots on the reticles at *C* and *D*. If the movable dot is shifted to *F*, it is evident that the dot in space will be seen at *G*. Thus by laterally moving one of the reticles the dot seen in

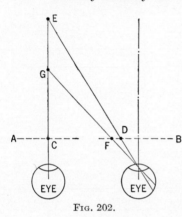

Fig. 202.

space will advance or retreat. In this way the observer can cause the dot (known as a *wander mark* or *measuring mark*) to stop over any object he sees through the instrument. He is then said to have established *stereoscopic contact*. By having the mechanism that moves the movable dot calibrated in terms of distance, he can read directly the range of any object over which he has stopped the mark. It is also possible to place a series of dots on the two reticles, these being ruled in pairs with different spacings. Because the pairs of dots on the two reticles have different spacings, they will appear to be located at different points in space. The ranges corresponding to the distances between the marks are of course known; thus, by observing which mark is nearest the target, its range is instantly determined. In practice, the first or wander-mark type of instrument is normally used. However, instead of changing the spacing between reticles to cause the mark to move in space, the reticles are fixed in position and one of the real images is laterally shifted instead, the theory of operation being exactly the same. The means employed to shift the image are the same as used for the coincidence-type instrument.

A stereoscopic rangefinder could have the appearance of the instrument shown in Fig. 201. In practice, however, it is found desirable to enhance the stereoscopic effect (see Chap. XIII) by artificially increasing the interocular distance. Magnification is used for the same reason and also to make distant targets more visible. The instrument accordingly appears as shown in Fig.

203. Images are formed by objectives $A$ and $B$ in the planes of the reticles $C$ and $D$. The rotating wedges $E$ vary the angle between the beams entering the two eyes until this angle is the same as that between the beams entering the observer's eyes from the reticles. Thus, the reticle image will appear as far away as the target. The angle at which the beams from the reticles enter the eyes may be controlled by the designer who should take into account psychological, as well as physical, factors. This is not usually done.

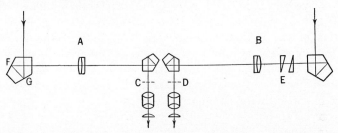

FIG. 203.—Optical layout of a stereoscopic rangefinder. The diasporameter prisms $E$ are shown, for the sake of clarity, rotated 90° about the optical axis from their true position. Neither halving nor infinity adjustments are shown.

The stereoscopic rangefinder resembles, externally, the coincidence-type instrument, the only difference being its possession of two eyepieces. However, it will be seen that internally there is no connection between the two halves of the instrument, which are essentially only telescopes. The images are fused by purely psychological means.

This type of rangefinder requires no aligning of two images. It may therefore be used on poorly defined images that may wander over the field of the instrument and cannot be kept on the dividing line of a coincidence instrument's field, aircraft being the most conspicuous objects in this class. However, although almost anyone can successfully operate a coincidence instrument, relatively few people can successfully use a stereoscopic device. Some people seem to lose this ability with time. Under strong emotional stress the accuracy of an observer is said to decrease. This has been offered as an objection to the use of the stereoscopic rangefinder. This point will probably be cleared up during the present conflict.

The Germans, who use the stereoscopic type of instrument for naval fire control, treat their rangetakers as "prima donnas," giving them all sorts of special privileges.

**Comparison of Coincidence and Stereoscopic Type Instruments.**—At the battle of Jutland, the German vessels were equipped with stereoscopic rangefinders, the British vessels with coincidence instruments. The results of this battle are used by the proponents of both types of instrument to support arguments in favor of their favorite device. It is pointed out that the British suffered greater numerical losses than the Germans, and this is taken as a point in favor of the stereoscopic instrument. The stock reply to this line of reasoning is that the British vessels contained a certain structural weakness that contributed to their losses, and this appears to be true. The supporters of the coincidence instrument state that the German fire became less accurate as the battle progressed, showing, allegedly, that the precision of setting of the German rangetakers suffered because of emotional strain. These arguments do not seem to settle the question.

In order to obtain some idea as to the relative merits of the two instruments, let us consider for a moment the ultimate limitations on the observer that control the precision of setting of which he is capable.

In Chap. V it was pointed out that under favorable conditions an observer could reproduce a single coincidence setting with a probable error of 2″. Under field conditions, it appears that an observer may work consistently to about 10 or 12″, although this undoubtedly varies from observer to observer and from test object to test object.

The ability of an observer to resolve stereoscopically two objects was discussed in Chap. XIII and was shown to be about 30″ under ordinary viewing conditions, although much better (10–12″) when an optical instrument was used. The Germans, who use this type of instrument extensively, find that their rangetakers average about 10″, although a few can give results good to 4″; a man whose precision is poorer than 20″ is rejected. Only about 15 per cent of the men they try can do better than 20″.

It is therefore evident that both types of rangefinder have about the same physiological limitations on the attainable precision and a 12″ Unit of Error is used for both types.

Generally speaking, when the ranges of straight, erect objects are to be taken, the coincidence type of instrument with erect

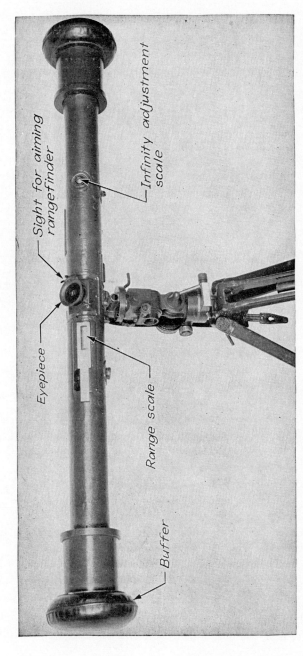

Sight for aiming rangefinder

Infinity adjustment scale

Eyepiece

Range scale

Buffer

PLATE X.—Rear view of a Bausch and Lomb 1-meter-base coincidence-type portable rangefinder. (*Official War Department photograph.*)

fields appears to be best. When rather indistinct objects such as trees are to be ranged upon, a coincidence-type device with an inverted field is useful. When rapidly moving objects of irregular shape, such as airplanes, are considered, the stereoscopic type of rangefinder is the most useful.

**Heightfinders.**—In directing antiaircraft fire it is desired to make measurements as rapidly and accurately as possible. Unfortunately the range of an airplane from a given point varies very rapidly, so that if range is used as a parameter in fire control it is difficult to transmit the range data to the guns in time for it to be of use. However, until recently, bombing planes commonly flew at a constant, or nearly constant, altitude, and their height changed much less rapidly than the range. Thus height was used as a parameter for fire-control purposes, and rangefinders for antiaircraft work were modified to determine height, these devices being designated *heightfinders*.

If the range $R$ to an airplane, from a rangefinder, and the angle of elevation $\theta$ of the plane are known, its height $H$ is easily determined from the fundamental equation

$$H = R \sin \theta \qquad (95)$$

Thus a rangefinder can measure the range of an airplane and its elevation simultaneously, and the results can be multiplied mechanically through a simple gear train to give height. This was done for many years, but more recently a new technique has been developed. An additional pair of prisms of the type shown in Figs. 203 and 208 are added to the instrument, these being so geared as to give a deviation that varies as the sine of the elevation angle. Thus, if a plane flies at constant altitude, both its range and elevation angle (usually) change, and the two sets of prisms rotate so as to give equal deviations. As they are geared together, they will under these circumstances show constant height for the target.

With the introduction of dive, low-altitude, and torpedo bombing the value of height as a parameter for fire-control purposes is largely lost.

**Coincidence Prisms.**—The type of ocular prism shown in Fig. 199 does not give a sufficiently narrow or sharp dividing line between the two fields to permit of accurate setting. Consequently much more elaborate devices have been developed.

A good deal of ingenuity is used in the design of these prisms, which are usually kept secret.

The coincidence prism shown in Fig. 204 is one that is used in Zeiss rangefinders. It consists of two prisms silvered along the contact face $AB$ and cemented together. In the silvered coating on the contact face is left a small rectangular opening, this being in the plane of the real image formed by the erector. Light from the left objective will be reflected from the silvered interface everywhere except at the small rectangular opening. Through this opening comes light from the right objective. Thus in the eyepiece will be seen a large image (formed by the left objective) in the center of which is located an image (inverted by the roof)

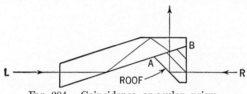

Fig. 204.—Coincidence, or ocular, prism.

from the right objective. The rectangular opening forms the dividing line between the two images. Inasmuch as this opening is not perpendicular to the optical axis of the eyepiece, it will not be in sharp focus even though the images themselves are. Thus the dividing lines between the two fields is apt to be indistinct except at the center, and this is a defect. This type of prism is used in present-day short-base rangefinders by the Germans.

A description of this prism has been included here only to illustrate the principles involved. The devices in present use are sometimes of a vastly more complex character and are generally expensive and difficult to manufacture.

**Penta Prisms.**—As has been mentioned, the light rays are deviated through 90° at the two ends of the instrument by use of penta prisms. These prisms have the characteristics of deviating a light beam in the principal plane through exactly 90° independent of the angle of incidence, a condition that must be fulfilled for proper performance of the instrument. In small instruments, these prisms are made of a single homogeneous block of glass, a difficult thing to obtain. Care should be taken in manufacture to have the two reflecting faces inclined at 45°, and the entrance and exit faces meet at 90°. This is necessary if the

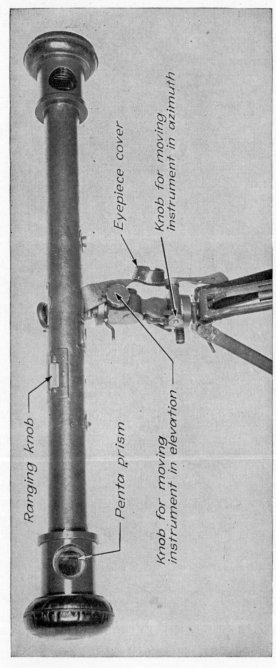

PLATE XI.—Front view of rangefinder shown in Plate X.    (*Official War Department photograph.*)

device is to function properly. A 5′ error in the 45° angle results in a 15′ error in the total deviation, and a 5′ error in the 90° angle produces an 8′ error in the 90° deviation.

It is practically impossible to get a large glass block sufficiently homogeneous to prepare suitable penta prisms for large rangefinders, so for these instruments two mirrors inclined to one another in the same fashion as the reflecting faces of the penta prism are used, these being called *penta reflectors*. They also give an exact 90° deviation in the principal plane for any angle of incidence.

Penta prisms are used for rangefinders of up to about 120 cm base length; larger instruments use penta reflectors.

Under the action of temperature gradients, the angle between the inclined faces of a penta prism or penta reflector can change and thus introduce error. Penta reflectors can come to temperature equilibrium more easily than penta prisms and are thus less susceptible to changes of this sort.

Small linear errors in the locating of these prisms have no effect upon the accuracy of the instrument. Rotational errors can cause trouble, however. A rotation of a penta prism about the axis of the rangefinder is rare and can occur only through a twisting of the outer tube of the rangefinder or incorrect assembly of the prism supports. The result is a rotation of one image with respect to the other, this making it difficult to effect coincidence with a coincidence instrument and disturbing the stereoscopic effect with a stereoscopic rangefinder. A rotation about the axis of the incoming beam is very rare, but it can cause an error of coincidence. A rotation about a vertical axis produces no effect. It is thus seen that the positioning of a penta prism or penta reflector should be performed reasonably carefully but is not extremely critical.

The mirrors in penta reflectors are made of plates of glass about 10 mm thick with faces made accurately plane and parallel. It is not desirable to silver the first surfaces of these mirrors because such silvered surfaces tarnish very rapidly. It is possible to silver (and protect) the second surfaces and use the reflectors without the introduction of spurious reflected images because these mirrors are working with parallel light, and their thickness has the effect of a plane parallel block of glass. Such a block will not deviate the image formed from a beam of parallel light.

Various attempts have been made to make these mirrors of metal, but they have not been very successful. More work is probably being done on this problem, however.

In order that the mirrors might be supported in their proper relationship to one another without being stressed by the supports, many elaborate techniques of mounting have been developed. It is necessary to incorporate in these mounts enough degrees of freedom to permit the mirrors to be properly aligned with the axis of the instrument.

**Optical Bar and Objectives.**—Generally, small linear displacements of the penta reflector or other optical elements located in the optical path before the objective are not serious because they are located in parallel light. However, after passing through the objectives, the light is convergent, and any displacement of the objectives or subsequent elements will seriously affect the accuracy of the instrument through the resultant motion of one image relative to the other. Therefore, the objectives and subsequent elements are mounted within the instrument in or on a structure of special rigidity known as the *optical bar*. Although this is normally made of manganese steel, aluminum is used in some portable instruments. It consists of a tubular or girder-like structure.

Changes in the length of this bar, such as might be caused by thermal expansion, will cause a shift, in a direction perpendicular to the optical axis, of the plane of the real image formed by the objectives. Such a shift will generally not seriously affect the accuracy of the instrument. However, a lateral displacement of the objective will move the image laterally in its own plane, and this can seriously affect accuracy by changing the coincidence setting. In an instrument of 2-meter base length, which would have objectives of about 50-cm focal length, a lateral shift of 0.01 mm of one objective would cause an error of about 270 yd at 5,000 yd. Thus it is necessary to fasten the objective in position on the bar so that it can suffer no displacement, but excessive pressure should not be applied to the objective because this could result in poor imagery. A mounting in which spring pressure is applied to the objective is often employed. Since the optical and mechanical axes of the objective will not in general coincide, it is necessary to keep the objective from rotating in its mounting because such rotation is equivalent to

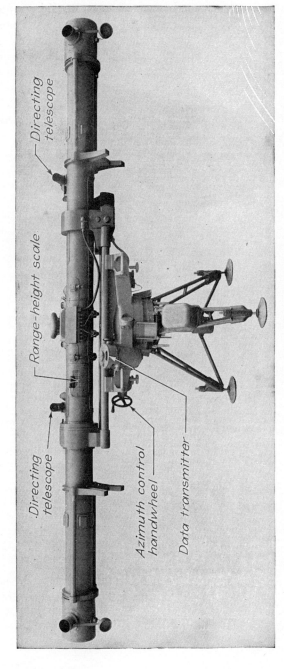

PLATE XII.—Front view of a Bausch and Lomb stereoscopic heightfinder of 13½ ft base length. The telescopes labeled "directing telescopes" are used by the handwheel operators to keep the instrument aimed at the target airplane; they are often called *tracking telescopes*. (*Official War Department photograph.*)

a lateral shift, which, as we have seen, is quite objectionable. Notches may be cut in the edges of the objectives; fixed pins in the lens cells can fit into these notches and prevent rotation.

When exposed to the sun, the top of a rangefinder usually becomes warmer than the bottom; thus a temperature gradient is apt to exist across the optical bar, from top to bottom. This causes an expansion of the top relative to the bottom and a consequent bending of the bar. With an optical bar of 1-meter length and 6-cm diameter a temperature gradient of 1°C across the bar can cause a lateral displacement of each objective of 0.03 mm. As will be seen from the calculations of the previous paragraph, such a displacement can have very serious results. An effort is usually made to keep the temperature gradients in the optical bar at a minimum by supporting it at only two points within one or more protective insulated tubes and thus keeping it more or less thermally insulated from the rest of the instrument. This method of support also reduces to a minimum the effect of the expansions of other parts of the instrument on the very sensitive optical bar. The bar is kept insulated from the outer tube by one or more dead-air spaces.

The weight of the various elements supported on the optical bar causes a bending that is of significance. Unless the supports of the bar are judiciously located with respect to the load, the bending will vary as the instrument is elevated and cause inaccuracy. This effect can be of great significance with height finders whose angles of elevation vary widely in use.

It is necessary that the two objectives used in an instrument have the same focal length so that the images formed by both may be of the same size. These objectives are usually air-spaced doublets (Fig. 142), and their focal length is adjusted by variation of the air space. Another method of making this adjustment is to place a weak negative lens behind the stronger objective and vary the focal length of the combination by moving this adjusting lens parallel to the optical axis. This is not a very good solution, because the extra lens causes some additional reflection loss and introduces an extra source of mechanical trouble and error. The focal length of a lens is apt to change with temperature because of changes in the radii of the surfaces and minor changes in index of refraction. If both objectives change equal amounts through this effect, very harmful results will not be suffered. In a coincidence instrument the images might move out of the focal plane of the line dividing the fields. This results in some inaccuracy but not too much. A similar effect is encountered when objects at widely different ranges are observed, *i.e.*, the planes of their images move slightly.

**Deviation Devices.**—It has been pointed out that in both the coincidence and stereoscopic types of instruments one of the two beams of light must be deviated in order to effect coincidence or move the wander mark. Various devices that may be used for this purpose are as follows:

1. *Plane Parallel Plate.*—This device is shown in Fig. 205. The deviation $D$ produced by a plate of thickness $d$ is given by

$$D = \frac{d \sin (I - I')}{\cos I'} \tag{96}$$

If the beam strikes the plate nearly normal to its face, this equation reduces to the form

$$D = Id \left( \frac{n - 1}{n} \right) \tag{97}$$

$n$ of course being the index of refraction of the glass. A beam of parallel light is homogeneous in that displacement of the beam produces essentially no optical effect. Thus, if such a plate were placed in a rangefinder before the objective and were rotated so that its tilt varied, it would produce no effect on the image.

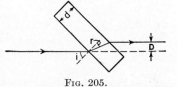

Fig. 205.

It would have to be placed behind the objective, in a convergent beam, to cause any displacement of the image. It gives too small a deviation to be of much use except as a halving or infinity adjuster (described below).

2. *Prism of Small Refracting Angle: Translated along Axis.*—If one were to consider a single ray striking a weak prism, such as the upper ray in Fig. 206, it would be found that the deviation $w$ of this ray would not change as the prism was translated parallel to the axis. However, when a cone of rays is considered, it would be found that although the rays would all be found to be shifted through equal angles by longitudinal motion of the prism their intersections would move, and the image at $A$ would be

found to shift laterally. If $Y$ is the distance between the deviated $(A)$ and undeviated $(B)$ images, it may be shown that

$$Y = wX \qquad (98)$$

$w$ is of course expressed in radians. For a weak prism of refracting angle $a$, we found the deviation produced by the prism

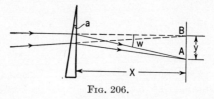

Fig. 206.

to be equal to $(n - 1)a$. Substituting this in Eq. (98) gives

$$Y = (n - 1)aX \qquad (99)$$

$a$, too, is measured in radians.

From these considerations it is evident that a deviation device of this type must be used in a convergent beam of light (behind the objective) and could not be used in a parallel beam between the penta reflector and the objective.

It will be realized that with this device, even when the target is at infinity, there will be a certain deviation produced by this prism. Thus one arm of the rangefinder must be considered, optically, to be slightly inclined to the other by this amount. This amount is kept small. The deviation $w$ is normally kept below 0.003 radian to avoid deterioration of the image by the prism. If the rangefinder is adjusted to an infinitely distant object and then directed at a target at a distance $r$, the deviation prism should be moved by an amount $dx$ to secure coincidence again.

$$dx = \frac{bf'}{wr} \qquad (100)$$

In this equation $b$ is the *base length* (distance between the centers of the penta prisms), $f'$ is the focal length of the objectives, and $w$ is the angle shown in Fig. 206. The scale is a reciprocal one. Thus for long ranges $dx$ will be small, *i.e.*, the scale will be cramped.

The prism is usually moved with a rack and pinion. The range scale may be moved past a fixed index mark by having it attached directly to the prism. This makes the device simple to construct. For this reason, as well as because it has only two surfaces at which reflection losses occur, it is used in many instruments. In practice the prism is normally made achromatic. A rangefinder containing this device is shown in Fig. 199. It is used widely in American (Bausch and Lomb), British (Barr and Stroud) and French (Société d'Optique et de Mechanique de Haute Précision or S.O.M.) rangefinders.

3. *Two Equal Prisms with Variable Spacing.*—This device, shown in Fig. 207, consists of two equal prisms with the thin

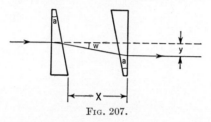

Fig. 207.

edge of one opposite the thick edge of the other. When they are in contact, *i.e.*, when X is a minimum, they act as a plane parallel slab of glass normal to the beam and therefore give no deviation. The arms of the instrument are consequently not inclined to each other as they were with the preceding device. As the distance between them increases, the displacement Y increases, the mathematical statement of this being

$$Y = wX \qquad (101)$$

As before, this may be reduced to the form

$$Y = (n - 1)aX \qquad (102)$$

This latter form is not particularly useful because the prisms are normally achromatic. In this case they consist of two components and $a$ is meaningless. As with the previous device, the spacings on the range scale are related reciprocally to range. It is used only in a convergent beam.

This device was used only in the rangefinders of the French firm known as the Société Optique et Précision de Levallois, or O.P.L.

4. *Diasporameter.*—This deviation mechanism is shown in Fig. 208. It consists of two prisms of equal refracting angles mounted in bearings so that they can be rotated in their own planes about

the optical axis.   When the prisms are in the orientation shown in the illustration, the deviation of one cancels that of the other.

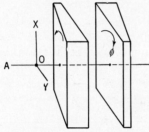

If they are rotated at equal rates in the directions of the arrows, they will always produce equal and opposite deviations in the plane $AOY$.   Thus the beam will be deviated only in the plane $AOX$.   In this plane the deviations produced by the prisms are added.

FIG. 208.—Diasporameter.

If each prism produces a deviation $w$ and if the two prisms are rotated through equal and opposite angles ($\phi$ and $-\phi$, respectively) from the position shown in the figure, the angular deviation, in the plane $AOX$, of the emergent beam is

$$h = 2w \sin \phi \qquad (103)$$

When both prisms have rotated through 90°, the deviation will be a maximum, $2w$.

The chief argument in favor of the diasporameter is that it can be located in front of the objective, between it and the penta prism.   It is thus not connected to the optical bar.   As the optical bar is very sensitive, this is a highly desirable feature. The objections to it are that it has two more glass-air surfaces than the single prism deviator, that it is usually difficult to avoid backlash between the prisms, and that the range scale is trigonometric in character and therefore difficult to rule.

It is possible to photograph the scale on a piece of glass fastened to one of the rotating prisms and project this directly into the eyepiece, next to the image field (Zeiss Em 34 rangefinder).   It is also possible to engrave the scale on a long helix and gear this to the rotating prisms.   This arrangement is usually afflicted with backlash unless special precautions are taken.

The diasporameter is used extensively in Zeiss and Goerz rangefinders as well as in some American instruments.

5. *Miscellaneous Other Devices. a. Tilting prism:* This is a prism rotating about an axis parallel to its base.   It may be used between the penta prism and the objective and thus need not be fastened to the optical bar.   It normally gives too small a deviation for obtaining coincidence because the deviation angle

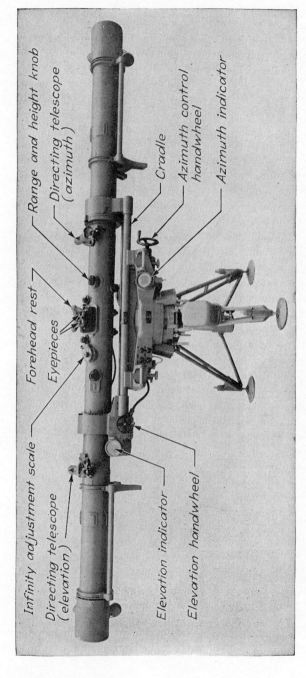

Infinity adjustment scale

Directing telescope (elevation)

Forehead rest

Eyepieces

Range and height knob

Directing telescope (azimuth)

Cradle

Azimuth control handwheel

Azimuth indicator

Elevation indicator

Elevation handwheel

PLATE XIII.—Rear view of 13½-ft stereoscopic heightfinder shown in Plate XII. (*Official War Department photograph.*)

must be kept small enough to avoid chromatic aberration, but it may be used for halving and infinity adjustments.

*b. Moving objective:* It would be possible to move one objective laterally, thus displacing one image. Mechanically this does not prove a desirable arrangement because of the great sensitivity of the image to such deviations. Rangefinders with this type of adjustment have been built by the German firm of Hahn.

*c. Sliding lenses:* If a positive and a negative lens are placed in contact and one is slid laterally over the other, the image they form is deviated. However, considerable aberration is introduced. This device is used in some modern German short-base rangefinders.

*d. Azimuth-type rangefinder:* Another method of effecting coincidence is by rotation of the whole rangefinder about a vertical axis. One type of instrument is constructed on this principle. The images formed by the two objectives are purposely made different in size by using objectives of different focal lengths. The images thus move at different speeds as the instrument is rotated. As the instrument is rotated, one of these images catches up with the other and then passes it. The point at which coincidence occurs is a measure of the range. The total length of the scale is limited by the length of the dividing line between the two images, and this sets a limit on the obtainable accuracy. Unfortunately, coincidence is usually obtained away from the center of the field, such a location being less suitable with regard to aberration than a central one.

This type of instrument is very simple in construction, having essentially no moving parts. It can easily be made waterproof because of the lack of apertures for adjusting levers. It is known as the *azimuth type* of rangefinder, and many 80-cm base instruments of this type have been used by our infantry. They are commonly of the invert type, being of 11 power and covering a 4°0′ true field. They have exit pupils of 2.8 mm. The objectives have focal lengths of 16.26 and 16.78 cm. The total length of the range scale is about 1 cm.

**Astigmatizers.**—Under conditions of night observation, the object being ranged might be a point source of light, as a searchlight. It is extremely difficult to bring such a source onto the dividing line between the two fields of a coincidence instrument. For this reason some rangefinders are equipped with arrangements designated as *astigmatizers*, these being merely cylindrical lenses that may be swung into the beams to draw the image of a point source into a thin line perpendicular to the division between the two fields. These lines may easily be ranged upon in the customary fashion.

**Reticles.**—Instead of containing a single wander mark, the reticles of stereoscopic instruments are commonly constructed with a series of marks so arranged that, to the observer, they appear as two lines of pickets in space that intersect at the target. Thus, with the central mark over the target, equal numbers of the pickets are seen before and behind the target.

PLATE XIV.—An 80-cm-base Barr and Stroud coincidence-type rangefinder. The instrument is of 10 power and covers a $3\frac{1}{2}°$ true field. One eyepiece is used to obtain coincidence; the other is used to read the range scale. This scale may also be read through the window in front of the rubber eye shield. (*Official War Department photograph.*)

It is claimed that this type of reticle gives more accurate results when an isolated object is being ranged than is obtainable with a single wander mark. This increased accuracy may be due to the fact that the observer's sense of symmetry is used in making the setting.

If a shell bursts before or behind the target, the additional marks assist in determining the range error. It is unfortunately not possible to assign definite range differences to the different marks, letting them represent, for example, 25-yd intervals in space, because their spacings actually represent angles, and the range differences they indicate thus vary with the range itself.

**Accuracy Limitations.**—Let us define the Unit of Error $a$ as the greatest angular deviation in the apparent field that one image can suffer without the lack of coincidence being almost certainly detected[1] (see page 88).  This definition holds only for a coincidence instrument.  With a stereoscopic rangefinder, we shall define $a$ as the greatest difference of the convergence angles[2] in the apparent field that can occur without apparent change in the position of the object under consideration.  With a rangefinder of base length $b$ and magnification $M$, the fractional error in range for a given range is then given by

$$E = \frac{dR}{R} = \frac{Ra}{bM} \tag{104}$$

Thus the percentage error in range increases directly with the range and is inversely proportional to base length and magnification.

It is commonly assumed that the Unit of Error $a$ is about $12''$ under field conditions; in this case, the percentage error at 1,000 yd is given by

$$\text{Percentage } E_{1,000} = \frac{6}{bM} \tag{105}$$

where $b$ is expressed in yards.  It will be noted in Eq. (104) that although the percentage error varies with the range, the actual error, in yards, varies as the square of the range.  If the actual error $dR_1$ at some particular range, say 1,000 yd., is known, the error $dR_n$ at any other range $R_n$ is given by

$$dR_n = dR_1 R_n^2 \tag{106}$$

where $R_n$ is expressed in thousands of yards, $i.e.$, in multiples of $R_1$.

The foregoing equations assume that the only source of errors other than systematic is the stereoscopic or vernier acuity of the eye.  This assumption is probably incorrect, and these equations are therefore to be regarded with a certain amount of suspicion.

If the Unit of Error is assumed to be $10''$, Table IV, calculated by Zeiss, gives the errors that will be expected at various ranges, assuming the rangefinder to be perfect.

It has been found that each observer has to calibrate a rangefinder for his own vision (see page 87).  The slight changes in

[1] With a $10''$ Unit of Error the average observer will make an incorrect setting one time in 1,000; with a $12''$ Unit of Error, once in 10,000.

[2] The convergence angles are the angles subtended by the observer's eyes at the image points, $i.e.$, the binocular parallaxes of the image points.

the functioning of the observer's eye that might occur from day to day are perhaps an additional source of inaccuracy. Various other sources of error that cannot be discussed at this time have also been found to affect results.

TABLE IV[1]

| Base length, meters | 0.50 | 1.0 | 3.0 |
|---|---|---|---|
| Magnification | 8 | 11 | 28 |

| Range, meters | Error, meters | | |
|---|---|---|---|
| 200 | 0.5 | | |
| 300 | 1.1 | | |
| 500 | 3.0 | | |
| 1,000 | 12.0 | 4.4 | 0.6 |
| 2,000 | 49 | 17 | 2.3 |
| 3,000 | 109 | 39 | 5.5 |
| 5,000 | ..... | 110 | 15 |
| 7,000 | ..... | 218 | 29 |
| 9,000 | ..... | 358 | 47 |
| 15,000 | ..... | ..... | 129 |

[1] GLEICHEN, "Die Theorie der modernen optischen Instrumente," p. 217, F. Enke, Stuttgart, 1923.

**Halving Adjustments.**—If the instrument were so misaligned that instead of giving an image as shown in Fig. 209 its field had the appearance of Fig. 210, it would be said to have a *halving*

FIG. 209.          FIG. 210.          FIG. 211.

*error.* Such an error occurs when one image is displaced vertically from its proper position. With an invert type of field the halving error would appear as shown in Fig. 211. This type of error is a source of annoyance but not necessarily a source of error unless the object being ranged upon is a line inclined to the division between the two fields of view. In this case a halving error can cause a large error in range. Rangefinders are provided with an adjustment known as the *halving* or *height-of-image adjustment* to eliminate this error.     Both coincidence and stereoscopic instruments must have this adjustment.

Such an adjustment should be capable of moving one image vertically but not horizontally, for a horizontal movement would produce a coincidence error.     The methods of obtaining the halving adjustment are as follows:

1. *Rotation of Penta Prism.*—Rotation of this element about *FG* as axis (Fig. 203) produces the required halving adjustment and also a small (and usually insignificant) change in coincidence.

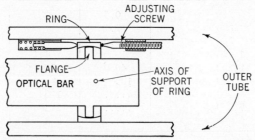

Fig. 212.—Method of obtaining halving adjustment by tilting optical bar. The adjusting screw rotates the ring about an eccentrically located axis. Rotation of the ring therefore moves the flange on the optical bar up or down a small amount.

This technique has been employed by Barr and Stroud on many short-base (66 to 100 cm) rangefinders.     It has the advantage of not introducing into the instrument any extra glass elements.

2. *Tilting of Optical Bar.*—If the optical bar can be tilted exactly in the vertical plane, the halving adjustment may be made without introduction of a coincidence error.     The method of application is shown in Fig. 212, which is self-explanatory. It is claimed that this method gives a very sensitive and quite fine adjustment.     It has been used by the French firm of S.O.M. in 70- and 80-cm base instruments and by Zeiss on a 70-cm base instrument.

3. *Plane Parallel Glass Plate.*—The glass plate is introduced behind one objective.     It rotates about a horizontal axis.     This solution is simple to attain in construction and is popular for that reason in spite of the fact that it involves the introduction into the instrument of an extra optical element.     The amplitude of rotation of the plate and, therefore, the amount of adjustment that may be obtained by its use are limited because excessive

rotation will place the plate at too large an angle of inclination to the beam and thus will introduce excessive astigmatism.

4. *Rotation of a Prism about Optical Axis.*—A prism of small refracting angle may be placed in the beam between the penta prism and the objective. This is mounted with its thickest edge vertical, and provision is made to rotate it about the axis of the objective. As it rotates, the beam is moved circularly; if it is turned through only a small angle, the motion of the beam is practically linear. Thus it effects a halving adjustment but introduces at the same time a small, and usually negligible, error in coincidence. This scheme is used by Zeiss.

5. *Tilting Prism.*—A weak prism is placed between the penta reflector and the objective and is supported on a horizontal axis parallel to its base. Rotation of the prism about its axis produces the halving adjustment, and no change in coincidence is produced. This was developed by H. Dennis Taylor, the famous British optical engineer.

**Infinity Adjustments.**—Because of the various sources of systematic error heretofore discussed, some of which may vary from day to day, it is necessary to check the accuracy of a rangefinder rather frequently. Since the observers, too, undergo change, frequent adjustments should be performed for this reason as well.

Adjustment is usually performed at a single fixed range, *i.e.*, the range scale is set so as to read correctly the range of a target at a known distance. If the instrument is not properly adjusted, coincidence will not be obtained with a coincidence instrument nor stereoscopic contact with a stereoscopic device. Coincidence, or stereoscopic contact, is then obtained by means of an extra deviation mechanism placed in the instrument for that purpose. The instrument is now in proper adjustment for the range selected for adjustment, and, if the scale has been properly constructed, it will be in adjustment for all other ranges too. The range commonly selected for making this adjustment is infinity, and it is therefore commonly called the *infinity adjustment*. To make the adjustment, it is necessary to provide a target of such a character that beams of light parallel to each other will enter the two objectives.

One of the very early methods of obtaining this adjustment involved the use of a board or flat metal tube (known as a *lath adjuster*) containing two marks separated by a distance equal to the base length of the instrument to be calibrated (see Fig. 213).

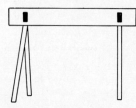

FIG. 213.—Lath adjuster.

This was set up several hundred yards from the rangefinder, and parallel to it. The rangefinder was then adjusted until the field appeared as shown in Fig. 214, at which time the light beams entering the two objectives were parallel (Why?).

This method was crude and cumbersome, but it is still applied to portable short-base rangefinders because the apparatus involved is cheap, easy to construct, simple, and portable. Each lath should be adjusted to the exact base length of the instrument with which it is to be used.

The lath has to be aligned accurately perpendicular to the line from its center to the center of the rangefinder. It is usually provided with special sighting equipment for this purpose.

Under some field conditions it is not possible to use the lath at the desired range of several hundred yards. In these circumstances it is permissible to use it at as short a distance as about sixty times the base length of the rangefinder. If the lath is located 50 meters from a rangefinder of 1-meter base, an error of $\frac{1}{4}$ mm in the length of the lath will result in an error of measurement of about 115 yd at 5,000 yd. As the lath is placed farther from the rangefinder the resulting error decreases (Why?).

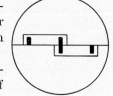

FIG. 214.—Appearance of the field of a coincidence (invert type) rangefinder when adjusted by means of a lath adjuster.

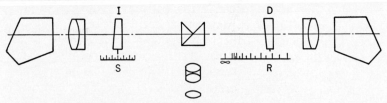

FIG. 215.—Coincidence-type rangefinder (no halving adjustment shown).

The method of making the infinity adjustment is shown in Fig. 215. The deviating prism $D$ is adjusted to the infinity position on the range scale $R$. The lath, or other adjusting device, is set up. The infinity adjusting prism $I$ is moved until coincidence is obtained, as shown in Fig. 214, and the reading on the infinity adjusting scale $S$ is noted. A number (usually ten) of such readings are taken and averaged. Each observer who will use the instrument determines the particular setting of $S$ that gives the best results for him.

Instead of the prism shown at $I$, any of the other deviation devices, such as a diasporameter, may also be incorporated into an instrument for the infinity adjustment. It is usually desirable to check the infinity adjustment very frequently, for it will change with the slightest provocation.

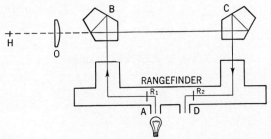

Fig. 216.—Abbe's infinity adjuster.

The other infinity adjusting devices to be described are used in a similar fashion to this one. They merely provide different methods of artificially obtaining an infinitely distant target.

In 1893, Abbe developed a practical technique which is illustrated in Fig. 216. The adjusting apparatus consists of the two penta prisms $B$ and $C$ placed in front of the entrance windows of the rangefinder, which is of the stereoscopic type. The wander marks for this instrument are on reticles $R_1$ and $R_2$. Let a source of light, such as a tungsten filament lamp, be placed at $A$. Light from the lamp passes through the left tube of the rangefinder. As the reticle $R_1$ is at the focus of the left objective, this reticle will be imaged at infinity by the beam entering penta prism $B$. Thus this reticle will be imaged at infinity by the light entering the right-hand objective, and it will be imaged in the plane of $R_2$. If the adjuster $BC$ has been set up properly, the beams entering and leaving the rangefinder will be parallel; consequently the instrument is working at infinite range. The observer looks into the right eyepiece $D$ and brings the images of the two reticles into coincidence with the infinity adjuster

The instrument is now correctly adjusted for infinity. Because the two prisms $B$ and $C$ are optical squares (*i.e.*, they give exactly 90° deviations in the principal plane even if they are not oriented properly), this device works very effectively. Additional prisms might be placed between $B$ and $C$ so as to give divergent beams of light corresponding to a definite range less than infinity, but this is not generally done.

This arrangement was modified by König so that both eyes could be used during calibration. He employed a collimator consisting of an objective $O$ with an illuminated reticle $H$ at its focus (Fig. 216). This reticle is imaged by the objective at infinity. Light from $O$ enters prisms $B$ and $C$, each of which

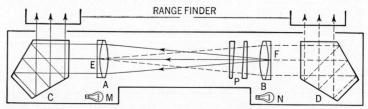

RANGE FINDER

Fig. 217.—Barr and Stroud type infinity adjuster. (The diasporameter $P$ has been shown, for the sake of clarity, rotated 90° about the optical axis from its true zero position.)

covers half the field, simultaneously, and reticle $H$ is thus seen at infinity in both eyepieces. Coincidence is effected, or the wander mark is brought over $H$, by means of the infinity adjuster, the scale having previously been set to infinity.

The method in most general use at present stems from apparatus developed in 1906 by Barr and Stroud and shown in Fig. 217. Each of the two objectives $A$ and $B$ carries etched on its surface a cross hair (located at $E$ and $F$) illuminated by the bulbs at $M$ and $N$. The objectives are so spaced that $E$ is at the focus of objective $B$, and $F$ is at the focus of $A$. Thus in light traveling to the left, $F$ is imaged at infinity by $A$, and this light enters the left objective of the rangefinder. In light traveling to the right, $E$ is imaged at infinity by $B$, and this light enters the right objective. The beams entering the rangefinder from the penta prisms $C$ and $D$ are parallel to one another, so the combined image of $EF$ will be seen at infinity. Thus the two cross hair images are fused into one in the rangefinder after the scale has been set to read infinity. This calibration apparatus can of course be used for both coincidence and stereoscopic instruments. It is particularly well regarded because it functions properly regardless of small lateral displacements of objectives $A$ and $B$ (Why?), or small rotations in their principal planes of prisms $C$ and $D$. The beams passing through the objectives $A$ and $B$ are always colinear.

If desired, the diasporameter $P$ may be added to diverge the beams to reproduce settings at any desired range. This refinement is generally not used.

Originally this adjuster was furnished as a separate piece of apparatus, as shown. Later it was mounted on the external framework of the rangefinder so that it could be swung up into position. In some modern instruments it is built within the rangefinder and may be swung into position when needed.

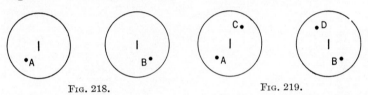

Fig. 218.                    Fig. 219.

**Pseudoscopic Rangefinder.**—An instrument which has not yet been constructed commercially but which is interesting on theoretical grounds is of the stereoscopic type. The fields of the two eyepieces are shown in Fig. 218. Now suppose we are sighting on a target, represented by the dot in the illustrations, and leave the deviation device set at a slightly different range from that of the target. The images of the target will now be represented by $A$ and $B$, which are farther apart than they would be if the instrument were set for the correct range. Now assume that by optical means we form in the upper half of the left eyepiece an image using light from the right objective, and in the upper half of the right eyepiece an image with light from the left objective. Then we shall have the fields shown in Fig. 219, where all the dots are images of the same target. The image seen by the observer of dots $A$ and $B$ will be seen in true perspective while that seen from dots $C$ and $D$ will be reversed in perspective, this latter being called a *pseudoscopic* image. As the deviation device is adjusted closer to the correct range, the two images will approach one another; at the instant the range is properly set, they will merge. If the range is overshot, the images will of course reverse. The geometry of this instrument is such that the parallactic angles are doubled, and thus the accuracy is doubled (theoretically). However, to the present time this device has not been constructed commercially because of technical difficulties. Because of psychological effects it may not be as accurate as expected.

## REFERENCES

"Dictionary of Applied Physics," Vol. 4, Macmillan & Company, Ltd., London, 1923.

GARDNER: "Elementary Optics and Applications to Fire Control Instruments," Government Printing Office, Washington, 1924.

GLEICHEN: "Die Theorie der modernen optischen Instrumente," F. Enke, Stuttgart, 1923.

KÖNIG: "Die Fernrohre und Entfernungsmesser," Julius Springer, Berlin, 1937.

MAZUIR: "Traité de télémétrie," Revue d'Optique théorique et instrumentale, Paris (XV$^e$), 1931.

## PROBLEMS

**1.** A 1-meter base coincidence type rangefinder, with 25-cm focal length objectives, is directed toward a target located 1,000 meters away. What is the parallactic displacement of the images of the target?

**2.** A stereoscopic rangefinger of 15-ft base length, using objectives of 4-ft focal length, is ranged on a target 1,000 yd away. How much movement of the wander mark is now necessary to make stereoscopic contact with a target 20,000 yd distant? (NOTE: Stereoscopic contact is obtained when the wander mark is so placed as to appear at the same distance from the instrument as the target.)

**3.** Assuming for an average observer a Unit of Error of 12″, what is the minimum difference in range that could be detected between the wander mark and the target with the rangefinder of Prob. 2, assuming it is an instrument of 20 power, when the target is 1,000 yd distant?

**4.** If a diasporameter were constructed by using two achromatic wedges, *i.e.*, prisms of small refracting angle, as calculated in the problem of Chap. XI, what would be the maximum obtainable deviation? What would be the deviation if the two wedges were rotated 30° in opposite directions from the position of zero deviation? Assume that you wish to use the diasporameter over a range in which the deviation produced varies approximately linearly with the angle of rotation. Plot the angle of rotation against the deviation and estimate what would be the maximum permissible angle of rotation to fill this condition.

**5.** An observer working with a Zeiss rangefinger of 70-cm base length and 11 power makes an error in setting of 12″ at 1,000 meters. What is the resulting error in range? What would be the range error if he had made a similar angular misalignment at a range of 500 meters?

**6.** An adjusting lath with an incorrect length of 70.1 cm between the centers of the vertical marks is furnished for use with the rangefinder described in Prob. 5. What angular error is introduced if this lath is used to adjust a rangefinger when the lath is placed 50 meters from the instrument? What is the error if this distance is changed to 150 meters? Which distance gives the more accurate adjustment? Which gives the more precise adjustment?

**7.** In order to make the functioning of a coincidence rangefinger clear, an exaggeration leading to an optical absurdity was necessary in Fig. 199. What was it?

# PART III

*Mechanical and Electrical Design*

# CHAPTER XVII

## OPTICAL INSTRUMENT DESIGN: GENERAL CONSIDERATIONS

If a detail draftsman were working on the design of an optical instrument and were engaged, for example, in the installation of a ball bearing, his interest would lie solely in the direction of knowing the necessary clearances and tolerances that should be obtained to install the bearing properly.

If a layout draftsman were working on the same element of the same instrument, he would have to decide what type of ball bearing should be installed in order to carry the load involved and position it to the desired accuracy. Of course, he would also have to select the bearing that would most economically meet his requirements. Thus he should possess the knowledge to make these decisions as well as possess the more specialized knowledge of the detailer.

The instrument designer, working on this same element, must decide whether ball or other types of bearings will be used, where they will go, and what effects the various bearings will have on one another and other elements of the device. In order to be able to do this effectively, he should have at his disposal the general theory of instrument design as well as the detailed knowledge of individual elements possessed by the layout man and the detailer.

Inasmuch as the fundamentals of layout and detail design spring from the more comprehensive work of the designer, we shall first consider the basic, underlying principles of instrument design.

There has been much discussion from time to time as to whether the optical or mechanical elements of an optical instrument should be designed first. Although the use for which a given instrument is intended sometimes stresses the importance of one or the other of these elements, the writer feels that the design of both types of elements should follow along parallel to one another and that both should, if possible, be under the supervision of a single designer. This is the best way to insure that the optical and mechanical elements in the complete instrument will function together in harmony.

Various theories and techniques of instrument design may be employed for optical instruments. The particular technique employed should be selected with reference to the specific type of instrument under consideration. Thus measuring microscopes, motion-picture projectors, and rangefinders are devices that, generally speaking, call for quite different approaches, for the fundamental problems involved are of quite different characters.

In many optical instruments results of the highest precision must be obtained. It is highly desirable to achieve these results with the most economical grade of workmanship. If we were to design optical instruments according to standard machine design practice, we would have to use a large amount of the highest precision machine work. The designer must, therefore, seek a design technique that will enable him to obtain results of the desired accuracy with as little precision machine work as possible. When faced with this problem (which, it should be remembered, is by no means encountered in all optical design problems), he may have recourse to a design technique known as *kinematic design*.

**Kinematic Design.**—If a body in space is to be accurately located with reference to another body, six coordinates must be used, for the spatial object has three degrees of freedom of translation and three of rotation. (The number of *degrees of freedom* a body possesses is the number of coordinates of translation or rotation required to specify completely its position.) A locomotive moving along a pair of straight tracks has only one degree of freedom: that of translation in a given direction. If the tracks were to curve, it might be argued that the locomotive has two degrees of freedom: one of translation and one of rotation. However, as the statement of the position of the locomotive along the track is sufficient to determine its position completely with reference to both translation and rotation, it is evident that the two degrees of freedom are not independent, and there is still only one independent degree of freedom. If a crane were to lift the locomotive from the tracks, it might then have all six degrees of freedom. From this elementary example it is immediately obvious that it would be extremely difficult to determine mathematically the number of degrees of freedom possessed by one body with reference to another, for this number will depend on the particular conditions obtaining at any given instant. The designer should use plain common sense to evaluate the number present in any given case.

As has already been indicated, if a given body is to be located accurately with respect to a reference object, six degrees of freedom should be eliminated. The minimum number of point contacts between the two bodies that can accomplish this is six. If $n$ degrees of freedom are desired, $(6 - n)$ point contacts are the minimum that may be used.

It is of course obvious that more than the minimum number of contacts, or constraints, may be used to position a body. Consider the case of a stool being placed upon a floor. The minimum number of degrees of freedom that determine the position of the seat of the stool relative to the floor are three, *i.e.*, three legs may be used. However, a fourth leg may be added. In this case more than the minimum possible number of constraints are used. If the four legs have not been made exactly equal in length, the weight of the stool will be supported by three legs instead of four. Even if all the legs do have equal lengths, any slight irregularity in the floor will cause the load to be again thrown on three legs and, as the stool is moved about the floor, different sets of legs will bear the load. Although this is not very objectionable in the design of chairs, it can be a source of major error in instrument design. One of the principles of kinematic design is that only the minimum possible number of constraints should be used, *i.e.*, no element of an instrument may be reduntantly constrained. Consider this matter from a different point of view: suppose it were desired, in an instrument, to clamp a flat metal plate temporarily to a flat, rigid support. This could be done by using four C-clamps, applying one at each corner of the plate. If the plate and the support were not parallel at all points (*i.e.*, if either were slightly rough or bent or warped) we might find that, after applying two or three of the clamps a remaining corner of the plate did not lie flat against the support. The remaining C-clamps would force it into position, but only at the expense of setting up heavy strains in the plate. In an optical instrument these strains could become a source of inaccuracy as will be appreciated from a consideration of Chap. XVI. Thus we see that overconstraint must be avoided.

There is one distinction between the two foregoing examples that should be kept in mind. In the case of the four-legged stool only relatively light forces (due to gravity) kept the stool in contact with the floor, and these forces were not sufficiently great to force all four legs into contact with the floor had one been shorter than the others. This case is designated *redundant constraint.* The plate, on the other hand, was forced into contact with its support at all four corners by means of the large forces brought into play through the use of C-clamps. This is a case of *overconstraint.* Each of these two forms of excessive constraint is of course objectionable.

The general principle involved in these examples is this: In kinematic design, overconstraint or redundant constraint must be avoided.

Suppose that we were designing a telescopic sight for a gun and placed the optics in a cylindrical tube. Suppose we place on the gun a V-shaped trough to act as the sight mount and that we attempt to mount the sight on the gun by laying it in the trough. If the cylindrical tube and trough had been machined perfectly smooth and true, the sight would fit the trough properly and would bear the same relationship to the bore of the gun every time it was placed in the trough. In practice there would always be slight irregularities on the surfaces of the tube and the trough. The sides of the trough would not be perfectly flat, and the wall of the tube would be neither perfectly flat nor truly round. Thus, every time the tube was dropped into the trough, it would in practice bear a different relationship to the bore of the gun, with resulting inaccuracy. The tube is redundantly constrained with relation to the trough and thus violates a fundamental principle of kinematic design. Note, too, that if the sight has not been collimated, *i.e.,* the optical axis and the tube axis made coincident, considerable inaccuracy would result from the tube being differently oriented with regard to rotation each time it was placed in the trough. As far as rotation is concerned, the tube is underconstrained, *i.e.,* there are too many degrees of freedom. If the principles of kinematic design were not being followed in designing this sight, the difficulty would probably be overcome by collimating the sight, a costly and time-consuming process. If we were following the precepts of kinematic design, we should probably eliminate the undesirable degree of freedom by an additional constraint such as a pin on the tube that might drop into a recess in the trough and would thus make rotation impossible. This example suggests one of the principal advantages of kinematic design; it enables the designer to obtain results of high precision without necessarily using the most expensive and time-consuming machining operations.

Again consider a leg of the stool that was used as an example. At the bottom of this leg is a small area that makes contact with the floor. In theory one might consider the whole bottom of the leg to be in contact. In practice, however, because of the fact that the floor and leg contain minute irregularities, only one, or perhaps a few, minute areas of contact between leg and floor exist, and these support a load that was intended to be supported by a much larger area. This has several important disadvantages. Because these points do support relatively large loads, they wear rapidly, transferring the load to other points. Again, the designer does not know at what points contact is actually obtained between the leg and the floor, and thus, if the leg happens to support the base of an instrument, he does not know the exact base length of the device. The distance between the instrument table supported by such a leg and the floor on which the leg rests might vary slightly, depending on what minute areas support the load at a given instant. In an optical instrument such a source of error might be of importance. Finally, it is obvious that if the designer is comparing various grades of machining that produce surfaces of varying degrees of smoothness and is trying to decide which to use for the "leg" or "floor" in his instrument, he has no way of telling the quantitative effect on the position of the table that will result from using these different machining operations. It is thus very evident that *areas of contact* are to be avoided in an instrument. This might be looked upon as an extension of the principle of the avoidance of overconstraint. This principle is of such importance that it is usually listed separately. It may be stated as follows: In kinematic design constraints should be applied through point contacts rather than area contacts.

Suppose that the bottom of the legs considered above had been pointed. The base length of the instrument would then be accurately known for it would be the distance between these points. The load would be distributed over an accurately known area.  If various grades of machining were to be considered for application to the base or "floor" surface, the variations in position of the pointed leg as it traveled across the surface could be accurately calculated.  The designer could determine the permissible variation in this positioning and then select the least expensive grade of machining that would give the desired accuracy.

Again consider the case of the flat plate fastened to a support by C-clamps.  It has been pointed out that large forces will probably be brought into play when the clamps are applied.  These forces are of unknown magnitude and might lead to serious trouble.  This is a general difficulty experienced with overconstrained elements.  In the case of a slide moving in a lathe bed there will always be a small amount of play so that the slide can be moved from side to side until its sideways motion is stopped by a bearing surface.  While moving from side to side the restoring force (tending to bring it to some desired position) is zero; when it is moved into contact with the bearing surface and an attempt is made to push it farther, a tremendous restoring force is brought into play by the elastic properties of the materials involved.  Such an arrangement is suitable for a machine tool, but it would not be suitable for an optical instrument because of the unavoidable play.  Thus another principle of kinematic design is that there shall always be *locators* to maintain the various constraints and keep all parts in known positions. Springs or gravity is generally used for this purpose.  In order to avoid overconstraint, restoring forces acting through the locators are always kept small.  The restoring forces are generally kept constant regardless of the relative position of the two objects being constrained, this, too, helping to keep the restoring forces light.  The fact that the restoring forces are kept light means that the friction forces throughout the instrument are small, improving its performance and making it possible to use light parts.  Also, the light forces reduce wear.

In any instrument in which moving parts are used wear must occur.  In general, this results in a change in the relationship of the various elements of the instrument.  In optical instruments such changes can lead to very large errors.  It is often possible, by the proper application of the fundamentals of kinematic design, to design an instrument so that the principal parts will maintain a desired relationship independent of normal wear. It is also possible to design two parts so that they will bear a fixed relationship to one another regardless of different thermal expansion properties.

In general, the advantages of kinematic design may be summed up as follows:

1. In a properly designed instrument relatively light and well-controlled forces are used to keep the various points of support in contact with one another. Only small amounts of friction are thus involved, and it is possible easily to predict such resultant displacement in the relative positions of the elements whose relationship is to be controlled as might result from any surface irregularity of the bearing surfaces. Thus the effects of various grades of machine work can be evaluated easily, and the most economical one is then selected.

2. Since the restoring forces and the frictional forces are small, sufficient stresses to call into effect the elastic properties of the members are not encountered and need not be taken into account.

3. The relative position of two bodies in a properly designed instrument does not depend on the accuracy of the dimensions of the positioning contacts. Consequently, this position can be maintained in spite of normal wear of the bearing surfaces. This desideratum cannot always be achieved, but it can be attained surprisingly often.

4. If differential measurements are to be made, it is often possible to design the instrument to give very precise results in spite of indifferent workmanship.

5. Because small parts and light forces are involved, it is often possible to minimize wear through the use of kinematic design. This is not always the case, however, for wear is sometimes accentuated because of the point contacts involved.

The principal disadvantages of kinematic design are as follows:

1. The fact that a given degree of freedom is limited by a point in contact with a surface means that the location of this point can be affected by minute irregularities in the bearing surface.

2. The fact that control is exerted over the positioning of elements by rather small forces means that the instrument will be somewhat "loose-jointed" in the presence of large disturbing forces that might be encountered in actual use.

3. As has been mentioned, the use of point contacts sometimes leads to accelerated wear because of the loads concentrated on these points.

Because of the use of point contacts and light restoring forces, kinematic design is eminently suitable for small instruments of the highest precision, but for the same reason it is not always usable in the design of larger devices. Therefore, in some cases compromises are made between practical considerations and the precepts of kinematic design, this combination being designated *semikinematic* design.

In the construction of bulky instruments it is often quite impracticable to use point contacts because of the excessive wear that would result. In this case

Fig. 220.

the points are expanded into areas small in comparison with the distance between them. A certain amount of predictability of the location of the elements is lost, but greater loads can be carried. The device is also more stable with regard to variations in the locations of the point contacts caused by irregularities in the surface on which they bear. This is an example of semikinematic design.

A second compromise is sometimes reached when the number of areas of contact is kept a minimum, but each area is itself overconstrained. Suppose that a three-legged pedestal were under consideration. With the first compromise the legs would have small areas rather than points to be placed in contact with the floor. Assume that this pedestal carries a fire-control instrument, which is to be mounted in a bombing plane (Fig. 220). Since the pitching of the plane might disturb the device, we use the second compromise. We might bolt the three legs to the floor. This technique results in large forces being imposed on the locators themselves, but, because of the small base over which these forces act (limited by the size of the contact area) and because the minimum number of locators has been retained, large stresses will not be set up in the instrument supported on the pedestal. The lower end of one of the legs is shown in Fig. 221. As the bolts in the three legs are screwed down, each bolt being tightened a little in turn, the stresses set up will have lever arms no longer than $b$; thus the torque produced will be moderate.

A third compromise would be the provision of redundant locators. The use of four legs on the tripod would represent

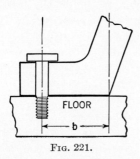

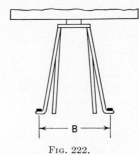

Fig. 221.                                        Fig. 222.

this case, and it might be necessary to use these four legs if the loads to be carried were large.

Finally, we can provide redundant locators that are over-constrained. If we used a four-legged support for our instrument and bolted all four legs to the floor of the plane, we should be employing this technique. In this case any three of the legs can define a geometrical plane. If the end of the fourth leg does not lie in this plane, large forces will be brought into play when it is forced into position. These forces will be applied over the lever arm $B$ in Fig. 222, and therefore large torques can be applied directly to the body of the instrument. It is possible to design

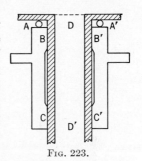

Fig. 223.

on semikinematic principle a firm support involving four bolts in which excessive torques will not be applied.[1]

An interesting application of the principles of semikinematic design occurred a few years ago when a certain surveying organization purchased a number of theodolites of high quality.[2] These theodolites (telescopic devices used for the precise measurement of angles in surveying) had their telescopes mounted on vertical

[1] Whitehead, "The Design and Use of Instruments and Accurate Mechanism," The Macmillan Company, New York, 1934.

[2] Rannie and Dennis, "Improving Primary Triangulation Theodolites," *Can. J. Research*, Vol. 10, No. 3, p. 346, 1934.

axes that were not kinematically designed. The design of these axes is shown in Fig. 223. The revolving telescope is mounted on the central member of this assembly. The load is carried by the ball thrust bearing at $AA'$. The axis is positioned by the cylindrical surfaces at $BB'$ and $CC'$. Although the tube $DD'$ and the bearing surfaces $BB'$ and $CC'$ were ground with the highest precision, it was just not possible to surface them perfectly, and it is evident that unless these surfaces are perfectly matched there will be some play in the axis. The purchasers of these instruments tested them very carefully and found that

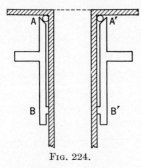

FIG. 224.

the angles measured by them were slightly in error. As it was suspected that the small amount of play that is inevitably associated with this design might be responsible, the axis was redesigned according to kinematical principles. The new design, which may be called semikinematic, is shown in Fig. 224. The load was supported by three balls in an angular-contact ball bearing at $AA'$. These balls also helped to locate the upper end of the axis (later more balls were added to give greater strength). The lower end of the axis was positioned by the rather narrow bearing surface $BB'$. It was realized that two solid pads located 120° apart combined with a third spring support pad would have represented somewhat better design practice, but it was desired to modify the existing instruments with as few actual changes as possible. It will be realized that any slight warpage of the axis in the design shown in Fig. 223 would lead to considerable overconstraint, while the reduction in the area of the bearing surfaces, as shown in Fig. 224, gives a design that will introduce very little constraint in this case. The theodolite axes were rebuilt according to this new design in the instrument shop of the surveying organization, and a few other minor changes were made. Upon retest the theodolites showed greatly improved performance.

Numerous other similar examples of the successful application of kinematical principles to optical instrument design could be recounted.

Point contacts represent the most difficult objects to lubricate that can be visualized, and they must often be replaced by antifriction bearings. This is another example of semikinematic design. It will be seen that it is possible to lay out an instrument generally following the precepts of kinematic design with regard to minimum constraints, etc., and then to use areas instead of points for some of the contacts. Macroscopically the instrument would be kinematically designed; microscopically it would not. It would thus be called semikinematically designed.

It is pointed out that, in cases where the instrument is apt to be subjected to large disturbing forces, non-kinematic designs are sometimes desirable.

### REFERENCES

MARTIN: "Optical Measuring Instruments," Blackie & Son, Ltd., Glasgow, 1924.

POLLARD: "The Kinematical Design of Couplings in Instrument Mechanisms," Adam Hilger, London, 1929.

WHITEHEAD: "The Design and Use of Instruments and Accurate Mechanism," The Macmillan Company, New York, 1934.

# CHAPTER XVIII

## MACHINING OPERATIONS AND CASTING METHODS

It is often easy to design an instrument to perform a given task, but it is definitely more difficult to design an instrument that can be made economically and can perform its function. If the designer has some knowledge of the principles of kinematic design, he may design an instrument that will give the maximum performance obtainable with a given grade of workmanship. However, unless the designer also has a good idea of the functions and limitations of the different types of equipment used in the machine shop, he will often include in his design one or more parts that just cannot be made with reasonable economy.

The various pieces of equipment used in the standard machine shop will be briefly mentioned:

**Shaper.**—The *shaper* is a machine (Fig. 225) in which a tool is moved back and forth over a piece of metal with a reciprocating motion, thus scraping it. Generally a chip is peeled from the metal only on the forward stroke. The piece of metal being worked is clamped on a table, and in many shapers this table is made universal, *i.e.*, it can be rotated through 180° and tilted through some 15°. The table is moved, either by hand or automatically, so that the tool scrapes a different part of the work at each stroke; thus a large surface can be finished. Shapers are usually described in terms of the table they have (plain or universal) and the size of the square area they can machine. If the stroke of a shaper is 24 in. and the table can be moved transverse to the stroke a distance of 24 in., then the machine is called a 24-in. shaper. The total range of vertical motion of the tool will generally be only a few inches. Besides obtaining flat surfaces, a shaper may be used to cut dovetail slots, keyways, etc. Machines in which the work is held on a horizontal table and the tool moves vertically are known as *vertical shapers*, a simple form of which is known as the *vertical slotter*. The vertical shaper may be used for work of the same general character as the horizontal machine. Tolerances of about ±0.001 in. can be held with shapers and planers, this depending somewhat on the size and shape of the work.

PLATE XV.—A vertical shaper.  (*Courtesy of Pratt and Whitney.*)

**Planer.**—The *planer* is a machine that differs from the shaper in that the table and the work move beneath a fixed tool instead of the reverse (Fig. 226). It is generally used for producing flat surfaces and is employed on work that cannot be surfaced on a milling machine because of excessive size, etc.   The work

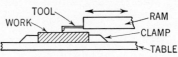

Fig. 225.—Principle of the shaper.

is clamped to a reciprocating table. This table is sometimes equipped with a chuck that can be rotated in a plane parallel to

PLATE XVI.—A vertical shaper surfacing a casting. (*Courtesy of Pratt and Whitney.*)

that of the table. The cutting tool is held in a horizontal bar mounted between two vertical uprights. At times the work is mounted between a pair of centers similar to those on a lathe, and the work may be rotated by means of a graduated circle on

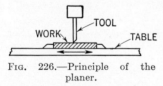

FIG. 226.—Principle of the planer.

one of these. One of these centers is made movable vertically so that the work might not be parallel to the table in case it is desired to machine bevels or tapers.

The size of a planer is designated by giving the distance between the uprights, the distance between the table and the horizontal bar in its highest position, and the maximum length of the stroke. Thus a planer could be specified by the dimensions 24 by 24 in. by 6 ft.

**Lathe.**—The *lathe* is one of the most important and versatile tools in the machine shop. It is shown in Plate XVII. The work is held between the two centers and is rotated by motion of the *live center*. The tool is held in the *tool post* and is moved by means of a carriage parallel to the axis of rotation of the work. The carriage is moved by the *lead screw* or the *feed rod*.

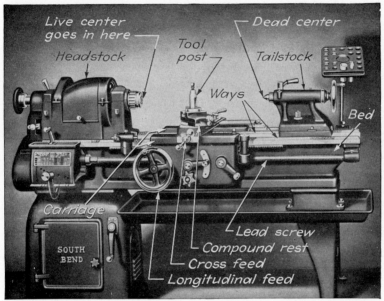

PLATE XVII.—A modern engine lathe. A precision engine lathe of this type is sometimes called a toolroom lathe. This particular lathe has no feed rod, all longitudinal motion being transmitted by the lead screw. (*Courtesy of South Bend Lathe Works.*)

The tool can be moved perpendicularly to the axis of rotation of the work by means of a *cross-feed*, which may be either hand or power operated. The speed of rotation of the live center may be controlled by proper selection of gears in the *headstock*. The machine may be adjusted to accommodate long or short work through motion of the *tailstock*. The carriage may be moved along the work in *ways*, this being accomplished either manually or by power delivered through the feed rod or the lead screw at the will of the operator. The lead screw, which is very accurate, is used only when threads are to be chased; the feed rod is used at all other times. The base of the machine supporting the hardened ways is known as the *bed*.

The type of machine shown in Plate XVII is an *engine lathe*, this being the type in most general use. Its size is usually specified in terms of the largest diameter piece that can be rotated over the ways and the total length of the bed.

By gearing the lead screw to the main spindle the tool can be made to move along the work at a rate governed by the rotation. By this means threads may be cut in the work. By proper selection of gears various pitch threads may be produced.

The *compound rest*, which supports the tool post, is commonly provided with cross ways for rotating and sliding the tool post so that the tool can be brought against the work in any desired orientation.

The lathe is provided with several special-purpose attachments. One of these is a taper attachment for turning and boring tapers. Another is for relieving; still another is for milling. The latter may be used to mill dovetail slots, perform end milling, and mill keyway slots. When a long thin rod is being worked, it is necessary to use special rests to support it to prevent tapering that could be caused by distortion or springing of the rod. One such rest is the *follower rest*, which is a rest that is attached to the carriage and thus follows along with the tool.

Work may be held at the headstock by two types of chuck. One has three jaws that move simultaneously. It is used for round stock because it is simple to adjust. The other commonly used chuck has four independently operated jaws. It is difficult to adjust but can be used with work of a great variety of shapes. If the work is being held between centers, special means must be provided to rotate it; special clamps, known as *lathe dogs*, are used for this purpose. Material much longer than the lathe may be worked by supporting it through a hollow chuck, known as a *collet chuck*. This type of chuck is also used for very accurate work. Note that, although the live center revolves with the work, the dead center does not and thus must be lubricated with oil.

Besides turning cylindrical forms and tapers, a lathe may be used for *facing*, *i.e.*, it may be used for smoothing a face perpendicular to the axis of rotation. It also may be used for straight or taper boring. By bringing a knurled cylindrical tool against the work the work itself may be knurled.

It has been mentioned that tapers may be cut with a taper attachment. This feeds in the tool automatically at the proper rate to give the desired taper. A taper may also be obtained by adjusting the compound rest so that the tool feed is at the desired angle, and the tool is then advanced by hand. By offsetting the tailstock, it also possible to obtain a taper.

PLATE XVIII.—A light turret lathe. (*Courtesy of South Bend Lathe Works.*)

A special form of lathe, known as a *turret lathe,* carries a rotating turret in which are fastened several tools. The turret is rotated so that one tool after the other is brought up against the work. It is used when a given series of operations is to be repeated many times. These devices may be built so that the work rotates about a horizontal axis (horizontal turret lathe) or a vertical axis (vertical turret lathe). It is sometimes possible, by the use of these lathes, to perform two operations, such as boring and turning, simultaneously. The vertical turret lathe is the fastest lathe to use for short or heavy work. When the horizontal turret lathe is provided with automatic controls to bring the various tools against the work in production, the device is known as an *automatic screw machine.* This is of course used solely for manufacturing purposes. It is capable of doing fine work if operated properly. Unfortunately some small shops equipped with screw machines do not obtain good results. Screw machines and turret lathes can hold dimensions to $\pm 0.001$ in. or better and can drill small holes to $\pm 0.00025$ in.

**Milling Machines.**—*Milling machines* are devices in which metal is removed from a piece being worked by means of a rotating steel cutter. The work is fed under the cutter (see Fig. 227). Provision is commonly made for horizontal and vertical motion of the table, leaving the cutter fixed in position. However, provision is sometimes made for vertical motion of the cutter. The most popular type of machine has a table that may be moved in two directions horizontally (longitudinally and transversely) and vertically as well. This is known as the *knee-and-column* type of machine. A machine with just these three movements is known as a *plain milling machine* and can be used to take heavy cuts at high speeds with coarse feeds. The rigid construction of this type of machine makes this procedure feasible.

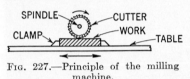

FIG. 227.—Principle of the milling machine.

Another type of machine of the knee-and-column type embodies the table movements of the plain machine and, in addition, its table may be moved diagonally in the horizontal plane. This machine thus attains greater versatility but only at the sacrifice of rigidity. It may be used to machine angular cuts, helical gears, etc. It is called the *universal milling machine.* A type of milling machine in which the table is horizontal but where the cutter revolves about a vertical axis is known as the *vertical spindle milling machine.* The table may be moved along the usual three axes and the spindle may be moved vertically. It is used for face milling, profiling, and similar applications. The *planer milling machine* is a large device resembling a planer in appearance. It is used for very heavy work.

Various attachments are available to extend the limits on the types of work that may be undertaken by milling machines. The *universal milling attachment* is employed to set the spindle at any desired angle to the work. *Rotary milling attachments* are tables or platens that may be rotated about a pivot to cut circular slots and keyways. They may be either hand or power driven. A device that supports the milling cutter on a shaft parallel to the direction of motion of the table is the *rack milling attachment.* This is used for machining teeth on racks, etc. An *index head* that rotates the work through a known angle

PLATE XIX.—A milling machine in operation. (*Courtesy of Cincinnati Grinders, Inc.*)

between cuts is available. This may be used to cut teeth on gears, etc. Various vises are available for supporting the work at various angles to the cutter.

Milling machine *cutters* are available in great variety. Figure 228a shows the *plain milling cutter.* Figure 228b shows a *convex cutter.* An *angular cutter* is shown in Fig. 228c. A quite different type of milling cutter is shown in Fig. 228d. This is known as a *face milling cutter.*　Milling is performed with this cutter with a face perpendicular to the spindle instead of parallel to it as with the ordinary milling cutter.　This device can surface fairly large areas rapidly.　Another type of cutter is the *end*

PLATE XX.—A knee-and-column-type milling machine (vertical type).　(*Courtesy of Cincinnati Grinders, Inc.*)

*mill* shown in Fig. 228*e.*　A cutter of this type with a narrow head can reach points within a device inaccessible to ordinary cutters.　The work in the last two is moved in the direction of the arrow, against the cutter.　If a sheet of metal is moved in a direction perpendicular to the spindle against the side of an end mill, a slot will be cut in it.　The cutter used for this task is a *slotting end mill.*　Keyways may be cut in shafts by means of a *Woodruff keyway cutter.*

By employing the indexing head, previously mentioned, which may be used to rotate the work through an accurately known angle, it is possible to cut odd shaped figures, such as cams, with a milling machine.

Milling develops a good deal of heat through friction, and it is generally necessary to provide a cooling liquid to remove the excess heat. Parts may be milled to a tolerance of $\pm 0.001$ in.

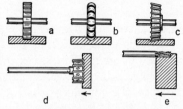

Fig. 228.—Milling cutters.

**Grinders.**—*Grinders* are machines in which the work is fastened to a table and then fed beneath a rapidly revolving abrasive wheel. This can be used to bring the work down to a required dimension and also to give it a fine finish.

Plate XXI.—Centerless grinder. (*Courtesy of Cincinnati Grinders, Inc.*)

The grinding tool is usually applied to the external surfaces of a device, but by special grinding tools (internal grinding attachment) the interiors may also be ground. If a large amount of internal grinding is to be done, special internal grinding machines may be obtained.

In finishing cylindrical work grinding machines are now replacing lathes, for they are cheaper, quicker, and more accurate. Then, too, it is possible to grind hardened steel accurately while it is difficult to surface such material with a lathe.

Although the work may be mechanically clamped to the table, as with other machines, the practice of holding it in place magnetically is becoming increasingly popular. This can be done because the grinding wheel exerts less tangential pull on the surface than does a shaper cutter, for example. When it is necessary to hold non-magnetic materials on a magnetic chuck,

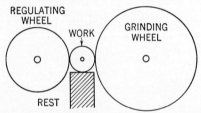

REGULATING WHEEL

WORK

GRINDING WHEEL

REST

FIG. 229.—Principle of the centerless grinder.

the work is reinforced by use of steel *V*-blocks or other magnetic materials.

Grinders intended for surface finishing are of two types. In the *planer type* the work moves back and forth beneath the grinding wheel in the same fashion as in a planer. In the *rotary type* the work revolves beneath the grinder on a rotating table. This is used for grinding circular surfaces. In most grinding machines the grinding wheel is in a vertical plane, and grinding is performed with its periphery. *Vertical spindle grinding machines* are also made in which the plane of the grinding wheel is horizontal, and grinding is performed with the flat side of this wheel. As this usually leaves many circular scratches on the work, it cannot produce so smooth a surface as the conventional type. The vertical spindle machine is faster for some types of work, and requires less attention in operation. Tolerances of $\pm 0.0005$ in. or better can be held with grinders.

When it was desired to grind a cylindrical rod, it was formerly the practice to mount the rod between centers (as on a lathe) and rotate it beneath the grinding wheel. This was a tedious process and required much care. It has now been largely replaced by the process diagramed in Fig. 229. Here the work is supported against the grinding wheel by a regulating wheel that also rotates it. The work may be fed in continuously. This technique, known as *centerless grinding,* is far more efficient than the older method, for no time need be spent in truing up the stock and adjusting the wheel. It is possible to take heavier cuts than with the old type of machine because the work is supported by the regulating wheel at the point being ground. If desired, the amount of material that must be removed can be made much less than with the old method. This re-sults in greater economy. The grind-ing and regulating wheels are usually not coplanar but are in slightly inclined planes. Thus the motion of the regulat-ing wheel has a component parallel to the work, and this feeds the work auto-matically. The work is of course kept strictly perpendicular to the plane of the

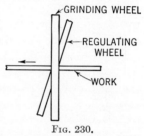

FIG. 230.

grinding wheel and is thus inclined to the plane of the regulating wheel. This is illustrated in Fig. 230. This procedure may be used with rings, disks, etc., as well as with shafts. A tolerance of ±0.0001 in. can be held with this process.

Grinding devices on flexible shafts may be introduced into complicated work. These are known as *flexible grinders.*

Ground parts may be finished by a process known as *lapping,* in which a soft metal lap charged with an abrasive is moved over the ground surface. The lap is made of materials, such as soft iron and brass, and the abrasive may be silicon carbide, emery, or similar materials. In order to remove tool marks by this process about 0.0003 in. of stock is removed. Consequently the part should be left oversize by this amount after grinding.

### CASTINGS

Castings play a very important part in the design of almost any optical instrument. The designer should be familiar with the factors involved in their use.

Generally speaking, two principal methods are employed for making castings:

1. Sand casting
2. Die casting

**Sand Casting.**—Assume that it is desired to make a large base plate on which will be mounted an optical instrument. Such a plate should be flat; furthermore, it should *stay* flat. Although it would be possible to use a machined steel plate for the base, it would generally be too heavy and cost too much to manufacture. It is thus desired to make the part out of a lighter metal, and it is also very desirable to keep the required machining at a minimum. A sand casting of a light metal may be used for this purpose. A wooden model of the desired base plate is made by a pattern maker, the model being known as a *pattern*. This will be used to make an impression in sand, in which the molten metal will be cast. To increase the rigidity of a part of the type under consideration, ribs which could be made as part of the original casting would be added. Instead of machining the whole top of the base plate to make it sufficiently flat for the mounting of the optical parts, the designer would probably employ a few raised bosses on the casting, one for each part to be fastened to the base. It would then be necessary to machine only these bosses instead of the whole plate. The designer would have to avoid undercuts so that the pattern could be removed from the mold. Furthermore he would have to taper the pattern to a certain extent to facilitate its removal from the mold. The amount of taper so added is known as *draft*.

Surfaces at right angles to the face of the casting are the only ones that require draft. For small patterns about $\frac{1}{16}$ in. of taper per foot of surface to be drawn is left. For large patterns this is increased to $\frac{1}{8}$ in. per foot.

Sand castings are made of various metals, of which aluminum, bronze, brass, and iron are particularly useful in instrument work. Magnesium and zinc are also cast.

Small and medium-sized patterns are made of hard woods such as mahogany and cherry, mahogany being preferable in spite of its greater cost because it is less sensitive to changes in humidity. For larger patterns, white pine is commonly used. For turned parts, woods that take a good finish are desired, and maple and birch are used for such applications. White wood and fir are also occasionally used. The finished pattern is coated with shellac, lacquer, or rubber cement to resist moisture. Metal patterns are more durable than wood and are used when many castings are to be made. Steel, aluminum, cast iron, and brass are used for this purpose.

After the casting has been made certain areas are machined to give them smooth surfaces. These must therefore be cast oversize to allow for the machining. About $\frac{1}{8}$ in. of metal may be left for machining on small parts, and about $\frac{3}{4}$ to 1 in. may be required on very large castings. In making castings, allowance should also be made for the shrinkage of the metal as it cools. This varies from metal to metal and also with the geometrical shape of the object being cast. Aluminum generally shrinks about $\frac{7}{32}$ to $\frac{1}{4}$ in. per foot of casting. Bronze shrinks about $\frac{5}{32}$ in. per foot; common brass about $\frac{3}{16}$ in. per foot; yellow brass about $\frac{7}{32}$ in. per foot; iron $\frac{3}{32}$ to $\frac{1}{8}$ in. per foot; and steel about $\frac{3}{16}$ in. per foot.

If a pattern for a given part is available, the weight of the casting may of course be determined from a knowledge of the density of the material used in the pattern and that proposed for use in casting.

**Die Casting.**—This is a process whereby molten metal is forced into a closed mold, allowed to solidify by cooling, and then ejected. The process is analogous to that of injection molding used with plastics. The finish of the mold is transferred to the cast part, so if the mold has been highly finished the cast part will be quite respectable in appearance. This process is important in optical instrument manufacture because parts may be made to very closely held dimensions. On very small parts it is sometimes possible to hold dimensions to within $\pm 0.001$ in. The tolerance on a given dimension varies with the size and shape of the part; in certain cases tolerances as large as $\pm 0.015$ in. are the best that can be held. This will be discussed later.

As has been noted, the cast part should be cooled before it is removed from the die. In order that rapid production may be possible, it is sometimes necessary to water cool the die. This makes die costs high. The simplest air-cooled dies cost about $100, and the cost increases rapidly with the complexity of the part. The materials used for these dies depend on the type of metal to be cast. For zinc alloy die castings, S.A.E. 1020 steel or case hardened 6140 steel is used. For brass or bronze castings semi-high-speed or high-speed tool steels are used, while the better grades of hot die steels are used for aluminum and magnesium alloys. In some cases in order to conserve material it is possible to use a plate steel or cast-iron die block, and insert in this block a piece of alloy steel in which the cavities may be made.

The die is of course made in two halves. One half, known as the *ejector* half, retains the casting when the die is opened. Ejector pins, which work through holes in this half, push the finished casting from the die. The other half of the die is known as the *cover* or *stationary* half. This is the half containing the *cavity* or *gate* through which the molten metal is introduced.

In designing a part to be die cast, it should be borne in mind that all corners should be filleted, and as large a radius as possible should be used in each case. Sharp angles should be avoided at all costs. It is practical to cast inserts in a die-cast part. These are of course preloaded in the die at the beginning of the casting cycle. The inserts should be grooved and knurled to prevent their rotating or pulling out. The possibility of electrolytic action between the insert and the casting should be investigated. Pre-cast parts may be used as inserts. This makes it possible, for example, to cast a ball inside a sleigh bell. This trick has many practical applications.

Dies may be "hogged" or milled in the steel blank. Vents are provided to permit escape of the air trapped in the mold. These vents are usually located along the parting line of the die at the points that the metal reaches last.

Metals used in die castings are alloys of the following bases: aluminum, zinc, copper (brass, bronze), magnesium, lead, and tin.

A thin film of casting metal is usually forced between the die halves at the parting line and also around the edges of any inserts or ejector pins in the die. This solidifies into an unsightly thin sheet known as *flash*, which must be removed by a subsequent cleaning operation.

Since the solidifying metal in the die shrinks on cooling, allowance must be made for this in designing the die. Unfortunately, it is very difficult to predict the amount of shrinkage in advance, but it usually varies between about 0.002 and 0.007 in. per inch. It is generally necessary to determine the value empirically in any given case.

Some external threads and other minute complicated shapes may be formed by die casting. Lettering may be added in relief to the finished part by milling it in the die. When die-casting contractors do work for a manufacturer, they usually add their insignia to the casting in this fashion. Unfortunately at times they are likely to do this in an undesirable location on the part, and it is generally a good policy to come to an understanding on this matter before the die is made.

Usually, machining is not required on a die casting, for the finish is very good. This alone is sometimes enough of an advantage to warrant the use of die castings. When machining is required, it is very difficult to predict in advance how much metal should be left on the part for this purpose. It is less, however, than is required on a sand casting.

It is possible to make many similar cavities in a die so that a number of similar parts are cast simultaneously. This increases the tool cost and the production rate. It is also possible to make in one die cavities for several different parts that will be required in approximately equal quantities. In practice, it is usually found that some parts are needed in greater quantity than others, through greater tendency toward breakage, etc., and thus it is often inadvisable to use a die of this construction. An effort is often made to make right- and left-hand parts of a unit similar so that tool cost can be reduced. When multiple cavity dies are used, this is obviously unnecessary.

Let us return for a moment to the base plate considered at the beginning of this section. If this plate is to be made by die casting and is to be really flat, it will have to be aged—to relieve all stresses and permit it to take its final shape—and then machined. It may then be necessary to age it again, and again machine the part, etc. The process may sometimes be speeded by annealing. If subsequent warping is to be avoided, it may be necessary to machine the part to equal depths on opposite faces.

As with sand castings, draft is required with die castings. About 0.01 in. per inch, on outside walls, is all that is required.

With regard to tolerances, it may be said that the dimension between two parts on the same half of a die may be held to about $\pm 0.005$ in. Dimensions between parts formed by opposite die halves can be held to about $\pm 0.010$ in. The tolerance for the dimension between two points made by a fixed and movable part of the die, respectively, is about $\pm 0.015$ in. On long dimensions a minimum tolerance of about $\pm 0.0015$ in. may be held.

### REFERENCES

BOSTON: "Engineering Shop Practice," John Wiley & Sons, Inc., New York, 1935.

BURGHARDT: "Machine Tool Operation," McGraw-Hill Book Company, Inc., New York, 1937.

CHASE: "Die Casting," John Wiley & Sons, Inc., New York, 1934.

COLVIN and STANLEY: "American Machinists' Handbook," McGraw-Hill Book Company, Inc., New York, 1940.

DAVIES: "Precision Workshop Methods," E. J. Arnold & Son, Ltd., London, 1935.

DE LEEUW: "Metal Cutting Tools," McGraw-Hill Book Company, Inc., New York, 1922.

"Machinery's Handbook," Industrial Press, New York, 1941.

"Manual of Engineering Design for Die Casting," Harvill Aircraft Die Casting Corp., Los Angeles, 1941.

"Shop Theory," Henry Ford Trade School, 1934. Rev. ed., McGraw-Hill Book Co., Inc., New York, 1941.

# CHAPTER XIX

## BEARINGS

In any device in which a shaft rotates with respect to a fixed member, friction will exist at the point of contact between the shaft and its support. Because of this friction, heat will be developed and wear will occur at the point of contact. As such wear can rapidly destroy an instrument, special means must be provided to reduce the friction and to have such rubbing contact as must exist take place between materials that do not wear readily. It will be appreciated that when friction occurs between various combinations of material more wear will occur with some combinations than with others. This should be kept in mind during this study. If we were to mount a steel shaft in a steel housing by merely drilling a hole in the housing of the same diameter as the shaft and permitting the shaft to rotate in it, wear would occur at a rate depending on the speeds and loads involved. In almost every case it would be found that the wear that would occur in a short time would be sufficient to impair the performance of the device. Consequently, it is necessary to place between the shaft and the housing some material or contrivance for reducing friction and wear. This is called a *bearing*.

When all the load on a given shaft is considered, this load can be resolved into two components: one perpendicular to the shaft and one parallel to it. The component parallel to the shaft will be called a *thrust* load; that perpendicular to it a *radial* load. Bearings to take up these components are called *thrust bearings* and *radial bearings*, respectively. These will be illustrated below. In general, both thrust and radial components will be present in a given case, and the designer should not forget to provide adequate bearing capacity for both. The designer usually remembers the radial component but occasionally neglects thrust.

**Sleeve or Journal Bearings.**—Let us return to the case of the steel shaft rotating in a steel housing. It has been pointed out that rapid wear will occur in this case. Now suppose we drill

313

a hole in the housing that is larger in diameter than the shaft and suppose we place in this hole a hollow cylinder of some material more resistant to wear than steel and with a low coefficient of friction. The shaft can then turn inside this cylinder, and we thus have a *sleeve* or *journal bearing*. With such a bearing it is generally desirable to have shaft and bearing made of different materials to keep heating, as well as wear, at a minimum, for excess heat can ruin one or both surfaces. The faces of the shaft and the bearing should of course always be truly parallel. In order to avoid excess heat and wear with this type of bearing, speeds and loads are kept reasonably low, although surprisingly high speeds are sometimes attainable. In instrument work sleeve bearings are usually constructed of bronze and may be either made by the user or purchased already fabricated, the latter generally being preferable. Since it is necessary to lubricate this type of bearing adequately, oil holes are often drilled through the wall of the bearing and housing, perpendicular to the shaft, so that oil may be introduced. It is also common practice to cut spiral oil grooves along the inner surface of the bearing in order that oil may be carried along the bearing from the point of introduction so as to lubricate all of the bearing surface. If the bore of the bearing is appreciably larger than the shaft, oil may work up and down in the clearance between the bearing and the shaft. The shaft may then ride up and down on this oil, this resulting in noise. If insufficient lubrication is employed, the shaft may overheat and expand, thus *seizing* in the bearing and jamming the mechanism.

Sleeve bearings are not used so widely as formerly because of the fact that the more desirable ball bearings are now being made

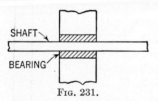

SHAFT

BEARING

Fig. 231.

available at only a slightly greater cost. The ball bearings are generally easier to install, give less friction, and are much easier to lubricate. However, sleeve bearings are much less bulky than ball bearings. This is also a very important consideration.

Sleeve bearings are usually made in the construction shown in Fig. 231. It will be noted that this form has no thrust capacity whatever, *i.e.*, it cannot accommodate a thrust load. Motors are often equipped with such bearings. They should not be used with thrust loads or should not be used where the motor shaft is vertical, as in a drill press because the weight of the shaft itself constitutes a thrust load. Flanged sleeve bearings may be used to take thrust and radial loads when used as shown in

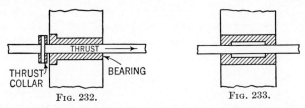

Fig. 232.        Fig. 233.

Fig. 232. The thrust collar, pinned to the shaft, takes up any thrust to the right. If thrust is also to be expected in the reverse direction, it can be taken care of by the use of a similar bearing, facing the opposite way, mounted elsewhere on the shaft.

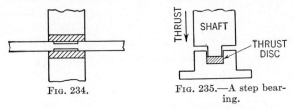

Fig. 234.        Fig. 235.—A step bearing.

Sometimes, to reduce friction, the bearing may be undercut, as shown in Fig. 233. This is difficult to manufacture, so more often the shaft itself is undercut in the fashion shown in Fig. 234. The undercut may take the form of a lead screw to conduct oil through the bearing.

It is pointed out that these sleeve bearings are very critical with regard to fit and should be lubricated frequently. Except where space conditions are critical, their use is not generally recommended.

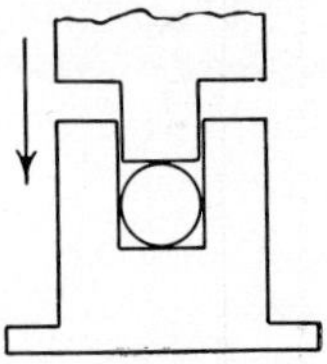

**Oil-impregnated Bearings.**—Several manufacturers are now producing sleeve bearings made of sintered phosphor bronze. These are very porous and absorb 35 per cent oil by volume. They thus reduce the lubrication difficulty normally associated with sleeve bearings, for this oil exudes continuously in use. They are furnished filled with oil by the manufacturer and may be recharged by pouring oil over them, for they absorb it instantly.

Fig. 236.—Another form of step bearing.

Oil holes similar to those provided for plain sleeve bearings are sometimes provided with the oil-impregnated bearings, but these bearings require only very occasional oiling.    It is claimed by one

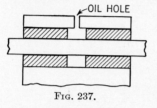

FIG. 237.

manufacturer that these bearings will outlast hardened and ground steel shafts at 30,000 rpm!  They do constitute a real improvement over plain bronze bearings and may be used to advantage in instrument design.   Oil-impregnated washers or disks suitable for the various thrust applications previously described may also be obtained.   When a very long bearing is required, two short impregnated bearings may be installed next to one another with a small gap between them.   An oil hole may be drilled into this gap, letting the gap act as an oil reservoir.   This is illustrated in Fig. 237.

In all the drawings of sleeve bearings they have only been shown pushed into their mounting holes.   A good press fit is usually employed, and the bearing is sometimes held in position with a retainer ring.

**Step Bearings.**—A pure thrust load, generally associated with a vertical shaft, may be taken up by a *step bearing* of the type shown in Fig. 235.   The small thrust disk carries the load. Bronze disks for this purpose may be obtained.   It is also possible to replace the disk with a ball thrust bearing; or the modification

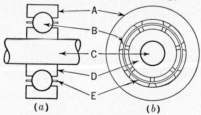

(a)                    (b)

FIG. 238.—A radial ball bearing.

shown in Fig. 236, in which the thrust is taken up by a hardened steel ball, may be used.

**Ball Bearings.**—The ability of a ball to carry a load has been extensively investigated both in this country and abroad, and the data have been applied to the design of a type of bearing that is of the greatest value to the optical instrument designer: the *ball bearing*.   Such a bearing is illustrated in Fig. 238, in

which are shown the principal components. On the shaft *C* is
fastened (usually by clamping) the *inner ring D*. The balls *B*
are carried between the inner ring and the *outer ring A*. This
outer ring is fastened (again usually by clamping or a retainer
ring) in a housing. Either the inner or the outer ring might
carry the rotating part, the inner ring being more commonly used
for this purpose.

PLATE XXII.—Ball bearing, external view. (*Courtesy of New Departure
Division, General Motors Corporation.*)

Two techniques of assembling balls in bearings are used. In
one case the two rings are held eccentrically and as many balls
as possible are dropped into position. The rings are then centered and the balls are uniformly distributed about the bearing by
means of a *ball retainer*, part *E* in Fig. 238. The other method of
assembly involves the use of a loading slot cut into the inner and
outer rings. Enough balls to fill completely the space between
the rings may be added through this slot. The ball retainers
mentioned are generally made of pressed steel. At very high
speed specially machined steel retainers may be used. If particular quietness of operation is desired, composition retainers
are employed, the composition used being plastic-impregnated

cloth or the like. Retainers fabricated of oil-impregnated sintered bronze have been used successfully to eliminate the need for periodic lubrication. This development will probably prove to be of considerable importance.

The type of ball bearing illustrated in Plate XXIII is the commonest in general use and is designated a *radial ball bearing*. In

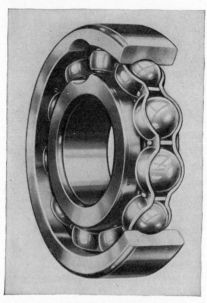

PLATE XXIII.—Single-row radial ball bearing. Note loading slot. (*Courtesy of New Departure Division, General Motors Corporation.*)

spite of its name, however, it is capable of carrying quite heavy thrust loads in addition to radial loads. The type of bearing containing the maximum number of balls has a greater radial capacity than the retainer type, but its thrust capacity is limited, by the presence of the filling notch, to one-half the radial capacity. With the retainer type of bearing, thrust loads equal to the radial loads may be carried, but a certain amount of radial load is required to position the balls properly, so they should not be used to take pure thrust.

It is common practice to manufacture ball bearings for shafts made to metric dimensions. However, a few manufacturers also make inch-dimensioned bearings.

For a given shaft diameter, each manufacturer generally makes several series of radial bearings for different load capacities, these generally being designated as light, medium, and heavy bearings. The medium and heavy series are generally too bulky for optical

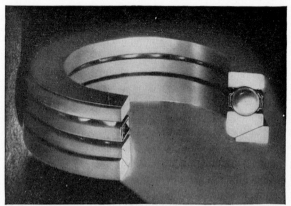

PLATE XXIV.—Ball thrust bearing with self-aligning mounting ring. (*Courtesy of SKF Industries, Inc.*)

instrument work. Several manufacturers also make lighter series of bearings under the names *instrument bearings, extra light series,* etc. These light series of bearings are particularly valuable for instrument work.

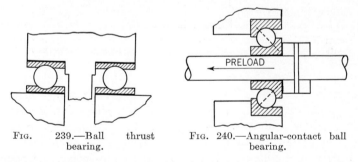

FIG. 239.—Ball thrust bearing.    FIG. 240.—Angular-contact ball bearing.

*Ball thrust bearings,* as illustrated in Fig. 239, are used for pure thrust loads and may be used in a step bearing of the type shown in Fig. 236. They have no radial capacity whatever.

A comparatively new innovation is the *angular contact ball bearing,* shown in Fig. 240. This is of the greatest importance to the optical instrument designer. It will be noted that the

axis of contact (dotted line) in these bearings is inclined instead
of occupying a radial position. They have great thrust as well
as radial capacity. However they must always bear a certain
minimum thrust load to position the balls. In practice, these
bearings are generally assembled in pairs facing in opposite
directions. A load is applied between them (by forcing the two

PLATE XXV.—Single-row angular-contact ball bearing. (*Courtesy of SKF Industries, Inc.*)

PLATE XXVI.—Double-row self-aligning ball bearing. (*Courtesy of SKF Industries, Inc.*)

inner rings together, for example) by tightening a nut. This is
known as *preloading*, the direction of preload in Fig. 240 being
indicated by the arrow. When properly preloaded, these bearings have much greater resistance to *deflection* (displacement
of one ring relative to the other) than any other commonly
available type of bearing. In optical instruments it is often
necessary to have a rotating shaft so supported that no angular
deflection is possible. The most economical way of obtaining
this desideratum is through the use of preloaded angular contact
bearings. Because of the very small friction in these bearings,
heavy preloads may be applied without causing binding.

It will be realized that each radial ball bearing defines the direction and location of the shaft mounted in it. If a shaft is to be supported by two such bearings, they must be carefully aligned so that they both define the same location for the shaft, *i.e.*, the axes of the two bearings must coincide laterally and angularly. This calls for very careful machining of the housing for the bearings. If the device in which they are mounted is lightly constructed, it may warp in use, or while being moved, in such a way as to throw the bearing axes out of coincidence and the results of all the initial careful machining will be lost. Both of these difficulties may be overcome by the use of *self-aligning ball bearings*, one type of which

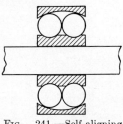

Fig. 241.—Self-aligning ball bearing.

is illustrated in Fig. 241. It will be noted that the shaft and the inner ring can rotate through an appreciable angle without causing the balls to be forced against the outer ring as would occur with the standard radial bearing. Thus the two bearings at the ends of the shaft can be displaced appreciably without unduly loading any part of the equipment. It will be noted that this technique will work with two bearings but not with three, and *in any instrument design the use of more than two separated bearings on a single shaft should be avoided whenever possible.* It is of course difficult to align properly more than two bearings separated by an appreciable distance, and a high grade of workmanship is necessary to obtain mediocre performance when this is attempted.

Various special types of bearings with flanges, oil retainers, snap rings, etc., are available to the designer for special applications and can be found in standard bearing catalogues. One special type of bearing is worthy of mention. This is the *magneto bearing*. It is a radial bearing so constructed that the outer ring may be removed for ease in assembly in magnetos, a bearing of this character being designated *demountable*. When the outer ring is removed, the balls are held in position on the inner ring by the ball retainer. In an optical instrument a bearing of this type may be assembled in a housing without the outer ring, thus using the inner bore of the housing for the outer ring. In this way the advantages of a ball bearing can be obtained at the

sacrifice of little space.   The inner surface of the housing must
be carefully machined and hardened for this to be accomplished
satisfactorily.   This technique can be successfully employed only
when the load is very light.   It can be used at
high speed, however.

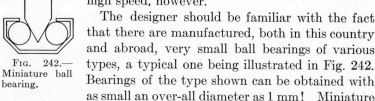

The  designer  should  be  familiar  with  the  fact
that there are manufactured, both in this country
and abroad, very small ball bearings of various
types, a typical one being illustrated in Fig. 242.
Bearings of the type shown can be obtained with
as small an over-all diameter as 1 mm!   Miniature

Fig.   242.—
Miniature  ball
bearing.

radial ball bearings having diameters as small as 3 mm are also
available.   Angular contact types may also be obtained.

Note should be taken of the fact that some manufacturers
produce special lines of bearings to very close tolerances and,
by inspection and selection, can furnish sets of bearings matched
extremely closely.   On one of these high-precision series of radial
bearings the bore diameter is held to dimension with a tolerance
of plus 0 and minus 0.00015 in.   These can be used at speeds up
to 42,000 rpm.

**Needle Bearings.**—Roller bearings are not generally used in
instrument design.   However, a special form in which the rollers
may be considered as shrunk down to the dimensions of pins is
used.   This is called a *needle bearing.*   It
consists of a series of needles, or rolls,
manufactured to close tolerance (0.0009
in.) and mounted in a surface-hardened
shell, as shown in Fig. 243.   It will be
noted that the shaft itself serves as the inner ring for this bearing.   For this reason
the shaft must be surface hardened to

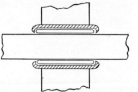

Fig. 243.—A needle bear-
ing.

a hardness equivalent to Rockwell C 52.   It will be seen that for
a given shaft diameter this bearing occupies much less space than
the corresponding ball bearing.   Thus, if bearings for a ½-in.
shaft are considered, a standard radial ball bearing has an outside
diameter (or OD) of 1⅛ in., while the needle bearing has an
outside diameter of only 11⁄16 in., a truly significant difference.
This is one of the principal advantages of the needle bearing in
instrument work.   Another point of some significance is the fact
that the needle bearing generally costs much less than the

corresponding ball bearing. Although the manufacturers claim that these bearings can be used with high speeds and heavy loads, they are usually restricted in use to low speeds and light loads because of the amount of friction involved. They are used frequently on control shafts in place of sleeve bearings. If it is not possible to harden the shaft that acts as the inner ring, it is possible to purchase a sleeve that slips over the shaft to form an inner ring. This is to be avoided if possible, for it is uneconomical in both material and space. It will be appreciated that these bearings are designed to carry solely radial loads.

**Bearing Installation.**—The corners marked *A* and *B* in Fig. 245 are rounded or filleted in any bearing; consequently both shafts and housings should be properly filleted so that the bearings may seat properly. These fillets must be of smaller radii than the corners on the bearing in order that interference of the corners might not displace the bearing axially (see Fig. 244). The Society of Automotive Engineers has established cer-

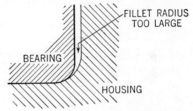

Fig. 244.—If a housing fillet radius is too large, a bearing may be displaced axially.

tain standard radii for this purpose. The bearing seats should always be ground; otherwise the bearing will make contact with only a few high points on the shaft.

In using a bearing one should employ as few spacers, washers, etc., as possible, for any or all of these may be sufficiently inaccurate to ruin the installation. Such spacers and washers as are used should be faced perpendicular to their bores to eliminate any tendency toward misalignment when the assembly is locked.

The general method of fastening the inner ring to the shaft is indicated in Fig. 245. There are various other methods in general use, but they are essentially variations of the one shown. Some use lock washers to protect the installation against loosening through vibration. If the inner ring has been properly fitted to the shaft, it will not turn on the shaft, and it is often unnecessary to provide for clamping by any other means than by providing good shoulders to take endwise play. The height of the shoulders should be proportioned properly with respect to the dimensions of the inner ring. Therefore a ball-bearing catalogue giving the proper shoulder height should be consulted before design is undertaken.   The shoulder must be high enough to take the load, but not too high to prevent removal of the bearing.   In applications in which both thrust and radial loads are present, it is often desirable to resist the thrust load with a single bearing, leaving the other bearing or bearings to take the radial load.   Under these circumstances the bearing taking the thrust should be clamped in place, and sufficient longitudinal clearance for the radial bearings should be provided so they can ˙ ıloat'' axially without absorbing any thrust.   Provision should always be made for removing the bearing from the shaft for cleaning, adjustment, etc.

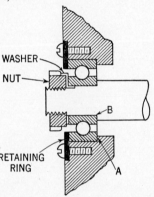

Fig. 245.—Installation of a radial ball bearing.

The clamping of the outer ring of the bearing in its housing is normally accomplished in the fashion illustrated in Fig. 245. Many variations of this general procedure are also employed. When the retaining ring extends all the way in to the shaft, a positioning flange may be employed to aid in preventing the ring from striking the shaft through misalignment.

The normal method of using a bearing is to have the outer ring stationary and the inner ring rotating.   In this case it is important that the inner ring does *not* rotate with respect to the shaft, for wear would result.   Thus a firm press fit, using several ten-thousandths of an inch of interference, is employed.   With the outer ring, on the other hand, it is desirable to have the ring rotate slowly with respect to its housing because fresh portions of the ball raceway are continually being brought into the heaviest loaded area, thus distributing the wear throughout the race and prolonging the life of the bearing. For this reason a close push fit, with several ten-thousandths of an inch clearance, is employed. Because this ring is push-fitted, and not clamped, it is possible to permit the bearing to move axially, thus avoiding the imposition of excessive thrust loads. Another important advantage derived from the use of this push fit is that it generally makes the assembly of the instrument easy to accomplish. If the inner ring is stationary and the outer ring rotates, the foregoing rules should be reversed, with the inner ring being push-fitted and the outer ring being press-fitted.

### REFERENCES

AHRENS: "Die Kugellager und ihre Verwendung im Maschinenbau," Julius Springer, Berlin, 1913.

"Machinery's Handbook," Industrial Press, New York, 1941, and other standard handbooks.

"New Departure Handbook," New Departure Division of General Motors Corp., Bristol, Conn., 1941, and other manufacturers' publications.

### PROBLEMS

**1.** You are designing a projection machine in which are carried slides, for projection purposes, on a metal disk 2 ft in diameter. This disk is mounted on the end of a shaft 15 in. long. It is necessary to mount this shaft so that there will be no angular deflection of the disk. Sketch the bearing installation you would use, naming the type or types of bearings employed.

**2.** In designing a high-speed camera you mount a light part that rotates very rapidly on a $\frac{1}{4}$-in. shaft. The housing that will contain the bearing for this shaft is only about $\frac{1}{2}$ in. in internal diameter. To what type of bearing would you give first consideration for possible installation in this machine?

# CHAPTER XX

## GEARS, CLUTCHES, COUPLINGS

### GEARING

Gears of one sort or another are often important auxiliaries in many optical instruments. At least an elementary knowledge of them is indispensable to the instrument designer. Fortunately the loads with which he deals are usually relatively light, so he is not often required to make calculations on the power transmitted by a set of gears. He is merely interested in getting motion of a certain character at a known speed.

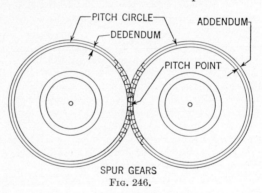

SPUR GEARS

Fig. 246.

**Spur Gears.**—*Spur gears* are used more often than any other type in instrument design. They are of course used in transmitting power from one shaft to another parallel to it, usually with a change in speed.

When two spur gears mesh, effective contact is obtained at a point on the center line of the gears known as the *pitch point* (see Fig. 246). Each gear can be represented on a layout drawing by a circle drawn with the shaft center as its center, and the distance from the shaft center to pitch point as its radius. This circle is known as the *pitch circle;* its diameter is called the *pitch diameter*. If one were to draw a circle around the gear at the tips of the teeth and another circle at the base of the teeth, the

326

pitch circle would be found to lie somewhere between the two. The distance from the pitch circle to the tip of the teeth is called the *addendum;* the distance from this pitch circle to the bottom of a tooth is known as the *dedendum.* The fact that a spur gear may be represented in a drawing by a simple circle is of the greatest importance to the designer, for by having the pitch circles of two spur gears tangent to one another he knows the gears will mesh properly. Thus with a knowledge of merely the pitch diameter of the gear he can properly position the gear on his drawing. If it were not for this concept, he would have to draw in all the teeth of his gears carefully and then position them by trial and error. In purchasing gears the designer specifies the pitch diameter he desires.

Spur gears can of course be made with teeth of different sizes, and the tooth size is usually effectively specified in terms of a quantity known as *diametral pitch,* or *pitch,* which is the number of teeth per inch of pitch diameter. Thus a gear of 32 diametral pitch and 1-in. pitch diameter (or PD) would have 32 teeth. A gear of the same pitch and $\frac{1}{2}$-in. PD would have 16 teeth. This system of nomenclature is very simple and effective. The teeth may also be specified by another quantity, known as *circular pitch.* This is the distance between the centers of adjacent teeth along the arc at the pitch circle. The thickness of a gear, measured across the base of the teeth, is known as the *face.* Thus a gear of $\frac{3}{16}$-in. face is $\frac{3}{16}$ in. thick at this point.

The speed ratio between the two shafts containing two meshing spur gears is equal to the reciprocal of the ratio of the number of teeth of the two gears and is also equal to the reciprocal of the ratio of the pitch diameters.

Most gears available today have teeth of involute shape. The circle used for the generation of the involute teeth is called the *base circle,* and the pressure on the engaging teeth of meshing gears is transmitted along a straight line which is tangent to the base circle and which passes through the pitch point. This is called the *line of action.* The angle between the line of action and the tangent to the pitch circle at the pitch point is called the *pressure angle.* If a slight change should be made in the center distance of meshing involute gears, the pressure angles and the diameter of the pitch circles will change proportionally, and there will be no change in the speed ratio. Slight variations in the center spacing of the gears may be made without interfering with their smooth functioning.

Spur gears are made with pressure angles of $14\frac{1}{2}$ and 20°. Various forms of involute gear teeth are available with both these angles. Greater care in gear manufacture is required to obtain quiet operation from combinations of 20° stub-tooth gears than from those of $14\frac{1}{2}°$ generated gears. Generally speaking, when more than 40 teeth must be used on a gear, the $14\frac{1}{2}°$ generated gears are preferable; when fewer teeth are required, 20° full-depth-tooth gears are to be preferred. A $14\frac{1}{2}°$ gear will not mesh with a 20° gear. If quietness of operation is desired, gears of not less than 20 teeth should be used with the $14\frac{1}{2}°$ system, and not less than 14 teeth should be employed on 20° full-depth-tooth generated gears.

Small spur gears are commonly made of brass and steel; large ones of cast iron. Lately a number of non-metallic materials have been used in the fabrication of spur gears, these materials consisting for the most part of canvas impregnated with a thermo-setting phenol-formaldehyde plastic. Layers of this impregnated canvas are fused together by the simultaneous application of heat and pressure. Since these materials are quite resilient, gears fabricated from them have the endurance of cast iron. Such gears are used primarily in high-speed applications where freedom from noise is essential. Gears of this type are not generally mated together in pairs but are used instead with gears of other materials, hardened steel being preferable and cast iron making a good second choice. The use of non-metallic gears mated with gears of bronze, brass, or soft steel generally leads to excess wear.

Spur gears, as well as the other types, are fastened to shafts by several methods. They may be merely press fitted to the shaft. If relatively large loads are to be carried, they may be pinned to the shaft. If very large loads are involved, the gears are keyed to the shaft. For light loads setscrews may be employed.

The instrument designer is interested in the degree of accuracy of the gears he proposes to use. If the angle at which one gear is set is known, he has to know to what degree of accuracy he can predict the angle of the mating gear. Unfortunately not a great deal of information is available on this subject. Under very carefully controlled conditions of manufacture it appears possible to hold gears in production to 0.005°; it is probably possible to do somewhat better than this if extreme care is used.

**Bevel Gears.**—*Bevel gears* are of the general form shown in Fig. 247. By proper selection of the angle of the teeth relative to the shafts, these gears may be used with shafts intersecting at *any* angle. They can be furnished for different speed ratios in the same fashion as spur gears. When used merely for a 90° change of direction without a change in speed, they are sometimes called *miter gears.* Bevel gears are made with both straight and curved teeth, the latter being able to transmit the greater loads. These gears cannot be used interchangeably as can spur gears but are generally purchased in pairs. When extreme quietness of operation is desired, lapped pairs of gears may be obtained.

Because of their shape these gears (particularly those with spiral teeth) exert considerable thrust. Thus, with a shaft containing such gears, provision should be made to take both radial and thrust loads. For this reason it is desirable to use an angular contact ball bearing at the end of the shaft containing the gear and a radial ball bearing at the other end. It is not necessary to use angular contact bear-

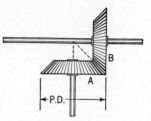

Fig. 247.—Bevel gears.

ings in pairs, preloaded, because the thrust of the gear furnishes all the preloading that is needed to position the balls in the bearing.

When one of the two components in a pair of these gears is larger than the other, the larger component is called the *gear* and the smaller the *pinion.* This terminology is common to the other types of gears as well.

The larger gears are made of cast iron, while steel is used for the smaller gears that are to carry heavy loads. Brass is also employed. In order to obtain maximum wear resistance, the pinion and the gear may be made of different materials, combinations of steel and bronze, and cast iron and steel, being frequently used. The pinion, being smaller, revolves more rapidly and thus should be made of the harder material. Non-metallic bevel gears are used for high-speed applications where noise is to be minimized.

Bevel gears, similar to spur gears, are specified in terms of pitch diameter (see Fig. 247), diametral pitch, and face. Also, 14½ and 20° gears are available.

As has been indicated, bevel gears are made with straight and curved teeth. The latter class are known as *spiral bevel gears*. These are particularly quiet in operation and can carry heavy loads. They have the additional advantage of being adjustable to some extent endwise without affecting performance.

It will be noticed that the shafts on which are mounted a pair of bevel gears lie in a single plane. If we now move the shafts into different planes and change the shape of the teeth so that we still get gear action, we have *hypoid* gears, as shown in Fig. 248. These run even more smoothly and quietly than spiral

Fig.   248.—Hypoid gears.

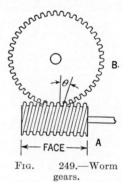

Fig.     249.—Worm gears.

bevel gears and have the additional advantage that both shafts can be continued in both directions without interference.

**Worm Gearing.**—*Worm gears* (Fig. 249) are much used in instrument design. They are employed as an efficient means of transmitting power, to obtain large forces, and to effect great reductions in rotational velocity. The types of worm gears used in instruments are usually self-locking in that they cannot be driven reversibly. This is often a great advantage.

The component $A$ of Fig. 249 is called a *worm*, while component $B$ is designated a *worm wheel* or *worm gear*. One or more continuous threads may be cut on a worm. When the number of threads is given, this refers to the total number and not the number per inch. The distance that any one thread advances per revolution is called the *lead*, while the distance between the center of two adjacent threads is called the *pitch* or *linear pitch*. For a single-threaded worm the lead and pitch are obviously equal, while for a double-threaded worm the lead is twice the pitch, and so on.

Worm wheels are specified in terms of diametral pitch and pitch diameter in the same fashion as spur gears. Worms are specified in terms of the diametral pitch of the worm wheels with which they are to be used, length of face, pitch diameter, and number of threads. For a single-thread worm used with a worm wheel of $n$ teeth, $n$ revolutions of the worm are required to obtain a single revolution of the worm wheel. If a two-thread worm is used, $n/2$ revolutions are required to turn the worm

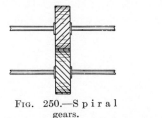

FIG. 250.—S p i r a l gears.

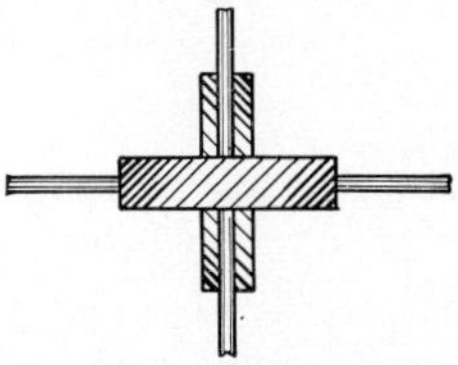

FIG. 251.—Spiral gears.

wheel once, and so on. Most worms have $14\frac{1}{2}°$ pressure angles, and these cannot be used with more than two threads without weakening the worm wheel teeth. If more threads are required, special worms of larger pressure angles are required.

The angle $\theta$ in Fig. 249 is termed the *helix angle* or *lead angle*. When the tangent of this angle equals the coefficient of friction, the gear is self-locking and the worm wheel cannot drive the worm.

It is occasionally necessary to position a worm wheel very accurately by means of a worm. Two thin worm wheels mounted together can be used. After they are engaged with the worm, they are rotated in opposite directions on their shaft until all the backlash is taken up; then they are locked or spring loaded. This arrangement will function satisfactorily, of course, only with a very precisely cut worm.

FIG. 252.—Spiral gears.

Worm wheels for instrument use are often made of cast iron and bronze and are used in combination with steel worms.

In designing bearings for use with worm gear installations the presence of thrust in hese gears should not be forgotten.

**Spiral Gears.**—Another type of gear used in instruments is the *spiral gear*, which may be used in various ways as shown in Figs. 250 to 252. These gears can be used interchangeably to obtain any desired speed ratio. They are specified in terms of diametral pitch, pitch diameter, and face width. They are furnished cut right hand and left hand. Those of the same hand operate at right angles, while those of opposite hand are used on parallel shafts. The spiral teeth slide over one another, so hardened steel is often used in the fabrication of these gears to minimize wear. Bronze is used also. In installing gears of this character the designer should provide adequate thrust capacity to provide for the thrust due to the gears.

**Herringbone Gears.**—These gears have the general form suggested in Fig. 253. They are rather expensive but have a number of important advantages. Since the load is passed from one tooth to another without shock, wear is greatly reduced. There is less bending action on the teeth caused by the load. The gears are silent in action and cause very little vibration. They exhibit nearly zero backlash. They can be used for large gear ratios and for large velocities. Cast iron and steel are used for the gears and hard steel for the pinions. These gears develop no thrust and so do not need thrust bearings.

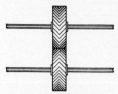

Fig. 253.—Herringbone gears.

**Use of Hunting Tooth in Gears.**—If gears of a 3:1 ratio were being designed, gears (spur, herringbone, etc.) of 90 and 30 teeth, for example, could be used. In this case a given tooth on the smaller gear would always mesh with the same three teeth on the larger. In practice, it is sometimes possible to use one extra tooth on the larger gear, thus having a ratio of 91:30. This is close enough to the desired 3:1 ratio for many purposes. By this means each tooth is made to mesh with every other tooth in turn. Thus wear is uniformly distributed, and, it is claimed, the teeth gradually wear to an "average" shape, which is more effective than the original.

## CLUTCHES AND COUPLINGS

Generally, in the design of any instrument that is to be driven by a motor, provision is made to transmit power from the motor to the driven unit through a clutch or coupling. If the motor shaft and the input shaft of the machine were connected directly, any linear or angular displacement between the two would cause malfunctioning of the equipment. The coupling is a form of linkage between the two shafts to permit freedom of the type desired in the relative positioning of the shafts without markedly affecting the performance of the equipment. The three types of freedom desired are the following:

1. *Axial Play.*—In order to permit the motor to perform satisfactorily, it may be necessary to permit the motor shaft to have a small amount of longitudinal freedom. Such freedom might also be desired if there is a possibility of longitudinal mis-alignment. If this longitudinal freedom cannot also be given the driven shaft, a suitable coupling must be used. This type of play is illustrated in Fig. 254.

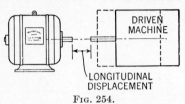

Fig. 254.

2. *Linear Lateral Displacement.*—If there is a possibility of the motor and the driven shafts being displaced laterally with respect to one another, while remaining parallel, a special form of coupling is required. This type of misalignment is shown in Fig. 255.

3. *Angular Displacement.*—In some assemblies there is always a possibility that the axes of the motor and machine shafts will

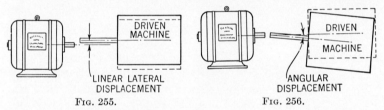

Fig. 255.    Fig. 256.

make a small angle with each other, as shown in Fig. 256. In this case a suitable coupling is provided.

In any given installation the coupling selected will depend on which of the three above defects might be encountered and on the amount of power being transmitted. Various combinations of these alignment defects are also frequently encountered, and these again call for special couplings.

A few typical couplings of use in instrument design are as follows:

**Multi-jaw Coupling.**—This is illustrated in Fig. 257. It is generally used for light duty. Because of the large number of teeth, the coupling has a large bearing surface and can thus transmit light loads without wear. These couplings are intended mostly for installations where some axial play is desired. However, they operate reasonably well for small angular displacements and have on occasion been used with displacements up to 10°.

This form of coupling has many variations, one of which is the saw-tooth form shown in Fig. 258. It can be so adjusted that it is held closed by axial pressure and will slip and open when overloaded. This can also be used as a positive drive when run in the opposite direction. In this case it has the advantage over the type shown in Fig. 257 of being capable of being engaged easily. The teeth may be undercut so that the coupling cannot become disengaged under load.

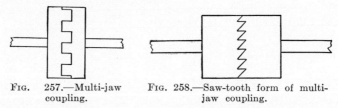

Fig. 257.—Multi-jaw coupling.
Fig. 258.—Saw-tooth form of multi-jaw coupling.

Other variations of the coupling shown in Fig. 257 may be obtained by rounding the teeth or making them slightly wedge-shaped, in order to get them to engage somewhat more easily.

Various other couplings of this type with particularly easy

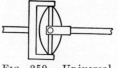

Fig. 259.—Universal coupling.

opening or closing characteristics are available.

This general form of coupling is known as a *positive clutch*, for it may be used in cases where inertia is so small that a machine can be started without slippage between the motor and the driven shaft. If slippage must occur because of inertia, a friction clutch is used.

**Universal Coupling.**—This is a familiar form of coupling, known to every machine designer. It is good for angular displacement, but it should not be used where linear displacement of the two shafts is likely to occur. It is shown in Fig. 259. This form of coupling has one objectionable feature that eliminates it from consideration for some applications. If the coupling is so arranged that some angular displacement exists between the driving and the driven shaft, the coupling does not give a uniform drive. This means that, if the driving shaft rotates with constant speed, the driven shaft will turn with non-uniform speed, its speed varying cyclically each revolution. By using two of these couplings in series with an intermediate shaft, a uniform drive may be obtained provided the couplings and the intermediate shaft are suitably oriented.[1]

These couplings should not be used where the angular misalignment is more than about 25°, although for light loads and low speeds they can be used to about 40°.

**Rubber Hose.**—This type of coupling, illustrated in Fig. 260, is useful for both angular and linear displacement of the shafts.

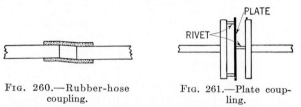

FIG. 260.—Rubber-hose coupling.

FIG. 261.—Plate coupling.

It is of course suitable for only light loads, but it has been used with considerable success in motion-picture projectors. It is not adapted to applications where a constant rotational relationship must be maintained between the driving and the driven shafts, for it acts as a spring and one shaft can get slightly behind the other. In starting, particularly, a rather large instantaneous rotational displacement can occur.

**Plate Coupling.**—This device is shown in Fig. 261. It can be employed in assemblies where angular misalignment is apt to occur. Any number of plates may be used in series in couplings of this form to give added flexibility.

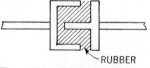

FIG. 262.—Rubber universal coupling.

**Rubber Universal Coupling.**—This device, illustrated in Fig. 262, consists of a pair of yokes joined by a block of rubber. It is useful for installations where angular freedom is desired.

**Flexible Shaft.**—These devices are familiar, for they are often seen in dental equipment. They consist of cables formed of layers of wire wound in opposite directions. They are usable when both angular and lateral displacements are to be encountered. They have rather small load capacities in general. They should be rotated in the direction specified by the manufacturer, otherwise the outer layer of wire will carry no load and the unit is likely to break if run nearly at capacity. When long installa-

[1] "Machinery's Handbook," p. 579, Industrial Press, New York, 1941.

tions of flexible shafting are contemplated, it is advisable to make sure that the external casing containing the shaft is fastened at several points; otherwise it will probably coil into one or more loops. It should be borne in mind that there is considerable rotational deflection between the two ends of such a shaft; consequently, one end of it lags behind the other. The flexible shafting may be attached to the motor and driven shafts by normal couplings, or by bayonet or spline type fittings, or it may be soldered into holes drilled in the shafts.

FASTENED HERE     NOT FASTENED HERE

FIG. 263.—Spring coupling.

**Spring Coupling.**—This device is shown in Fig. 263. The spring is fastened on one shaft but not on the other. Such a device transmits power when running forward but not backward and is thus a form of over-running clutch. This is a very useful property and has many practical applications.

**Viscous or Fluid Drive.**—This drive, shown in Fig. 264, consists of two bladed elements so arranged that their blades are very close together. The box containing these blades is filled with a viscous fluid, which serves to transmit energy from one shaft to the other. If constant speed of the driven shaft is

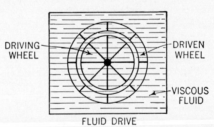

DRIVING WHEEL

DRIVEN WHEEL

VISCOUS FLUID

FLUID DRIVE

FIG. 264.—A form of fluid drive. The radial lines represent blades perpendicular to supporting disks, which are shown by the circular lines.

desired, it is possible to place a heavy flywheel on it. Its speed will then be independent of minor rapid fluctuations in the speed of the driving shaft because of the lack of a solid coupling between the two. This type of drive or clutch is quite sensitive to temperature variations because of viscosity changes.

**Overrunning Clutch.**—This device, used frequently in many types of optical instruments, is shown in Fig. 265. The inner plate $A$ is connected to the driving shaft, the outer ring $B$ to the driven shaft. When the driving shaft rotates in direction $a$, the balls are wedged between the plate and ring and transmit the driving power to *B*. When the driving shaft moves in direction *b*, the coupling is automatically broken and no power is transmitted. This type of coupling is capable of transmitting surprisingly large amounts of power. It is also available in another form known as a *single revolution clutch*. This is constructed similar to the device shown in Fig. 265 but has in addition a ball retainer, somewhat similar to that of a ball bearing, which can cam the balls out of the power-transmitting position. This cam plate can be tripped by a lever attached to a fixed part of the machine and will then instantly break the driving connection. In this way it is possible to stop a rotating shaft very accurately in a predetermined angular position, and the inertia of the motor does not have to be overcome in bringing the machine to rest. Because the cam plate cannot be stopped

FIG. 265.—Overrunning clutch.

instantly, it is necessary to make provision for absorbing the shock between it and the trip lever.

If the outer ring *B* is caused to rotate faster than the driving plate *A* in direction *a*, the linkage between the two is broken. This property is of value in obtaining a multiple speed drive.

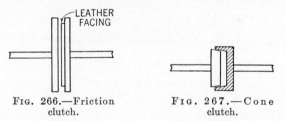

FIG. 266.—Friction clutch.

FIG. 267.—Cone clutch.

**Friction Clutches.**—These are obtainable in many different forms. In general they are useful in applications where the driving shaft runs more or less continuously and the driven shaft runs intermittently. The simplest form is the single-disk clutch shown in Fig. 266. The facing material should be chosen with regard to ready availability and high coefficient of friction. The best material for general use is leather. The opposing face of the clutch is usually left uncovered so leather-metal contact is secured.   Another useful facing material is cork.   When more power than a single disk can handle must be transmitted (and this is unusual in instrument work), multiple disks may be employed.   Another type of clutch capable of handling more power than that shown in Fig. 266 is the cone clutch shown in Fig. 267.   This is commonly faced with leather.   When so faced, the angle between the clutch surface and the shaft axis should be kept between 8 and 13°, an angle of about 12.5° being very common.   Multiple cone clutches may be built to transmit large amounts of power.   More complicated friction clutches are of the radially expanding and contracting band types.   The names of these are self-explanatory.

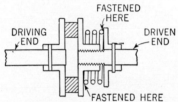

Fig. 268.—Constant-torque friction clutch.

An important variation of the disk clutch is the magnetic clutch, in which pressure is applied between the faces by means of an electromagnet contained in one clutch member.   Current to operate the electromagnet is transmitted to the rotating clutch by means of slip rings.   This is a particularly useful device for instruments provided with automatic electric controls.

Another form of friction clutch, developed by the Eastman Kodak Co., is illustrated in Fig. 268.   This gives constant torque because of the interaction between the torque operating through the spring and that through the thread.   When the spring torque gets too strong, the plate backs up the thread and frees itself, thus keeping the driving torque constant.   This device has a tendency to oscillate in operation, and provisions should be made for damping the oscillation in use.   The system may be run in oil for this purpose.

**Pin-and-slot Coupling.**—This is illustrated in Fig. 269.   It can be used for angular misalignment.   It permits some lateral displacement, but in this case it gives a non-uniform drive, *i.e.*, if one shaft rotates at constant speed, the speed of the other will vary cyclically. As it is sometimes desirable to obtain a non-uniform drive, this is a useful device for the purpose. By making the driven shaft movable laterally, the degree of non-uniformity, *i.e.*, the percentage variation in speed in each rotation, may be predetermined.

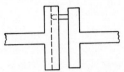

FIG. 269.—Pin-and-slot coupling. The pin fastened to one disk engages in a slot cut in the face of the opposing disk.

There are many other general and special types of clutches and couplings available for various purposes. An attempt has been made here merely to illustrate a few types and show their general properties.

### FLEXURE PLATES

Although flexure plates are not couplings used to transmit power between rotating members of a machine, they are sufficiently important static couplings to warrant inclusion in this text.

In designing mounts for optical instruments it is often desired to obtain a joint or sliding connection in which there is no looseness or play. Flexure plates may be used for this purpose, for they can be arranged to give either angular or linear motion.

These plates are strips of phosphor bronze, spring steel, or other suitable material. Because of its machinability, corrosion resistance, etc., phosphor bronze is commonly used.

The method of obtaining angular displacements by the use of a flexure plate is shown in Fig. 270. Here it is desired to tilt the

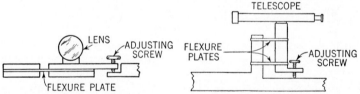

FIG. 270—Use of flexure plate in obtaining angular deflection.

FIG. 271.—Use of flexure plate in obtaining linear displacement.

lens in its own plane. As the adjusting screw is rotated, the flexure plate bends and permits the lens to tilt. There is no lost motion in the system and, because the plate has been made of flexible material, the system can be readjusted as often as desired.

The method of using flexure plates to obtain linear displacement is shown in Fig. 271. In this case it is desired to make provision for moving the telescope vertically without rotation. The illustration shows how this is accomplished.

This type of mounting is eminently practical and can be successfully employed in many cases of semikinematic design.

The same general idea can be used by mounting a mirror support on a steel post perpendicular to the reflecting surface and near the center of the support. By bending the post

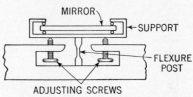

Fig. 272.—Use of a flexure post.

(through screw adjustments), the plane of the mirror can be tilted slightly in any direction to obtain adjustment. The post is called a *flexure post*. This arrangement is shown in Fig. 272.

### REFERENCES

FAIRES: "Design of Machine Elements," The Macmillan Company, New York, 1934.

HYLAND and KOMMERS: "Machine Design," McGraw-Hill Book Company, Inc., New York, 1943.

KIMBALL: "Elements of Machine Design," John Wiley & Sons, Inc., New York, 1935.

"Machinery's Handbook," Industrial Press, New York, 1941.

TRAUTSCHOLD: "Standard Gear Book," McGraw-Hill Book Company, Inc., New York, 1935.

### PROBLEMS

**1.** The centers of two parallel shafts are separated by a distance of 3 in. It is desired to make the second shaft run at three times the rotational velocity of the first by the use of spur gears. What are the pitch diameters of the two gears that will be used? If gears of 16 diametral pitch are employed, how many teeth will each have?

**2.** Two shafts are to be connected with worm gearing so that a speed reduction of 64:1 will be effected. A double-threaded worm is to be used. How many teeth should the worm wheel have? If a worm wheel of 4-in. pitch diameter is employed, what should be its diametral pitch?

# CHAPTER XXI

## LENS MOUNTINGS, PARALLEL DISPLACEMENTS

### LENS MOUNTINGS

After a lens has been ground and polished, it is reduced by grinding to its final diameter. As the periphery of the lens will be used to position it in its mounting, it is necessary to have the *optical axis* (the line joining the centers of curvature of the two surfaces) of the lens coincide with its mechanical axis. The lens is centered by fastening it with wax or shellac to a spindle in a lathe in the fashion shown in Fig. 273. The operator, whose eye is located at $E$, observes the reflections of the light source $L$ formed by both surfaces. If, as the lathe spindle rotates, the reflections of $L$ moves in a circle the optical axis of the lens does not coincide with the axis of rotation of the spindle. In this case the operator heats the spindle enough to loosen the lens and then manipulates it with a wooden stick until the images of $L$ formed by reflection remains stationary. He then cools the spindle, thus fastening the lens in position. The optical axis now coincides with the axis of the spindle. An abrasive wheel may now be brought against the lens and the lens can be ground to a disk with the optical and mechanical axes coinciding by slowly rotating the spindle while keeping the distance from the periphery of the grinding wheel to the center of the spindle constant. The lens may now be called *centered*. If it is dropped into a closely fitted lens cell, its optical axis will automatically be brought to the center of the cell. The centering of a lens may be checked by measuring its thickness at several points around the edge. These thicknesses should be equal.

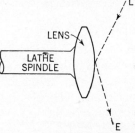

FIG. 273.—Method of centering a lens.

The problem of mounting a round centered lens in a tube is one peculiar to optical instrument design. Many methods have been tried, and experience has shown certain of these to be satisfactory. As will be seen, the method adopted in any specific case depends to a large extent upon the particular use for which the lens is intended. The most common methods are as follows:

1. The lens may be mounted against a shoulder and held in place with a threaded retaining ring (Fig. 274). This technique is used frequently in military instruments such as telescopes, binoculars, and rangefinders, for mounting objectives and erectors. It gives a firm mounting that can be easily disassem-

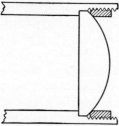 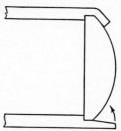

Fig. 274.—Method of holding lens in cell with retaining ring.

Fig. 275.—Method of holding lens in cell by burnishing.

bled for cleaning when necessary. The retaining ring is sometimes turned into position very firmly with a key and should be removed only with a similar key. In certain cases, to avoid the possibility of tampering, the retaining rings are shellacked into position. There is often a temptation to use aluminum retaining rings and lens cells for the sake of lightness, but the rings are apt to bind and cannot be unscrewed. Brass is usually satisfactory.

2. A second useful technique involves holding the lens against its positioning shoulder by burnishing. This is illustrated in Fig. 275, in which the lower part of the illustration shows the cell before burnishing and the upper part shows the cell after the operation has been completed. For this method to work satisfactorily it is necessary for the lens to fit the cell quite closely. Burnishing generally holds the lens firmly in position and is therefore satisfactory. It is in addition comparatively inexpensive. It is used in locations where it is desired to fasten the lens permanently in position and is thus employed in eyepieces, microscope objectives, etc. The operation is of course performed by chucking the cell in a lathe and rotating it. A

tool is brought against the projecting strip of tubing, forcing it in against the lens.

3. The burnishing technique may be modified by placing a spring between the lens and the positioning shoulder. The

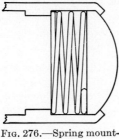

FIG. 276.—Spring mounting for lens.

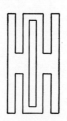

FIG. 277.—
Spring formed
by slotting
brass tubing.

spring may also be added to the retaining ring type of mounting This spring mounting, shown in Fig. 276, is sometimes found useful when the element is to be subjected to severe shock or where it is desired to avoid stressing the lens. The type of spring formed from a piece of tubing (Fig. 277) is often used for this purpose.

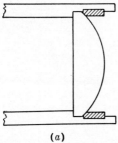
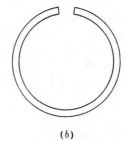

(*a*)  (*b*)

FIG. 278.—Method of holding lens in cell with retaining spring.

4. The lens may be held against its positioning shoulder by a retaining spring, as shown in Fig. 278*a*. The retaining spring itself is illustrated in Fig. 278*b*. It may be circular or rectangular in cross-section. This is not so satisfactory in general as the first and second methods.

5. Lenses may be cemented in place with Canada balsam, shellac, pitch, de Khotinsky cement, etc. This is done where the element is to be positioned permanently. It is a very inexpensive

method but does not give highly accurate positioning.   It is thus

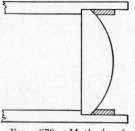

used on elements (eye lenses, etc.) where positioning is not very critical.

6.  The lens may be fastened in position with a flat ring press-fitted against it. This is shown in Fig. 279.   The ring is installed under pressure.

7.  When the lens is to be mounted in the center of a section of tubing, a slot

Fig.   279.—Method   of holding lens in cell by press-fitting a ring against it.

may be cut in the tubing (Fig. 280) and the lens dropped into position.   It may be held in place by wedging or by means of an external ring.

8.  It is possible to hold a lens in position in a cell by punching a few projecting ears against the lens, as is shown in Fig. 281.

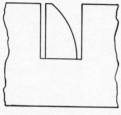

Fig. 280.

Fig. 281.

9.  For a condenser lens in motion-picture projection apparatus the method shown in Fig. 282 can be employed.   The lens

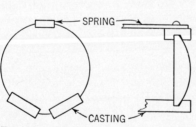
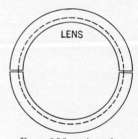

Fig. 282.—Method of mounting a condenser lens.

Fig. 283.—Another method of mounting a condenser lens.

is held in position in the two castings by the retaining spring. This method is cheap and leaves a good deal of the edge of the lens exposed to the air, this being advantageous because of the heat problem encountered in equipment of this type. Should the lens expand under heat, the spring gives and thus breakage is avoided.

10. For these same condensers two castings may be used in the manner shown in Fig. 283. This is not so useful as method 9 from the point of view of heat dissipation.

11. Another good mount for condensers is shown in Fig. 284. This consists of three springs, spaced 120° apart and fastened to a ring. It has the advantages mentioned under 9 and, in addition, keeps the lens better centered when expansion occurs.

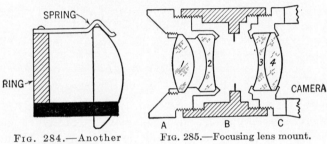

FIG. 284.—Another method of mounting a condenser lens.

FIG. 285.—Focusing lens mount.

The mounting of a good photographic lens is shown in Fig. 285. It will be noted that elements 1 and 2 are mounted in ring $A$, and that elements 3 and 4 are mounted in $C$. With this type of lens (Tessar) the spacing between elements 1 and 2 is very critical. Thus this spacing is maintained by accurately machined shoulders. Study of the drawing will show that the spacing will be held constant regardless of variations in thickness of the individual lens elements. Lens 1 is held in place by a threaded retaining ring, while the other elements are burnished in position. The airspace between elements 2 and 3 can be varied by the rotation of ring $B$. Thus focusing is accomplished.

With complex photographic lenses the optical system will not in general be found to be collimated, *i.e.*, rotation of the lens system about the axis of the mount would produce a shift of the image. It would thus be undesirable to focus the lens for precision photography by rotating the whole lens and mount in the usual fashion. In this case the focusing mount shown in Fig. 285 may be used, for focusing is accomplished by changing the spacing between two of the elements without rotating the lens.    Thus a shift of the image will not occur on focusing.

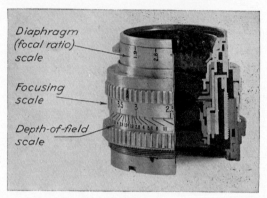

PLATE XXVII.—Modern lens mount.    (*Courtesy of Eastman Kodak Company.*)

Microscope lenses are usually burnished in position.    If an attempt were made to take a single mount and center and burnish one element after the other until the entire system were mounted, the difficulties to be faced would be considerable.    Hence a

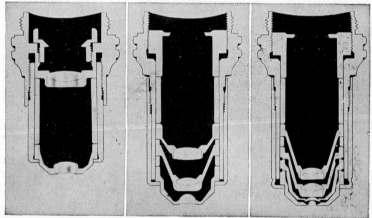

PLATE XXVIII.—Method of assembling optical elements in microscope objectives.    (*Courtesy of Bausch & Lomb Optical Company.*)

microscope objective may be made in such a fashion that each lens is centered and burnished in its own cell.    These cells are then assembled together in a nest to form the complete objective. This is shown in Plate XXVIII.

Returning to the focusing mount for photographic objectives shown in Fig. 285, it will be noted that a fine focusing adjustment may be obtained with comparatively coarse threads. This is accomplished with differential threading. The threads connecting $A$ and $B$ might be made 32 turns per inch (TPI), while those connecting $B$ and $C$ might be 54 turns per inch. If the threads were made subtractive, 86 turns per inch would be obtained. Thus one revolution of the focusing ring would close the gap $\frac{1}{32}$ in. at one end but open it $\frac{1}{54}$ in. at the other. Therefore a change in spacing of only $\frac{1}{32} - \frac{1}{54}$ in. would be obtained, and very fine focusing could be accomplished. If rapid focusing were desired, the threads could be made additive, giving 22 turns per inch (effective), which is comparatively coarse.

It is interesting to note that the centering of a lens system can be checked to some extent by holding the system at waist level and looking in it at the reflection of a light source above the head of the observer. There will be a reflection from each reflecting surface; if the system is properly centered, these reflections will be colinear. By noting the size and orientation (erect or inverted) of these reflections, as well as the direction in which they move when the lens is tilted, one may tell, with a little experience, the general character of the system, *i.e.*, number, type, and arrangement of components. Each glass-air surface will give a bright reflection, and each glass-glass reflection will give a weak one. Thus, if one should wish to determine whether a simple telescope objective were a single lens or a doublet without removing it from its cell, he could do so by determining whether the lens gave two or three reflections. A cemented doublet would of course give two strong reflections and one weak one. By noting the size of the reflections one could make some estimate of the relative curvatures of the different surfaces. When considering the reflection from a single glass-air surface, one can take as a general rule the fact that a large reflected image corresponds to a large radius of curvature.

## PARALLEL DISPLACEMENTS

In the design of optical instruments it often becomes necessary to displace the axis of a light beam parallel to itself. An example of this is a device for varying the interocular distance in a rangefinder and the apparatus for obtaining a rangefinder halving or coincidence adjustment in a convergent beam of light is another. In this section a few general methods of solving this problem will be indicated. These are by no means all the possible methods but merely indicate several solutions of the problem that have been found to be practicable.

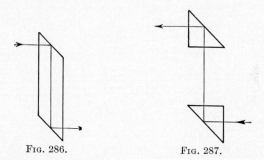

FIG. 286.                    FIG. 287.

1. A rhomboidal prism may be used, as illustrated in Fig. 286. This technique is employed in providing a means of varying the interocular distance of the eyepieces on stereoscopic rangefinders.

2. Two right-angle prisms may be used, as indicated in Fig. 287. This combination is used in simple periscopes and some

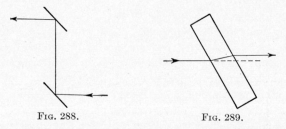

FIG. 288.                    FIG. 289.

types of panoramic sights. Their limitations for this purpose have been discussed in Chaps. XIV and XV. Various other prism combinations may of course also be used, and many examples have been given in preceding pages.

3. A pair of simple mirrors may be used (Fig. 288). This arrangement has been used in very simple trench periscopes, etc. If these mirrors are to be used with a convergent beam of light in precision optical instruments, it is generally necessary to use first surface mirrors, for they do not give the double image formed by second surface mirrors.

4. A plane parallel plate of glass inclined at an angle to the optical axis may be used. The displacement produced by such a plate is given by Eq. (96). By rotating the plate about an axis normal to the plane of the drawing a variation in displacement may be produced. These plates are used in high-speed cameras, rangefinders, and so on. This type of device is shown in Fig. 289.

5. Figure 290 shows the use of two prisms to obtain a variable displacement of the optical axis. The variation is obtained through changes in the spacing between the prisms. It might be thought that the aberrations introduced by one prism are canceled by the other, but this is not the case. Thus the prism angles must be kept small to minimize aberration, and the device

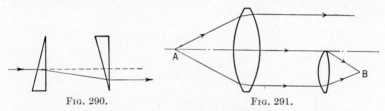

FIG. 290.                    FIG. 291.

is thus generally restricted to small deviations. In practice it is usually advisable to use achromatic prisms.

6. The scheme shown in Fig. 291 has been used successfully in some photographic devices. The large lens has the source *A* located at its first focal point. Thus light from *A* traversing the lens emerges as a parallel beam. This parallel beam enters the small lens, and is of course brought to a focus at its focal point *B*. Thus an image of *A* is formed at *B*. If the lenses are properly designed, excessive aberration will not be introduced. It will be noted that, with the arrangement as shown, only the light striking the small lens is used, the rest is lost. However, by placing a number of small lenses in front of the large one, a number of images of *A* may be formed. These small lenses may be located at various distances from the large lens and thus may form images of *A* in various places. Small lenses of various focal lengths may be used to obtain images of different sizes.

# CHAPTER XXII

## ELECTRICAL CONTROLS

Many optical instruments involve the use of electrical apparatus to control or indicate motion, to transmit information, etc. Consequently, a knowledge of some of the modern pieces of electrical control equipment is indispensable to the designer. A few devices of considerable importance will be discussed in this chapter.

**Snap-action Switches.**—In recent years there have appeared on the market several switches of the snap-action variety (see Fig. 292). These switches all have contacts mounted on the end of a

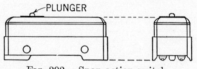

Fig. 292.—Snap-action switch.

leaf spring. Their construction is such that when the operating plunger is placed under a few ounces of pressure nothing happens. When a small extra pressure is added, the switch snaps abruptly. When part of the pressure is released, the switch snaps back. Only a very small movement of the operating plunger is required. Each manufacturer produces several switches with different operating characteristics. Thus *operating pressures, i.e.,* pressures required to operate the switch, of from 4 to 30 oz may be obtained. After the switch has been snapped, the amount of pressure that must be released to have the switch snap back to the original position (known as the *pressure differential*) varies from about 25 to 50 per cent of the operating pressure. The amount of movement necessary to snap the switch is called the *movement differential* and varies from 0.0002 up to 0.001 in. After the switch has snapped, the operating plunger moves a short distance, this being known as the *overtravel*. The overtravel varies from 0.005 to 0.020 in. A typical standard switch intended for general use has an operating pressure of 12 to 14 oz, a pressure differential of 3 to 4 oz, an overtravel of 0.005 to 0.007 in., and a movement differential of 0.001 in. A typical sensitive type switch has an operating pressure of 7 to 8.5 oz, a pressure differential of 1.25 to 2 oz, an overtravel of 0.005 to 0.020 in., and a movement differential of 0.0002 to 0.0003 in. These switches usually come in small box-like cases molded from phenol-formaldehyde or other plastics and have dimensions of about $1^{15}/_{16}$ by $1^{1}/_{16}$ by $2^{7}/_{32}$ in. A small metal plunger ($^{3}/_{32}$ in. in diameter) projects from the top of the case $^{35}/_{64}$ in. from the front end. Two 0.139-in. holes for 6-32 screws are molded through the body for mounting purposes. The total weight is about 1 oz. It should be borne in mind that not all switches necessarily conform to these same dimensions. One manufacturer makes several extra varieties of container including various water- and moistureproof cases, metal cases for use on machine tools, special airplane casings, etc.

These switches may be obtained in the single-pole single-throw variety with the contacts either "normally open" or "normally closed." They may also be obtained with single-pole double-throw contacts. In purchasing a number of these switches for instrument work, it is often advisable to purchase only the last-named variety, for it can also be used for either of the first two applications and is thus a good general-purpose article. The extra cost of a few cents is generally negligible. In production, of course, the situation is different. There is a great need for snap-action switches of the double-pole double-throw variety. The manufacturers are trying to develop this item but at the present writing have not succeeded.

After one of these snap-action switches has been snapped through the application of pressure to the operating plunger, it automatically snaps back to the original position when the pressure is released. In certain switches, known as *maintained-contact* types, the switch remains tripped until a reset button is pushed, thus returning the switch to its initial setting. These are very useful for many purposes.

These switches are obviously useful for a large number of applications in machine design work. Their principal use in optical instruments is as *limit switches*—switches that limit the motion of an electrically driven component of a device by having the part strike the operating plunger of the switch when it has reached a predetermined position. The switch of course then stops or reverses the moving part.   A limit switch can stop a rotating part through the use of a lever or cam attached to that part These switches can also be used to illuminate pilot lights when a part of the instrument has reached a desired position.   The fact that the switch needs only a very small movement differential for operation insures that each of the foregoing operations will be performed with great precision.

In each of these applications the operating part will normally move through a greater distance than the usual overtravel of the switch before the part can be stopped or reversed.   This could result in destruction of the switch, so for applications of this type the switches are usually equipped with a special spring-plunger

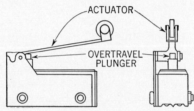

Fig. 293.—Snap-action switch equipped with lever actuator and overtravel plunger.

operating button which allows about $\frac{1}{16}$ in. overtravel, this usually being enough.   If more overtravel is needed, it can be obtained in other ways.   This type of spring plunger gives increased overtravel without changing any of the other characteristics of the switch, *i.e.*, there is no increase in movement differential or operating pressure.   A switch equipped with a spring plunger can have added to it a long ($2\frac{9}{16}$ in.) lever to increase further the sensitivity of the device and give increased overtravel (see Fig. 293).   This is usually equipped with a roller that bears against the moving part.   It is a very useful type of device for limit switches on optical instruments, for it gives low operating pressures ($\frac{1}{2}$ to $1\frac{1}{2}$ oz), fairly small movement differential (0.005 to 0.020 in.), and large overtravel ($\frac{1}{2}$ in.). The rollers on these levers are generally equipped with oil-impregnated bearings and thus, because of the small pressure involved, require no lubrication.

Snap-action switches are able to carry a surprisingly large amount of power (15 amp at 110 volts) when alternating current is used.   With direct current, the story is somewhat different.

A switch of this type can *carry* large amounts of power when direct current is used, but trouble occurs when an attempt is made to open the switch. As the switch opens, an arc is formed and is maintained as the switch continues to open. With alternating current, this arc is immediately extinguished upon reversal of current; with direct current the arc remains. Thus the circuit is not broken, and the arc rapidly destroys the contacts. Consequently, it is not generally advisable to use these switches for d-c applications. However, they can be used with small direct currents in some cases. If an application of this sort is being considered, it is advisable to consult the manufacturer. One switch manufacturer produces a special snap-action switch for d-c circuits. This is somewhat larger than the normal switch and is equipped with a magnet to "blow out" the arc when it is formed. Such a switch has a capacity of 17 amp at 110 volts d.c. If large amounts of direct current are

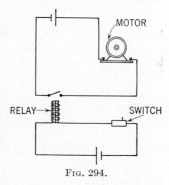

FIG. 294.

to be controlled with a snap-action switch, it is of course possible to close the d-c circuit with a relay whose coils are a-c energized by means of a snap-action switch.

**Relays.**—Suppose that, in designing an instrument, we found ourselves confronted with the problem of designing a circuit to control a heavy motor by means of the motion of a moving part. We could use a heavy switch and have this struck by the moving part, thus closing it. However, we should probably find that the switch was not well suited to this application and could not be precisely operated. We should prefer to use a snap-action switch, but this might be found to have insufficient current capacity. We should then have recourse to the solution indicated in Fig. 294. This involves the use of a *relay*, which is merely a switch operated by an electromagnet. We should have the relay contacts close the main power circuit. The snap-action switch would be located in the electromagnet circuit and would have to carry only enough power to close the relay, a very small amount indeed. This is only one example of the use to which a relay might be put. Another typical example is that in which an electrical contact operated by a moving part is desired to close a motor circuit. This contact, let us assume. would be able to carry sufficient current to operate the motor, However, frequent making and breaking of the current would soon pit this contact, which might be inaccessibly located. Hence the contact would be made to carry only the very small amount of current necessary to close a relay, and the relay would

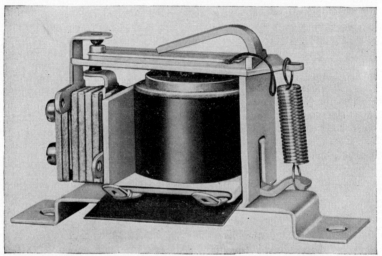

PLATE XXIX.—A typical electric relay. (*Courtesy of Guardian Electric Mfg. Co.*)

operate the motor. Frequent replacement of the contact would thus not be necessary. Countless other applications are also to be found, some of which will be mentioned.

The relay shown in Fig. 294 has contacts of the single-pole single-throw variety, which close when the electromagnet coil is energized. Almost any other desired combination of contacts may be obtained, these either opening or closing when the coil is energized. Relays may be obtained that close several circuits and open several others simultaneously.

Relays are made by a large number of manufacturers in a great variety of styles and sizes. The factors that should be taken into account in selecting a relay for a given application are (1) contact arrangement, (2) current to be carried by contacts, and (3) power available to operate the electromagnet, or coil, as it is usually known. Small relays of the "midget" class generally have contacts that will carry 6 amp at 110 volts a.c. or 1 amp at 110 volts d.c. The difference between the a-c and the d-c capacities is due to the arcing effect mentioned under Snap-action Switches. Electromagnet coils are available for either alternating current or direct current. The a-c coils take about 4 watts and can be obtained for operation at 6, 12, 24, or 110 volts. The d-c coils draw about 2 watts and may be obtained for use on 6, 12, 24, 32, and 90 volts. If the coil is to be energized by a switch circuit, the voltage should be kept as low as possible to limit sparking and arcing at the switch. On the other hand, if it is kept too low, the contact resistance at certain types of contacts might be sufficiently large to interfere with the proper functioning of the circuit. In comparison with the "midget" relay, a large power control relay carries 20 amp at 110 volts

a.c., and 2 amp at 110 volts d.c. The a-c coil takes 8 watts and may be obtained wound for 6, 12, 24, 110, 220, or 440 volts. The d-c coil draws 4 watts and is obtainable for use on 6, 12, 24, 32, 115, and 230 volts.

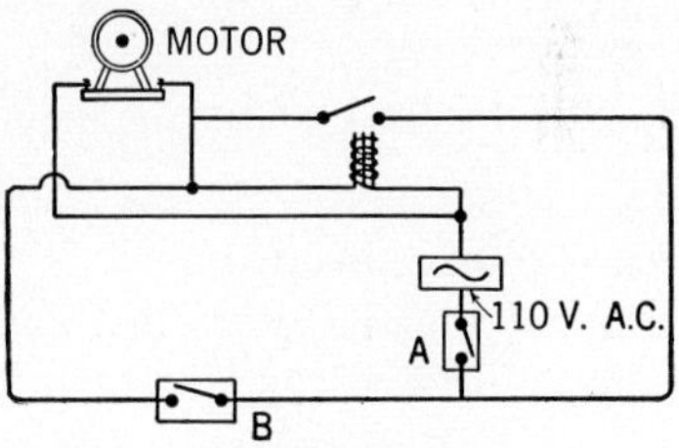

The contact points may be obtained fabricated from many

Fig. 295.

types of metal. Generally speaking the material best suited to instrument work is silver. On some relays the contact points are so designed that the movable contacts, after closing, slide for a short distance along the face of the fixed contacts, thus wiping off any dirt or surface film that might have formed on either. Such contacts are known as *self-wiping*, and contacts of this sort are usually desirable.

An interesting and useful control circuit using a simple relay is illustrated in Fig. 295. Switch *A* (snap action) is normally closed, switch *B* (push button) is normally open. Assume that the motor shown is to operate a moving part of an instrument. The motor is controlled by the relay, which has a 110-volt a-c coil. Thus, one power supply is used for motor and relay coil. By pushing the starting switch *B* the operator snaps shut the relay, thus starting the motor. The circuit is so arranged that now some of the current passing through the relay contacts also passes through the coil, thus automatically keeping the relay shut and permitting the motor to keep running in spite of the fact that switch *B* has been released and is now open again. When the moving part reaches the desired position, it strikes the limit switch *A*, opening all the circuits.   Thus only a single push on the control button was required to start the operation, and the operation automatically completed itself and then stopped.   The circuit may be reset, or another identical circuit may be used to return the moving part to its initial position. Many unique control operations in an instrument may be performed with variations of this circuit.

Besides the standard type of relay first described, a large variety of special relays are available for particular applications. A few will be described.

In some relays, instead of employing the usual contacts, the coil acts to close a snap-action switch of the type described previously, while in other relays the coil closes a mercury switch. This latter type of relay has high current capacity and in addition is non-sparking, an important factor in mounting relays in an explosive atmosphere.

A normal relay with a single-pole single-throw contact takes about 0.004 second to open and a similar time to close.   It is occasionally necessary to have one circuit in an instrument function before another (it may be desired, for example, to have a clutch close before it starts to rotate), and then a relay of slower operating characteristics is desired.   Such a device is known as a *time-delay relay*.   Time delay is obtained with a large variety of techniques: inertia, bimetallic elements, hot wires, condensers, dashpots, etc.   Time delays of from a fraction of a second up to one or more minutes may be obtained by proper selection of the relay.

Another type of relay has a mechanical latch that holds the contacts closed once they have been closed by the coil, even after the coil has been de-energized.   The latch may be released mechanically, with a lever, or electrically, by an additional built-in electromagnet.   These are known as *latch-in* or *locking relays*.   The two types described are known, respectively, as *mechanical reset* and *electrical reset* types.   They are apt to prove unreliable under continued use, and a circuit of the type shown in Fig. 295 should be used instead when possible.

Some motors are reversed by reversing a set of connections. The operation can be performed with two relays, each of which drives the motor in one direction. If the two relays should through some mistake be closed simultaneously, trouble will

PLATE XXX.—A stepping relay. (*Courtesy of Guardian Electric Mfg. Co.*)

develop. Thus two relays connected mechanically so that only one can be closed at a time can be used in this case. These are known as *interlock relays*.

It is sometimes desirable to have a relay, operated by a single push button, that will close one circuit after another each time the button is pushed. Such a relay can be obtained with provision for as many as 50 or more circuits, the contact being moved by a ratchet from one circuit to the next.    This is known as a *stepping relay*.   The movable contact may be reset to the starting position either mechanically or by an electrically operated reset coil. Many ingenious variations of this type of relay are also available, and numerous useful functions may be performed with their assistance.

PLATE XXXI.—A typical solenoid.    (*Courtesy of Guardian Electric Mfg. Co.*)

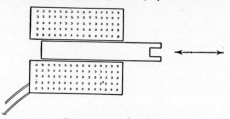

FIG. 296.—Solenoid.

There are also available relays that close two circuits alternately by a ratchet device and are known as *ratchet relays*. A number of other types are also procurable.

**Solenoids.**—Many control operations in optical instruments may be performed automatically by the use of solenoids, which are electromagnetic coils wound around a hollow core containing a plunger sliding parallel to the axis of the coil.   When the coil is energized, the plunger snaps into the coil, thus performing an operation.   When the coil is de-energized the plunger may be returned to its initial position by means of a spring.   The device is illustrated in Plate XXXI and Fig. 296.

In selecting a solenoid for a specific application the designer should take note of the distance that must be traveled by the plunger (known as the *stroke*) in performing the control operation, and the total force (called the *lift*) that it must exert. He can obtain solenoids wound to 12, 18, 24, 36, 115, and 230 volts a.c., and 6, 12, 18, 24, 36, 115, and 230 volts d.c. For a given solenoid size, coil voltage, and stroke, a solenoid is usually given two "lift" ratings. One of these is for continuous operation; the other is for intermittent operation. Coils wound for intermittent usage have considerably higher lift ratings than those designed for continuous use, but overheat dangerously if energized for more than 5 minutes. Obviously, they should be used only where a short period of operation is involved. Solenoids with strokes of $\frac{1}{8}$ to 2 in. and lifts of 1 to 81 oz may be obtained.

**Motors.**—Many optical instruments contain electrical motors. These motors are generally small, developing less than 1 hp, and are thus known as fractional horsepower motors. Common sizes range from $\frac{1}{50}$ to $\frac{1}{80}$ hp. Generally, the motor speed is much higher than that required for a specific application, and it is necessary to use reduction gears to obtain the desired speed. By far the best way of doing this is by the use of motors containing built-in reduction gears, these being designated *speed reducer* or *gear-head motors*. A well-built speed reducer motor is little more bulky than a motor without a gear unit. In some cases it is possible to purchase a motor with built-in gears for less than the cost of a reduction gear assembly alone.

Normally, motors are rated according to horsepower (rate of doing work). This is not a generally satisfactory method of measuring the performance of a speed reducer motor because friction losses in the reduction gears absorb some of the power. Different sets of reduction gears attached to the same motor will have different efficiencies. The efficiency of a given combination will vary with speed. Thus gear-head motors are generally rated in terms of the torque and speed of the slow speed shaft.

When a speed reducer motor is to be selected to drive a machine, the torque of the machine is measured by placing on its input shaft a pulley of radius $r$. A cord is wrapped around this pulley, and a spring scale is fastened to this in the manner shown in Fig. 297. The ring of the scale is grasped and pulled, and the scale reading is noted when the shaft is turning at roughly the desired speed.  The scale reading as the pulley is brought to speed is also noted.  The highest scale reading (in ounces) is multiplied by the pulley radius (in inches) to give the required torque (in inch-ounces) and from this figure and the required speed a motor may be selected.

It should be remembered that these gear reduction units cannot drive backward and they should not be used indiscriminately with loads of high inertia, for such loads can damage the gears while starting or stopping.  A friction clutch or shear pin safety arrangement should be used in this case.

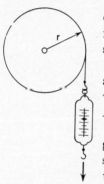

F I G . 2 9 7 . —
Measurement of
torque.

As motors with various types of windings are available, it is important that the proper windings be selected for a given application. A few notes on this subject follow.

**Split-phase motors** are a-c units intended for general-purpose use.  They have fairly constant speed and can be used where the starting torque does not greatly exceed the full-speed torque.  They are provided with a starting winding that is cut out by a centrifugal switch as the motor comes to speed.  They have four leads and can be reversed by reversing the two starting leads. They can be reversed only when the motor is standing still. This is a handicap for some applications.  Because of the centrifugal cutout mechanism, these motors are not particularly well adapted to frequent starting and stopping, for this mechanism would not stand such usage.

**Capacitor motors** may be used for frequent starting because they have no internal switches.  They are very reliable and are unusually quiet and vibrationless.  For these reasons they are well adapted to instrument applications.  However, they have low starting torques, and this is sometimes disadvantageous.  If high starting torque is desired, a special starting capacitor is added, but this involves the use of a cutout switch, which is objectionable because it will not stand frequent starting.  Such motors are of the "capacitor start-and-run" variety.  Most capacitor motors have four leads, two of which must be interchanged to reverse the device.  However a few light capacitor motors are made with three external leads, and these may be reversed with only a single-pole double-throw switch, which is advantageous. The capacitor for these various motors is rather bulky and must be mounted either on top of the motor or elsewhere in the apparatus.

**Shaded pole motors** have only one moving part: the rotor-and-shaft assembly. They have no commutators, brushes, or insulated rotor windings. They are thus very simple and reliable, but they have low starting torques and low power output for a given frame size. They are quite constant in speed in spite of normal line voltage changes and are unusually quiet in addition. They are not reversible.

**Polyphase motors** are generally used on three-phase 220-volt a-c lines. They contain no internal switches and are thus very reliable. They have practically constant speed regardless of the magnitude of the load. They can be reversed, when either running or motionless, by reversing two of the three line connections. This ability to be reversed while running is often very important. It should not be done too frequently, however, or the motor will overheat. These motors develop high starting torques, this being another important advantage.

**Synchronous motors** are used when it is desired to maintain constant speed regardless of load or line voltage variations. These motors give constant speed unless heavily overloaded, when their speed falls off. Split-phase synchronous, capacitor synchronous, and polyphase synchronous motors are commonly used.

The split-phase synchronous motor has high starting torque and is usually low in cost. It has a starting winding which is cut out by a centrifugal switch. The objection to this has already been mentioned.

The capacitor synchronous motor, like the plain capacitor motor, has no starting winding and thus may be started and stopped frequently. It is quiet in operation and free of vibration and is thus often used in preference to the split-phase type. The starting torque is less than that at full load. This is the chief disadvantage of this motor compared with the split-phase. These motors are reversible.

Three-phase synchronous motors combine some of the advantages of the two preceding types and are thus frequently used when a three-phase supply is available. They have no centrifugal switches and so may be started and stopped frequently. In addition they have high starting torque.

Although synchronous motors give constant speed regardless of normal line voltage variations, their speed will vary with normal changes in line frequency. In some localities these frequency variations are of sufficient magnitude to present a serious problem. In this case constant speed may be obtained with governor-controlled motors. For a given motor frame size a synchronous motor of a given type (such as capacitor) has less output than a non-synchronous motor of the same size and type.

Because of the fact that these synchronous motors operate in synchronism with the line frequency, resonance conditions are set up in electrical circuits and this results in mechanical vibration. Hence synchronous motors are normally characterized by greater vibration than the corresponding non-synchronous types. This cannot be eliminated even by the most careful static and dynamic balancing of the armature.

**Series motors** are rather simple in construction, for the armature and field windings are merely connected in series. No starting windings are used. They can be used interchangeably on alternating and direct current, and are thus often called *universal motors*. However, the output and speed are somewhat higher on direct current than on alternating current. If it is desired to have the motor perform the same with either type of supply, it is usually necessary to have an extra resistance that can be switched in series with it for d-c operation. The difference in operation with the two types of supply is due to the higher impedance of the windings with alternating current. An important advantage to be gained through the use of these motors is variable speed, for this may be obtained by placing a rheostat in series with the motor. However, when speed is decreased by the use of such a resistance, the power of the motor is similarly reduced.

These motors have higher starting torques for a given rating than do any other types. They operate most efficiently at speeds of 4,000 to 8,000 rpm and are normally used at such speeds. Large gear reductions are needed for most purposes. Higher speeds may be obtained with these motors than with any others. They give higher outputs for a given frame size than do other types.

These motors are reversible at standstill or while running. With some types reversing is accomplished with single-pole double-throw switches. These have two windings, one of which is selected by the switching operation. Other types are reversed by reversing the connections between the armature and the field. This is done by the use of double-pole double-throw switches.

One of the most serious disadvantages to the use of the series motor is lack of constancy in speed. The speed varies with the load. As the load might be different from motor to motor because of difference in bearing fits, etc., it is difficult to get two of these motors to run at the same speed. Furthermore, the speed varies greatly with normal line voltage variations. This is a further disadvantage. Motor operation may be stabilized to a certain extent by placing a resistance across the armature. This also helps to minimize the difference between a-c and d-c operation.

Note should be taken of the fact that because of their high-speed armatures, series motors usually have short brush life. The brushes may be mounted most advantageously when rotation is to occur in one direction only. Some sacrifice in this respect must be made when the motor is equipped for reversing service.

When very high speeds are desired for short periods of time, it is possible to run these motors at much higher voltages than those for which they were designed. This gives large speed and large output simultaneously. These are of course accompanied by a very rapid temperature rise.

**Constant speed motors** of the series type are available. These employ a small resistance that is cut in and out of the circuit by a centrifugally operated governor. The motor starts with the resistance out of the circuit. It gets up to the desired speed and begins to move still faster when the centrifugal switch throws in the extra resistance. This slows down the motor, the resistance is cut out, and so forth. When conditions are critically established, the contacts on the centrifugal switch can operate as frequently as 400 times per second. The speed changes involved are thus very small (about 3 per cent) and the motor speed is essentially constant regardless of load, line voltage, or line frequency. The speed may be varied by adjustment. The motor gives the same speed on alternating and direct current.

It has all the other advantages of the usual series type as well. However, in spite of all these advantages, the motor has not become very popular because of the frequent failure of the centrifugal switch either through mechanical trouble or because of the pitting of the contacts caused by their excessively frequent operation.

**Direct-current motors** of fairly constant speed may be obtained. These have good starting torques, approximately $1\frac{1}{2}$ times the full load torque. Their speed may be set at any desired value through insertion of resistance in the circuit. They may be reversed while rotating or standing still.

When the load varies, comparatively small speed changes are obtained. The speed changes obtainable with resistance are not so wide as those that may be got from a series motor.

Constant speed d-c motors may be obtained with both shunt and compound windings. There is little to choose between the two. The compound motors have a few turns of the field winding in series with the armature winding, and they thus have high starting torque. Compound windings are used on the larger size ($\frac{1}{8}$ hp or more) motors.

## REFERENCES

Catalogue of Bodine Electric Co., Chicago, Ill.
ROTERS: "Electromagnetic Devices," John Wiley & Sons, Inc., New York, 1941.
SHOULTS, RIFE, and JOHNSON: "Electric Motors in Industry," John Wiley & Sons, Inc., New York, 1942.
VEINOTT: "Fractional Horsepower Electric Motors," McGraw-Hill Book Company, Inc., New York, 1939.

# CHAPTER XXIII

## PHOTOELECTRIC CELLS

The human eye is an optical device capable of great precision in some types of measurements and rather poor precision in others. In general, it cannot make a protracted series of measurements over a period of hours without suffering a marked loss in efficiency because of fatigue. It is sensitive to some regions of the spectrum and insensitive to others. It is often necessary to make measurements with greater precision and accuracy, or with greater speed, than can be obtained from the eye. Sometimes optical measurements must be made continuously for days at a time; it is often necessary to make measurements in regions of the spectrum in which the eye is totally insensitive. For these various cases it is necessary to obtain a device responsive to light but with properties rather different than those of the eye. Various types of photocells are used.

We shall define a photocell, for the purposes of this discussion, as a device whose electrical properties are changed when the illumination on the device is varied. There are three general types of photocells, and we shall consider each.

**Photoconductive Cells.**—These are cells containing some element or material whose resistance changes with illumination, typical materials being selenium and thallium oxysulphide. They require external sources of potential. These cells are not widely used in optical instruments because they possess the following adverse characteristics:

1. Although the current passed by the cell, at constant impressed voltage, increases with an increase in illumination, the increase is not a linear one, for the current varies as the square root of the illumination. A linear response is highly desirable in cells intended for instrument use, for it enables them to be calibrated with a standard and the measured quantity can then be expressed accurately in terms of per cent of the reference quantity. If the response is non-linear, this cannot be done.

365

In this book the term "linearity" will refer to the curve of current vs. illumination.

2. The sensitivity of these cells decreases with temperature. Any measuring device whose sensitivity varies with temperature is something less than ideal. This is particularly true with many optical measuring instruments using photocells, for such instruments often have built-in light sources and are thus subjected to large temperature changes. The non-linearity of the response of these cells precludes the possibility of recalibrating them as their temperature changes. If the cells had linear response, this would be possible.

3. After the cell has become illuminated, there is a lapse of about $\frac{1}{5}$ second before the cell response approaches its final value. Although this defect does not eliminate the cell from consideration in all optical instruments, it is definitely a source of annoyance and might be considered sufficient reason of itself to reject the device from possible use.

4. Most of these photoconductive cells have their peak sensitivity in the far red, *i.e.*, at one end of the visible region of the spectrum. Thus their response differs widely from that of the human eye, and the effect of light on the cell would therefore be different from its effect on the eye. These cells are sensitive to infra red radiation and thus give a response to such radiation while the eye gives none. If one desires to make infra red measurements, this is a desirable property; if one wishes to obtain results that may be explained in visual terms, it removes the cell from consideration unless suitable filters can be provided.

5. The resistance of these cells is low; hence it is difficult to amplify the output.

**Photoemissive Cells.**—These are chronologically the oldest of the photocells. Their general character is suggested by Fig. 298, which may be considered as a section taken through a cylindrical object. The incident light strikes the cathode which consists of a monomolecular layer of a metal, such as caesium, deposited on a composite surface consisting of an oxide layer (as caesium oxide) on a metallic film. When the light contains sufficient energy, electrons are ejected from the monomolecular layer. The anode is made positive with respect to the cathode so that the negative electrons are attracted to it. Thus, as long as enough light is incident on the cell to eject the electrons and as long as there is sufficient potential to attract them to the anode, a current flows in the cell circuit and may be detected by the galvanometer $G$.

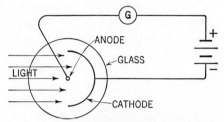

Fig. 298.—A photoemissive cell.

These devices are sealed in glass bulbs, which may be evacuated or may contain a fraction of a millimeter of pressure of some inert gas. The former type is known as a *vacuum cell*, the latter as a *gas-filled cell*.

Besides the caesium mentioned above many other types of metal may be used for the sensitive surface. These have different sensitivities and different spectral responses. It may be noted that the spectral responses of potassium, rubidium, and caesium cells cover the whole visible spectrum. By various special techniques (gas discharges, etc.) many types of cell can be given greatly enhanced sensitivity.

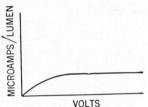

Fig. 299.—Characteristic curve of vacuum-type photoemissive cell.

In a vacuum cell the only electrons that reach the anode are of course those emitted by the cathode. As the voltage across these two elements is increased, more and more electrons are pulled to the cathode until, when a certain voltage is reached, they are practically all pulled over. Thus any further increase in voltage causes no further increase in photocurrent because there are no more electrons left to attract (see Fig. 299). This saturation voltage varies somewhat with the level of illumination, being about 15 volts for 0.10 lumen with a representative cell, and 65 volts for 1.0 lumen. The saturation current is about 0.4 microamperes at 0.10 lumen and about 4.9 microamperes for 1.0 lumen. It is obvious that, if the voltage across the cell is kept well above the saturation value, the current delivered will depend only on the amount of light incident on the cell and will be independent of any variations in voltage. This is a very important property for many photometric instruments, for it is often hard to find a source of voltage that is really constant; thus normally one has to worry about variation in output because of voltage variations. With this arrangement, voltage variations have no effect on the device.

Vacuum-type cells are noted for their ability to give a linear response, *i.e.*, the current produced by the cell (at constant

PLATE XXXII.—Three typical photoemissive cells. (*Courtesy of R.C.A. Mfg. Co.*)

voltage) is directly proportional to the flux incident on the cell. A typical cell yields about 5 microamperes per lumen. However, it should be borne in mind that with practically all photoemissive cells there is a slight fatigue effect (decrease in output with time under constant conditions). Thus a slight departure from linearity is apt to be encountered. If critical photometric measurements are to be made, each cell to be used should be checked for linearity. It should also be kept in mind that departure from linearity varies with wavelength. In some cases it may be found that an improvement in linearity might be obtained through the use of proper filters.

These vacuum cells are normally assembled in a bulb resembling a radio tube in appearance and having a similar base. In many such cells both anode and cathode connections are brought out to separate prongs in this base. Owing to the fact that the voltages applied across such cells are moderately high (some-- times 50 volts or so), a certain amount of leakage occurs across the base between the two terminals. This leakage current is very small (less than $10^{-8}$ amp), but it is appreciable in comparison with the regular photocurrent, which is also very small. The effect of this leakage is to destroy the linear response of the cell, and it also gives rise to "dark current," *i.e.*, a current is detected even when no flux is incident upon the cell. This leakage can be greatly reduced by bringing the cathode and anode connections out at opposite ends of the cell so that leakage currents must travel the length of the glass. This is done in many modern cells. Even in this case a certain amount of leakage takes place across the glass between the terminals. In wet weather, when moisture condenses on the glass, this can become a major source of error. This difficulty can be almost entirely overcome by placing a guard ring, consisting of a few turns of fine wire, around the glass bulb between the points of emergence of anode and cathode. This guard ring is connected into the photocell cir- cuit to a point of appropriate potential, *i.e.*, its potential is made roughly the same as that of the cathode. Some cells acquire, during manufacture, a deposit on their inside walls which causes a decrease in the insulation resistance. This must be overcome by means of internal guard rings, which are regularly furnished on some types of cells. These leakage currents have been found to decrease considerably as the temperature of the cell is lowered, and sometimes in critical work it is desirable to use the cell in a refrigerated chamber for this reason.

These vacuum cells are very stable in operation, always giving nearly the same results under the same conditions. There are, however, slight temperature and fatigue effects. As has already been mentioned, their output at normal levels of illumination is rather low. The output may be greatly increased by admitting to the cell a fraction of a millimeter of an inert gas, thus giving what is termed a *gas-filled cell*. In these cells the electrons emitted by the cathode strike the gas molecules under the imposed voltage and "knock" more electrons loose from them. These in turn eject further electrons, etc. Thus, for a given flux, much greater currents are obtained than would be received

from vacuum cells operated at the same voltage.   It is possible
to get as much as 100 microamperes per lumen from these gas-
filled cells.

We saw that for a vacuum cell, with constant flux, the current
reached a saturation value as the voltage increased.   This was
shown in Fig. 299.   With a gas-filled cell an increase in voltage,
under the same conditions, causes the electrons emitted from the
cathode to bombard the gas molecules heavily, thus causing the
emission of more electrons.   The result is an increase in current.
This effect is shown in Fig. 300, which should be compared with
Fig. 299.   As the voltage is increased
more and more, a point will be reached
where the gas will ionize and a glow
discharge will occur.   This can seriously damage the sensitive surface of
the cell.   Again, it is possible to have
the cell at a potential somewhat below
the critical discharge voltage.   The incidence of light upon the cell can release
sufficient electrons from the cathode

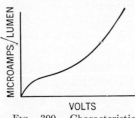

FIG. 300.—Characteristic
curve of gas-filled type of
photoemissive cell.

to start the discharge.   This should be guarded against.   Most
cells are so constructed that they should not be used at more
than 90 volts at ordinary levels of illumination.

Gas-filled cells are rather unstable and this condition increases
with the voltage, the stability becoming very poor near the glow
voltage.   This is one reason why these cells are not generally
used in photometric devices.   Another and more important
reason is that these cells give a non-linear response at ordinary
levels of illumination, and this has already been shown to be
quite objectionable.   However, at very low levels, these cells give
nearly uniform responses; they, of course, give much more current
for a given flux than do vacuum cells.   Thus they are sometimes used for photometric purposes under these extreme conditions.   They are generally disliked, however, because of their
lack of stability.

Gas-filled cells are used in the sound heads of motion-picture
projectors, this being their most general application.   The
caesium oxide type is used almost exclusively for this purpose
and is filled with argon.   These cells have practically no time
lag, the only factor to be taken into account in handling high

frequencies being the capacitance of the cell. Audio frequencies are handled uniformly without attenuation. Caesium oxide cells are responsive to wavelengths between 250 and 1,100 m$\mu$. They have two peaks in their spectral sensitivity curves: one at about 350 and the other at about 800 m$\mu$. With appropriate filters the response of these cells can be made similar to that of the human eye, but a great loss in sensitivity would necessarily result because of the absorption of light by the filter. These cells have rather large dark currents because of leakage across the insulation.

Photoemissive cells may be made using various other types of sensitive surfaces, and these have peak sensitivities at various points throughout the spectrum. Thus a wide range of sensitivities is available to the instrument designer. However, the spectral response as well as the over-all sensitivity of these cells changes with time, and it is thus difficult to obtain reproducible results in making photometric measurements unless the cell is calibrated frequently or a null method is used.

The use of the photoemissive cell in the instantaneous measurement of flux is well known and understood. However, it is not always realized that these cells may be used to integrate flux over a given interval of time. Thus these cells may be connected into a circuit so that they charge a condenser at a rate proportional to the flux incident upon them at a given instant. Thus, when the flux is small, the condenser charges slowly; when it is large, the condenser charges rapidly. Every time the condenser is fully charged, it discharges automatically and operates a counter. It then starts to charge again. The reading on the counter at any time thus is a measure of the total amount of light that has struck the photocell since the measurements began.

It is possible to construct photoemissive cells in which the primary electrons, ejected from the cathode, strike another light sensitive surface, ejecting more electrons. These in turn strike another sensitive surface, and so on. The effect is one of amplification of the original photocurrent, and the equivalent of several stages of vacuum-tube amplification can be obtained in this fashion inside the photocell. As far as the author knows this type of cell, known as a *secondary emission cell*, has not yet been used for photometric purposes. To operate these devices a rather large amount of cumbersome apparatus to give strong magnetic or electrostatic fields is required, and even with this auxiliary equipment the output is small, being of the order of milliamperes.

**Photovoltaic Cells.**—These cells, commonly known as *barrier layer cells*, consist of a layer of a semiconductor between two metallic layers, the upper layer being either a grid or a transparent metallic film (gold, platinum, etc.). Combinations in present use are copper–copper oxide and iron–iron selenide. Light incident on these cells sets up a potential that causes current to flow in the external circuit. Thus no batteries are required and compact instruments may be developed.

The copper–copper oxide cells are nice in that they have a spectral response similar to that of the human eye. However, their sensitivity decreases with time, and for this reason they are rather limited in application.

The iron–iron selenide cells do not lose sensitivity with time and are used in most applications calling for barrier layer cells. If the resistance in the external circuit of these cells is kept very low, the current output is directly proportional to the illumination. As the resistance is increased, the departure from linearity of response becomes very marked (see Fig. 301). Several manufacturers make two types of iron–iron selenide cells, differing in output, stability, etc., which differ in their departure from linearity with increasing external resistance. When these cells are used for the direct measurement of illumination, linearity is highly desirable; thus special low-resistance microammeters are used to measure the current. Generally, sensitive electrical meters have high resistances, and it is sometimes difficult to obtain a suitable low-resistance instrument. The two classes of this type of cell develop about 145 and 400 microamperes per

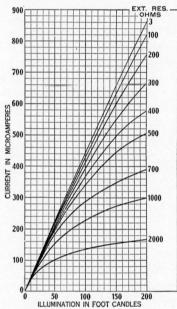

FIG. 301.—Response of a barrier layer cell. (*Courtesy of Weston Electrical Instrument Corporation.*)

lumen, respectively. The sensitivity of the surfaces of these cells varies somewhat from spot to spot, and the effect of this variation should be guarded against in designing some types of instruments.

When light strikes a surface at an angle $i$ to the normal, the illumination $E$ on the surface is given by the illumination $E_o$ in a plane perpendicular to the direction of the light multiplied by $\cos i$ [Eq. 42]. Hence, when a cell is used for the measurement of illumination, it is desirable to have its response vary with $\cos i$. Unfortunately, barrier layer cells do not obey this law but read relatively lower than they should as angle $i$ increases. Because the edge of some of these cells is more sensitive than the center, the situation may be helped somewhat by the addition of an external stop, as shown in Fig. 302. With the early types of cells an error of 50 per cent was obtained for an angle of incidence of 70°. Present cells have a mat lacquer on the upper

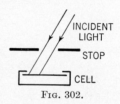

FIG. 302.

surface, which helps decrease the error, and they can give results correct to 99 per cent if the angle of incidence does not exceed 30°, and correct to 80 per cent for angles up to 90°.

One cell manufacturer points out that the departure from the cosine law is not wholly undesirable because most reflecting surfaces show departures from Lambert's law of about the same magnitude. Thus the cell gives an indication of the visual effectiveness of the illumination in some cases.

The layers in these cells function as the plates of a condenser. For this reason these cells cannot be used even at audio frequencies because of the leakage of the a-c pulses through the capacitance.

The voltage output increases approximately logarithmically with the illumination. When exposed to constant illumination, the current output of these cells comes up to a maximum and then decreases. The decrease, known as *fatigue*, is rapid at first and then becomes increasingly slower. This effect lasts over a rather long interval of time and should be taken into account in making precision measurements. This effect is stronger in the red than in the violet, so when possible it is wise to filter out the red component of the incident radiation. The use of filters to reduce the illumination on the cell also produces another beneficial effect, for the departure of the cell's response from linearity increases with illumination. Therefore, at low levels of illumination, the cell can be held closer to linearity.

The output of these cells is affected by temperature, the effect being that of a change in their resistance. The actual change in output per degree change in temperature depends for its value on the level of illumination and the external circuit resistance. Generally, the current output decreases with an increase of tem-

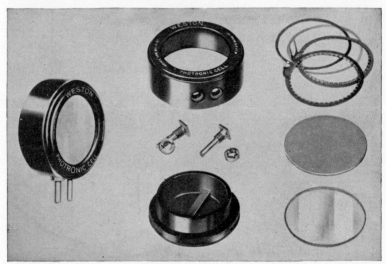

PLATE XXXIII).—A typical photovoltaic cell. The assembled cell is shown at the left, and its components are at the right. (*Courtesy of Weston Electrical Instrument Corporation.*)

perature. In critical work it is desirable to make special provisions for holding the temperature of the cell constant. The writer has found that a satisfactory means of accomplishing this is to locate the cell in an enclosure through which a thermostatically controlled stream of warm air is blown. By proper adjustment of the thermostat, the air temperature may be brought to any desired value. Note should be taken of the fact that special cells with particularly low temperature coefficients may be obtained.

The range of spectral response of these cells exceeds that of the eye in both directions, going down into the ultra violet and up into the infra red. However, they may be purchased with special filters (called *Viscor*) that give them an over-all response very close to that of the eye. These filters reduce the sensitivity of the cell (microamperes per lumen) to about 40 per cent of its initial value. When light of a single wavelength is being measured, there is nothing to be gained through the use of such a

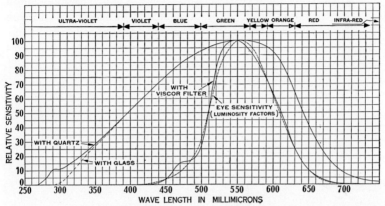

FIG. 303.—Spectral sensitivity of a barrier layer cell. (*Courtesy of Weston Electrical Instrument Corporation.*)

filter; when light containing many wavelengths is being evaluated and the effect to be produced on the human eye is to be determined, the cell must be equipped with such a correcting filter. The spectral responses of a typical cell with and without a filter are shown in Fig. 303.

For making transmission measurements, as in a densitometer, the simplest method of using these cells is merely to connect

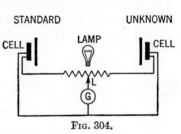

FIG. 304.

one in series with a low-resistance microammeter. A transmission standard is placed in front of the cell, which is set at a fixed distance from a constant light source, and the reading on the meter is noted. Then the standard is replaced by the unknown, and the reading again noted. The ratio of the two readings is taken and gives the transmission of the unknown expressed as a function of that of the standard. A somewhat quicker method of making this type of measurement is through the use of a circuit of the type shown in Fig. 304. The standard is constantly kept in front of one cell, and the unknown is placed in front of the other.    The slide-wire is moved until the galvanometer $G$ or other indicating meter indicates zero.    The slide-wire is of course directly calibrated in some convenient units.    One may also use a more elaborate form of the same circuit in which an additional resistance is provided for resetting the slide wire to zero.    These methods are useful only for measuring samples that do not scatter light.

This double cell type of circuit may be applied to the measurement of small areas with surprising precision.    The setup used

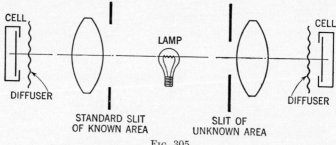

FIG. 305.

is that shown in Fig. 305.    The light source is imaged by the two lenses on the cells.    Since uniform illumination over the surface of the cells is desired, a diffusing medium might be introduced at the source or in front of the cells to accomplish this.    Assuming that a slit width is to be measured, the standard slit is placed against the left lens and the unknown against the right.    After the circuit is balanced, the area of the unknown may be read directly from the slide-wire.    The electrical details of the photocell circuits are similar to those of Fig. 304.    The reason that lenses are used is that the placing of the unknown in the plane of a lens reduces the illumination uniformly over the surface of the unknown-measuring cell.    This is necessary because of the unevenness of response over the surface of these cells.    Had the setup of Fig. 304 been used, the unknown might have covered an unusually sensitive, or insensitive, area of the cell, and thus excessively decreased or increased the output, obtaining an erroneous reading.    With the arrangement of Fig. 305, a slit 0.01 in. in width can be measured to within $\pm 0.0001$ in.

The double-cell type of circuit requires two cells similar in characteristics.    These usually have to be obtained through special arrangement with the manufacturer.

It has been shown that a decrease in the external resistance of a barrier layer cell circuit causes an increase in linearity. One would expect, then, that if it were possible to use the cell under zero external resistance (*i.e.*, short-circuit) conditions, linearity of response would be obtained. Consequently, various techniques have been developed to achieve this end.[1] It has been found that these techniques markedly help achieve linearity but are not a guarantee of it.[2]

Barrier layer cells are not as stable as photoemissive cells and exhibit much more fatigue. They have other special characteristics, as previously outlined, that must be taken into consideration in designing an instrument that will employ them; however, when properly used they are capable of producing excellent results.

Some problems in instrument design call for vacuum or gas-filled photoemissive cells, and some call for photovoltaic cells. Many, however, can be solved by the use of either. In this case the writer has found that it is generally more desirable to use the barrier layer cells because they can ordinarily be employed without the amplifying circuits required of photoemissive cells. They are therefore much simpler to handle.

### REFERENCES

BARNARD: "The Selenium Cell," Richard R. Smith, New York, 1930.

CAMPBELL and RITCHIE: "Photoelectric Cells," Sir Isaac Pitman & Sons, Ltd., London, 1929.

GUDDEN: "Lichtelektrische Erscheinungen," Julius Springer, Berlin, 1928.

HUGHES and DU BRIDGE: "Photoelectric Phenomena," McGraw-Hill Book Co., Inc., New York, 1932.

KIRCHNER: "Allgemeine physik der röntgenstrahlen," Akademische Verlagsgesellschaft m.b.H., Leipzig, 1930.

LANGE: "Photoelements and Their Application" (trans. by A. St. John), Reinhold Publishing Co., New York, 1938.

WALKER and LANCE: "Photoelectric Cell Applications," Sir Isaac Pitman & Sons, Ltd., London, 1933.

ZWORYKIN and WILSON: "Photocells and Their Applications," John Wiley & Sons, Inc., New York, 1934.

[1] CAMPBELL and FRIETH, *J. Sci. Instruments*, Vol. 11, p. 125, 1934.

[2] BUCHMÜLLER and KÖNIG, *Bull. Schweiz. elect. Ver.*, No. 5, p. 89, 1937.

ATKINSON, CAMPBELL, PALMER, and WINCH, *Proc. Phys. Soc.*, Vol. 50, p. 934, 1938.

# PART IV
## Optical Design

# CHAPTER XXIV

## RAY TRACING

Sufficient has already been written in the course of this book to indicate that the ultimate test of the performance of a lens system is the actual trigonometrical tracing through the system of a series of rays. Ray-tracing equations are all derived from one *exact* law: Snell's law. Thus they will give results that are correct to the limits of the accuracy of the data and calculations used.

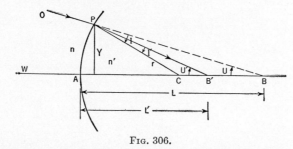

FIG. 306.

The fundamental quantities used in ray tracing are all shown in Fig. 306. A single refracting surface is shown. The medium in front of this surface has an index of refraction $n$, that behind the surface an index $n'$. The vertex of the surface is at $A$; the center of curvature is at $C$. A ray $OP$ is incident on the surface. This ray is directed toward $B$, which must be considered the object point even though the object is actually at $O$. The incoming ray makes an angle $U$ with the axis and an angle $I$ with the radius $PC$, which is the normal to the refracting surface at the point of incidence of the ray. After refraction, the ray is directed toward the image point $B'$, and this refracted ray makes an angle $U'$ with the axis and $I'$ with the normal. The object distance $AB$ is designated by $L$ and the image distance by $L'$. Note that quantities associated with the ray before refraction are unprimed (*i.e.*, $I$, $U$, $L$, $n$) while those associated with the ray after refraction are primed (*i.e.*, $I'$, $U'$, $L'$, $n'$).

381

It is pointed out that when a ray is to be traced through a system from an object point $O$ (Fig. 306) off the axis, the direction of the ray striking the first surface of the system is determined by joining the object point $O$ with whatever point $P$ on the surface of the lens it is desired to have the ray strike. The two points $P$ and $O$ define the direction of the incoming ray, and this ray is extended until it strikes the axis at $B$. $B$ is taken as the fictitious object point for the purpose of applying the ray-tracing equations; the object distance $L$ is taken as $AB$ and not as $OP$. To reiterate, in applying the ray-tracing equations the object point and the image point to which the distances $L$ and $L'$ are measured, respectively, are always taken on the axis of the system. If, instead of being at $O$, the original object had been at $W$ *on the axis* of the system, the object distance $L$ would have been $WA$ and the incident ray would have been defined by the line $WP$. Thus it is seen that any incident ray, provided it is not parallel to the axis, must cross the axis at some point, and this point is taken as the object point. If the incident ray is parallel to the axis, it is described in terms of its distance $Y$ from the axis.

If the locations of $O$ and $P$ are known, the location of $B$ and the values of $U$ and $L$ may be easily computed from the laws of geometry and trigonometry. This is all that is necessary to begin ray tracing.

With these data the standard ray-tracing equations are applied. These equations are the following:

$$\sin I = \frac{L - r}{r} \sin U \tag{107}$$

$$\sin I' = \frac{n}{n'} \sin I \tag{108}$$

$$U' = U + I - I' \tag{109}$$

$$L' = r \frac{\sin I'}{\sin U'} + r \tag{110}$$

By applying these equations, one after the other, the ray is traced through the first surface. It is then necessary to transfer the data to the next surface and continue the calculations. Transfer equations are used for this purpose. Let the distance from the vertex of the surface just completed to the vertex of the next surface, measured along the axis, be $t$. Then we can use the following:

$$L_2 = L_1' - t \tag{111}$$
$$U_2 = U_1' \tag{112}$$

The subscripts merely indicate the surface from which the data are obtained, $L_2$ being the value of $L$ for the second surface, etc. Of course $n_2 = n_1'$. By successive application of these equations a ray may be traced through the entire system.

There are a few special cases in ray tracing that are encountered sufficiently frequently to warrant attention. Assume that parallel light from an infinitely distant axial object point is incident on the first surface. Then evidently $U_1$ will be zero. It thus is not possible to calculate sin $I$ by means of Eq. 107. In this case we use the formula

$$\sin I = \frac{y}{r} \tag{113}$$

$y$ is of course the height of the incident ray. It should be remembered that Eq. (113) is valid only with parallel light.

Another special case is that of a plane surface. The equations used here are the following:

$$I = -U \tag{114}$$
$$\sin U' = \frac{n}{n'} \sin U \tag{115}$$
$$I' = -U' \tag{116}$$
$$L' = L \frac{\tan U}{\tan U'} \tag{117}$$

or

$$L' = L \frac{n'}{n} \frac{\cos U'}{\cos U} \tag{118}$$

Either Eq. (117) or (118) may be used, but because (118) depends on the use of cosines, which may be more accurately determined for small angles than tangents, it is to be greatly preferred.

It is patent that it is necessary to use the proper sign conventions in applying all these formulas. These sign conventions are simple and should be memorized. All linear quantities ($r, L, L'$) except $t$ are considered positive if the points to which they refer lie to the right of the vertex of the lens. The thickness $t$ is always positive. In Fig. 306 all these quantities are positive. The quantities are negative if the points lie to the left of the vertex. The *incidence angles* $I$ and $I'$ are positive if the incident and refracted rays respectively can be made to strike the normal $PC$ by a clockwise rotation of less than 90° about the point of incidence $P$. The *slope angles* $U$ and $U'$ are positive if the axis can be made to strike the rays $PB$ and $PB'$ respectively by a clockwise rotation of less than 90° about $B$ or $B'$.

Generally speaking, five-figure accuracy in these calculations is sufficient for most optical work. However sines to six decimal places and angles to $\frac{1}{10}''$ are used for long focal length lenses when angles of not more than 2 or 3° are involved. Also, when the results of ray tracing are to be used for interpolation purposes it is often desirable to use six-place computations. These ray-tracing calculations may be performed either with logarithm tables or with computing machines. The computing machines are so much handier and faster than logarithms that they are essential for any serious work. However, certain computers with many years of experience have attained phenomenal speeds with log tables. In performing these calculations some systematic system of recording the computations should be adopted. Lined paper with appropriate vertical rulings should be obtained. By using properly spaced divisions it is possible to get trigonometrical and paraxial tracing for as many as 10 surfaces on a single $8\frac{1}{2}$ by 11-in. page. The trigonometric tables used for the calculations should have degrees expressed decimally rather than in minutes and seconds for ease in interpolation. Even preferable to such tables (Peters's,[1] for example) is a table in which the angle is expressed in radians, and the difference between arc and sine is given in an adjacent column. The use of this type of table (in the form prepared by Chrétien,[2] for example) eliminates all interpolation and expedites the work greatly.

In making these calculations it is very easy to make errors; in fact for the beginner the probability of so doing is about unity. It is quite possible to make an error that will not be detected for several days, and then the work must all be done over.

[1] BREMIKER, "Logarithmisch-trigonometrische Tafeln mit sechs Dezimalstellen," C. E. Stechert & Company, New York. This is used for logarithmic computations.

PETERS, "Siebenstellige Werte der trigonometrische Funktionen," B. G. Teubner, Leipzig, now available through D. Van Nostrand Company, Inc., New York. This is used with computing machines.

[2] CHRÉTIEN, "Nouvelles tables des sinus naturels," Revue d'Optique théorique et instrumentale, Paris (XVe) 1932.

Therefore, for the beginner, it is practically imperative that he check the calculations at each surface before proceeding to the next. He could do this by going through the standard equations twice at each surface. As experience has shown that he will frequently make the same error both times, this form of check is not satisfactory. What is desired, then, is an independent method of calculating that may be used as a check on the standard equations, and luckily such a check is available.

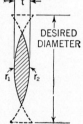

For the usual spherical curved surfaces, after $L'$ has been calculated by means of the foregoing equations, it should be re-computed by using

$$L' = L \frac{\sin U \cos (I' - U')/2}{\sin U' \cos (I - U)/2} \qquad (119)$$

If the values of $L'$ obtained by these two methods do not agree closely, an error has been made. However, if an error is made in the calculations associated with Eq. (108), it will not be detected by the use of this check formula, for such an error has the same effect as an incorrectly chosen value of $n$ or $n'$, and the equation cannot know whether the computer has chosen the correct type of glass. A check formula that is used with plane surfaces is

Fig. 307.— Insufficient center thickness $t$ has been selected for this lens, giving negative edge thickness. The ray-tracing equations would not reveal the error.

$$L' = L - L \frac{(n - n') \cos \frac{1}{2}(U' - U)}{n \cos U \cos \frac{1}{2}(U' + U)} \qquad (120)$$

As the computer gathers experience, he finds that he is able to sense even minute errors and is then able to discontinue the use of the check equations. A large amount of experience is necessary before this stage is reached, however.

It should be borne in mind that, if the computer has selected insufficient thickness for his lens, the equations will show up no error even though, for given radii and thickness, the lens has negative thickness at the edge. Thus when radii are selected for a lens it is important that the lens be actually drawn to scale to make sure that the trouble illustrated in Fig. 307, in which $t$ was chosen too small, does not occur.

If during the course of computations a value of sin $I$ greater than 1 is obtained and no computational error exists, then the situation diagramed in Fig. 308 has occurred, *i.e.*, the ray has missed the lens. If a value of sin $I'$ greater than 1 is encountered, the difficulty shown in Fig. 309 has been experienced, *i.e.*, internal reflection has occurred because the critical angle has been exceeded. This can happen only in going from a denser to a lighter medium, *i.e.*, from a medium of higher to one of lower index.

The foregoing discussion applies to rays that have been trigonometrically traced. As the rays are traced through zones that

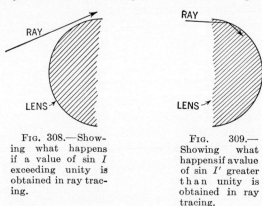

Fig. 308.—Showing what happens if a value of sin $I$ exceeding unity is obtained in ray tracing.

Fig. 309.—Showing what happens if a value of sin $I'$ greater than unity is obtained in ray tracing.

approach the axis the angles $I$, $I'$, $U$, and $U'$, all become smaller when an axial object point is considered. As these angles decrease, they approach the condition that the sine of the angle equals the angle itself. The sine and angle are exactly equal only at an angle of $0°$; with small but finite angles the difference between the angle and the sine is too small to be of consequence. Thus for these very small angles we can replace Snell's law with the satisfactory approximation $nI = n'I'$. The rays coincident with, or very close to, the axis do follow this equation, and of course they continue to obey Snell's law. In this region the difference between Snell's law and the foregoing equation is vanishingly small. Rays that make such small angles that they can be traced with the equation $nI = n'I'$ are called *paraxial rays*. It will be remembered that this equation is rigidly correct for a ray passing through the exact center of a lens from an axial object point.

The paraxial focus of a lens is easily located and is always used as the focal point in lens calculations. The stated focal length of a lens is always computed with paraxial rays. Consequently we must develop special equations to trace paraxial rays. These equations are as follows:

$$i = \frac{u(l - r)}{r} \tag{121}$$

$$i' = \frac{n}{n'}\, i \tag{122}$$

$$u' = u + i - i' \tag{123}$$

$$l' = r + \frac{i'r}{u'} \tag{124}$$

The transfer equations are as follows:

$$l_2 = l'_1 - t \tag{125}$$
$$u_2 = u'_1 \tag{126}$$
$$n_2 = n'_1 \tag{127}$$

It will be noted that capital letters have been used to refer to trigonometrically traced ray data, and that small or lower-case letters refer to paraxial ray data. $r$, $t$, $n$, and $n'$, being the same for trigonometrically traced and paraxial rays, have arbitrarily been chosen as lower-case letters. The check formula used for paraxial work is

$$l' = l\,\frac{u}{u'} \tag{128}$$

The formulas used for plane surfaces and parallel incident light are similar to those given for trigonometrically traced rays with the sines of angles replaced by the angles themselves.

A very important characteristic of these paraxial calculations that is not immediately evident from a consideration of the foregoing equations is the fact that the same result as to the final $l'$ will be obtained regardless of the height of the ray chosen. Thus, if several paraxial rays are traced at different heights, all should give the same $l'$ after each surface within the limits of computing accuracy. Therefore, the paraxial ray being traced need not be confined to the paraxial region and the same starting data may be used for a paraxial and trigonometrically traced ray. It is generally desirable to use large initial angles when tracing paraxial rays, for this contributes to computing accuracy. It is advisable to carry on parallel calculations of trigonometrical and paraxial rays surface by surface. The computer is not likely to make many errors on the paraxial trace and may use this as a rough check on the marginal or zonal trigonometrical trace. In addition it will be informative to him to see how the two rays vary from surface to surface.

Another equation which may be used for paraxial ray tracing and which is somewhat simpler and easier to use than those given above is

$$\frac{n'}{l'} = \frac{n}{l} + \frac{n' - n}{r} \tag{129}$$

This equation gives indication of the fact that the intercept length $l'$ is independent of the height of the paraxial ray traced. However, this equation does not give the incidence or slope angles. As these angles must be known for the determination of focal length and aberration characteristics, Eq. (129) finds very limited application in practice.

For paraxial rays the linear lateral magnification is given by the ratio $u_1/u_k'$. The subscripts refer to the first and last surfaces of a system, respectively. For trigonometrically traced rays the linear lateral magnification is given by the ratio $\sin U_1/\sin U_k'$.

It is occasionally desirable to know the height at which a ray is striking a given surface. This may be easily calculated from

$$y = r \sin (U + I) = r \sin (U' + I') \tag{130}$$

It will be noted that these ray-tracing equations all apply only to the case sketched in Fig. 306, *i.e.*, that in which the incident ray, refracted ray, and optical axis all lie in the same plane. The rays in this case are called *tangential* or *meridional rays*. For most problems of lens design the performance of the tangential rays may be taken as representative of that of the entire system. Only tangential rays can "emanate" from an object point on the optical axis. Object points off the axis can "emit" rays that do not lie in a plane containing the optical axis; these are called *skew rays*. The sagittal rays illustrated in the section on Astigmatism (page 36) are of this class. Skew rays are very tedious and difficult to compute, and their computation is avoided at all possible costs. Only in the design of photographic objectives of very high aperture ratio should skew rays be traced. In very fast photographic systems they are found to give rise to unusual aberrations different from those considered in Chap. II.

Various methods of tracing rays other than those given here have been proposed, but none have been found practical. One such method, involving the use of vectors, has been proposed by Silberstein (see references). The method appears to have little merit for the tracing of tangential rays, although it may prove useful in tracing skew rays. The writer has found it to be very nice for the tracing of rays through prisms when the effects of minute inaccuracies in the angles are being determined and the ray must be considered in three dimensions.

## REFERENCES

CHRÉTIEN: "Cours de calcul des combinaisons optiques," Revue d'Optique théorique et instrumentale, Paris (XV$^e$), 1938.

CONRADY: "Applied Optics and Optical Design," Vol. I, Oxford University Press, London, 1929.

CZAPSKI and EPPENSTEIN: "Gründzuge der Theorie der optischen Instrumente nach Abbe," p. 75, J. A. Barth, Leipzig, 1924.

"Dictionary of Applied Physics," pp. 289 and 209, Macmillan & Company, Ltd., London, 1923.

"Handbuch der Physik," Band XVIII, Julius Springer, Berlin, 1927.

HARDY and PERRIN: "The Principles of Optics," McGraw-Hill Book Company, Inc., New York, 1932.

MARTIN: "An Introduction to Applied Optics," Vol. I–II, Sir Isaac Pitman & Sons, Ltd., London, 1930, 1932.

MERTÉ, RICHTER, and VON ROHR: "Das photographische Objektive," p. 151, Julius Springer, Vienna, 1932.

NUTTING: "Outlines of Applied Optics," p. 60, The Blakiston Company, Philadelphia, 1912.

SILBERSTEIN: "Simplified Method of Tracing Rays," Longmans, Green and Company, London, 1918.

STEINHEIL and VOIT: "Applied Optics," (trans. by French), Blackie & Son, Ltd., London, 1918.

TAYLOR: "A System of Applied Optics," Macmillan & Company, Ltd., London, 1906.

## PROBLEMS

**1.** Starting with Eq. (129), derive an expression relating the image and object distances, radii, and index of refraction of a single thin lens.

**2.** Solve Prob. 1 for a lens of thickness $t$.

**3.** Using the paraxial ray-tracing formulas, show that, for a single spherical refracting surface,

$$\frac{n}{l' - r} - \frac{n'}{l - r} = \frac{n' - n}{r}$$

**4.** Given a single refracting surface of radius $+5$ in., with air to the left of the surface and glass of index 1.513 to its right, trace through the surface rays parallel to the optical axis at heights of 2 in., 1 in., and 0 in. (paraxial). Plot a curve of spherical aberration vs. zone height.

**5.** You are given a lens with these constructional data: $r_1 = +2$ in., $r_2 = -10$ in., $t = 0.43$ in., clear aperture = 2 in. It is made of glass with $n_D = 1.56822$, $n_C = 1.56529$, $n_F = 1.57521$. What is the marginal spherical aberration? How much longitudinal chromatic aberration does it have at the center and margin? Assume an infinitely distant axial object.

# CHAPTER XXV

## SPHERICAL ABERRATION

Consider Fig. 310, which shows parallel light incident upon a convex spherical surface. It will be noted that the rays striking the surface at various heights intersect the axis at different points

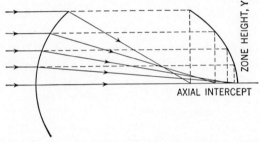

Fig. 310.—Spherical aberration of a single refracting surface. The curve at the right shows the axial intercept distance plotted as a function of zone height.

instead of coming to a common focus. Thus the image of the infinitely distant axial object point will be blurred because of the presence of what is termed *longitudinal spherical aberration.* If we were to plot this aberration, termed $LA'$, against zonal height $Y$ of the incident ray, we would get a curve of the form of Fig. 311, which is taken directly from Fig. 310. If we desired to study this aberration, we could trace trigonometrically through the system the various zonal rays shown and compare their intercept distances. We should also trace a paraxial ray through the surface and use this as a reference point, *i.e.,* we should take the distance from its intercept to the intercept of any zonal ray as a measure of the spherical aberration of the zone through which this ray was traced. A positive surface or simple positive lens always gives

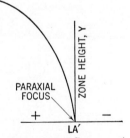

Fig. 311.—Curve of spherical aberration vs. zone height, derived from Fig. 310.

391

spherical aberration of the type shown, in which the intercept distance for the marginal ray $(L'_m)$ is shorter than the paraxial intercept distance $(l')$ when an infinitely distant object is considered. Thus, spherical aberration in which $l' - L'_m$ is positive is called *positive;* conversely, if $l' - L'_m$ is negative, the aberration is designated *negative.* A lens with positive spherical aberration is termed *spherically undercorrected;* one with negative spherical aberration is called *spherically overcorrected.*

In this book, we shall be concerned solely with the longitudinal aspects of spherical aberration, and we shall consider it as primarily a longitudinal aberration. However, if the various rays shown in Fig. 310 are continued until they intersect some plane perpendicular to the axis (the paraxial image plane, for example), they give a blurred pattern instead of a point image. Hence this aberration is seen to be measurable laterally as well as longitudinally. The lateral measure of the aberration is not very useful, and it is used only rarely.

It will be appreciated that, in practice, spherical aberration is determined as the difference (usually small) between two comparatively long intercept lengths. Mathematically, such a difference is always inaccurate, for it bears the full uncertainty of the two large numbers involved, and thus it is difficult, in practice, to make an accurate determination of spherical aberration. When short-focus lenses of relatively great aperture are being computed, this method of determining spherical aberration is fairly satisfactory; with long-focus telescope objectives of small aperture, it is too inaccurate. In this case the following rather cumbersome equation should be applied:

$$LA' = LA \, \frac{n}{n'} \, \frac{l'L'}{lL} + 2 \, \frac{n}{n'} \, l'L' \left( \frac{1}{r} - \frac{1}{L} \right) \left( \frac{\sin \dfrac{I' - U}{2} \, \sin \dfrac{I - I'}{2}}{\cos \dfrac{I' - U'}{2}} \right)$$

$$(131)$$

In this equation, $LA'$ represents the spherical aberration of the light after passage through a given refractive surface; $LA$ represents the spherical aberration present in the incident beam. For the first surface of a lens system, if a real object is used, $LA$ is zero. The equation is used to compute the $LA'$ after each surface, and this value is used as $LA$ for the next surface. Thus the calculation is carried on surface by surface, and the result after the last surface gives the $LA'$ for the whole system. It is quite obvious that paraxial and zonal ray-tracing data must be available. This equation gives results that are much more accurate than those obtained by the usual method of subtracting intercept distances. In practice, its use is avoided whenever possible because of the tedious calculations involved. It thus finds very infrequent application.

From a study of this equation it is easily shown that $LA'$ for a single surface is zero for certain special cases, and we shall examine these. In each case the term "object point" will have the special meaning designated at the beginning of Chap. XXIV.

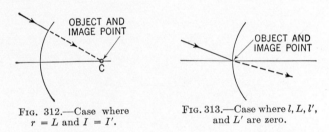

FIG. 312.—Case where $r = L$ and $I = I'$.

FIG. 313.—Case where $l, L, l'$, and $L'$ are zero.

1. $r = L$. This is the case of a ray entering the surface radially, *i.e.*, coinciding with the normal at the point of incidence. Thus no refraction occurs, and $I$ and $I'$ are zero. Image and object are located at the center of curvature $C$. This is an important case and is used in the design of photographic and microscope objectives. It contributes no aberration to a system but adds power to the extent $y \left( \dfrac{n' - n}{r} \right)$. It is illustrated in Fig. 312.

2. $I = I'$. This is similar to the preceding case and gives the same results.

3. $l' = 0$. In this case the object and the image are located at the vertex (see Fig. 313). This surface contributes nothing to either power or aberration (except Petzval curvature). In practice this represents a field lens at the plane of a real image.

4. $L' = 0$. This case is essentially the same as the preceding.

5. $I' = U$. This, known as the *aplanatic case*, is the most important case of all. For the surface to contribute zero $LA'$

the object must be located a distance from the refracting surface given by

$$L = r \left( \frac{n + n'}{n} \right) \tag{132}$$

For a typical case, let $n$ be 1 and $n'$ be 1.5. Substitution in the above equation gives $L = 2.5r$. Inasmuch as no optical glass will differ much in index from the value chosen, this means that to take advantage of this property the object must be located from the vertex of the refracting surface a distance of about $2\frac{1}{2}$ times the radius of curvature. Furthermore, the object must be on the same side of the vertex as the center of curvature. The location of the image for this case is given by

$$L' = r \left( \frac{n + n'}{n'} \right) \tag{133}$$

Substitution of the above data here gives $L' = 1.66r$. This case is shown to scale in Fig. 314, in which $A$ is the object point (known

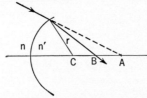
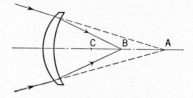

FIG. 314.—The aplanatic case.          FIG. 315.—Aplanatic lens.

in this case as the *aplanatic point*). $B$ is the image point, and $C$ is the center of curvature. Note that both object and image must be located on the *same* side of the refracting surface. Thus we can use this phenomenon only to increase the convergence of a converging beam or to increase the divergence of a diverging beam. As we cannot change a diverging beam to a converging beam with an aplanatic surface, we in general cannot construct an optical system of aplanatic elements alone, as would be very desirable. It is of importance to note that a surface is also free of coma at the aplanatic point. An interesting and important application of this principle is shown in Fig. 315. The center of curvature of the first surface is at $C$, and a ray incident on the lens is aimed at the aplanatic point $A$. The ray is thus refracted at the first surface to the conjugate aplanatic point $B$. The second surface of the lens has its center of curvature at $B$, and, as we saw in the first case, no spherical aberration or coma is introduced here.   Thus no spherical aberration or coma whatever is introduced by this lens.   Lenses of this sort are widely used in microscope objectives with the object at $B$ and the rays traveling in the opposite direction from those shown.   In a microscope objective of the oil immersion type the object is located in a medium optically similar to glass.   The first lens is hemispherical and the object is located at its aplanatic point.   (Question: What is the function of the oil?)   Next, several lenses of the type shown in Fig. 315 are used to decrease further the divergence of this beam without introducing any spherical aberration or coma. However these aplanatic lenses cannot change a diverging beam to a converging beam, and this task is performed by a Petzval-type objective located behind the aplanatic lenses.   Because of the work performed by the aplanatic lenses, this Petzval objective has to introduce only a fraction of the convergence that would have been necessary had the aplanatic lenses not been used.   An *aplanatic lens* is, by definition, a lens free of spherical aberration and coma.

As has been indicated, the variation of spherical aberration with height of incidence $Y$ is shown in Fig. 311.   The equation of the curve shown is

$$LA' = aY^2 + bY^4 + cY^6 \cdots \qquad (134)$$

This series converges very rapidly, the first term being the most important.

In a single lens the power contribution of the first surface is proportional to its curvature, $c_1 = 1/r_1$, and that of the second surface is proportional to $c_2 = 1/r_2$.   The total power of the lens is proportional to $c_1 - c_2$, or $(1/r_1) - (1/r_2)$.   It is evident that if $c_1$ is increased and $c_2$ is correspondingly increased, the power of the lens can be kept constant.   Thus it is evidently possible to change the shape of the lens without changing its power.   This process is known as *bending* a lens.   The importance of this is that by bending a lens the shape of the curve of spherical aberration (Fig. 311) may be changed.

Thus Figs. 316 to 318 represent three shapes of a lens.   The spherical aberration curve is shown with each.   It will be noted that the shape in Fig. 316 shows much less marginal aberration than that of Fig. 317. The shape with the least possible aberration is shown in Fig. 318. It will be seen that this shape, known as the *crossed* shape, is only slightly more effective than the plano-convex form shown in Fig. 316. It is evident that, when a plano-convex lens is used with parallel light, the convex surface should face the distant object, *i.e.*, the long conjugate of the beam. This principle is used in orienting lenses in simple condenser systems.

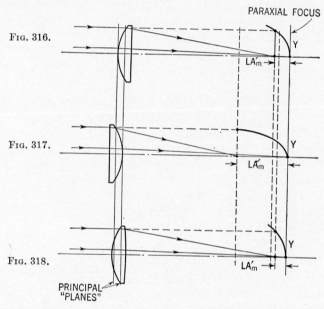

FIGS. 316, 317, 318.—These figures show, at the right, the spherical aberration curves for the three lenses shown at the left. All the lenses have the same focal length; they differ only in shape.

We can use various methods of quantitatively designating the shape of the lens. One of the simplest of these is to take the curvature of the first surface, or $c_1 = 1/r_1$. The value of $c_1$ and the power $\phi$ completely define the shape. If the shape of the lens is continuously varied between wide limits and the spherical aberration for the marginal ray $LA'_m$ determined for each shape, a curve of the form shown in Fig. 319 is obtained. It will be noted that for a certain shape (that shown in Fig. 318) the marginal $LA'$ is a minimum, but that for a single lens it can never be made zero. These curves are all made with infinitely distant objects (parallel incident light); thus the aplanatic case is not involved. The simplest way to eliminate spherical aberration for a distant object is by the use of a doublet consisting of a positive and a negative lens of different types of glass. If the two components are cemented together and the combination as a whole is bent (this entire bending may be measured by $c_1$ of the first component), an aberration curve of the shape shown in Fig. 320 will be obtained. This curve will be essentially a parabola. It will be noted that two solutions are obtained, *i.e.*, $LA'_m$ is zero for two values of $c_1$, and the one best suited to the designer's needs may be chosen. By varying the glasses used

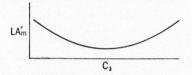

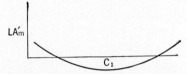

FIG. 319.—Variation of $LA'_m$ with lens shape. (Power of lens is constant.)

FIG. 320.—Marginal spherical aberration of a cemented doublet as a function of bending.

in the doublet, this aberration parabola may be pushed up or down at the will of the designer. As it is pushed farther down, the points at which the curve crosses the axis move farther out, and this represents solutions that are extreme in shape, *i.e.*, strongly curved meniscus lenses. If the glasses have been injudiciously selected, the minimum may appear so high that no solution at all is possible. The larger the difference in index between the two components, the lower the minimum of the curve falls. Too low a minimum is objectionable for a telescope objective because the objective will then be afflicted with coma and other aberrations. The glasses should be so chosen that the minimum of the curve falls just slightly below the axis.

Returning for a moment to the question of the single thin lens, it should be noted that the minimum spherical aberration is obtained when the refracted ray undergoes equal deviations at the two surfaces.

By the application of Maclaurin's theorem, it may be shown that the sine of an angle may be expressed in terms of the following infinite series:

$$\sin U = U - \frac{U^3}{3!} + \frac{U^5}{5!} - \frac{U^7}{7!} + \cdots \qquad (135)$$

If we apply this expansion to the slope angles $U$ and $U'$ of rays
that are very close to the axis (*i.e.*, $U$ and $U'$ are very small), we
may use only the first term on the right of the equation and
neglect the higher order terms, thus writing sin $U = U$. This
of course is valid only for very small angles. If we were to substitute this simplified expression for $U$ in the regular trigonometrical ray-tracing equations, we should get the paraxial equations.
This substitution is valid only for paraxial rays. Because the
first term in the expansion is the only one used, theory derived
by means of this substitution is known as *first-order theory;*
calculations based on this theory are called *first-order calculations.*
Rays traced by means of first-order theory will show only a few
of the aberrations. However, if we take the first *two* terms into
account, we find all the aberrations. Because the second term
on the right is of the third order, theory derived from the assump-

tion that sin $U = U - \dfrac{U^3}{3!}$ is known as *third-order theory.* Third-

order theory holds so closely to what one obtains in taking all
orders into account that it is used extensively for the preliminary
design work on optical systems. Most of the aberration equations to be given in subsequent chapters will be based on third-
order theory. If the first three terms in the expansion are used,
one has *fifth-order* theory. Aberration equations derived with
this theory are too cumbersome for most practical uses. Thus
fifth-order theory is not widely used in design work. Generally
the fifth order and subsequent terms are described by the expression *higher orders.*

Let us consider a doublet that has been corrected for spherical
aberration. It would be nice to have all the rays at all zonal
heights intersecting at a single focus. Unfortunately this is not
possible. The reason for this is as follows: We may select a
positive and a negative lens of such powers and shapes that the
combination is corrected for spherical aberration at the marginal
zone. If the various orders of the spherical aberration were
calculated for each lens by means of Eq. (134), it would be found
that the coefficients $a$, $b$, $c$, . . . would not be equal. Therefore
the spherical aberration of the two lenses could be made to
cancel at only a single value of $Y$; they would be unequal for all
other values. Hence all the other zones would manifest this
aberration. Most of the aberration in a single lens is of the third

order (see Fig. 321). With this third-order aberration there is always present some fifth-order, and unfortunately this order gives increasing negative aberration with increasing zone height (Fig. 322). If only third-order aberration were present, it would

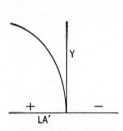

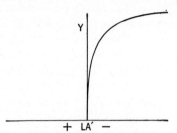

FIG. 321.—Third-order component of spherical aberration.

FIG. 322.—Fifth-order component of spherical aberration.

be possible to combine a positive and negative lens with equal amounts, and the resulting doublet would be corrected for spherical aberration at all zones. The fact that the two components have different amounts of higher order aberration means that correction can be obtained only for a single zone height. The resulting curve for such a doublet is that shown in Fig. 323. The ray passing through any zone, *i.e.*, at any height from the axis, may be brought to the same focus as the paraxial ray, and the lens is then said to be corrected for the zone of this ray. The best state of correction is obtained when the marginal and paraxial rays have the same focus.[1] A lens corrected in this fashion is termed "corrected for the marginal ray." Thus

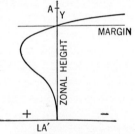

FIG. 323.—Spherical aberration curve of doublet telescope objective corrected for spherical aberration (*i.e.*, $LA'_m = 0$).

in Fig. 323 the ray showing zero $LA'$ comes from the margin of the lens. Note that, after the curve comes to zero at the margin, the aberration increases very rapidly. This is due to the fact

---

[1] This conclusion is reached on the basis of path-difference theory. Considerations of a purely geometrical character lead one to believe that a lens should be left spherically undercorrected at the margin (Baker, *Proc. Phys. Soc.*, Vol. 53, p. 531, 1941). However, the conclusion reached on the basis of path differences appears to be the more reliable.

that the fifth order component has taken hold here, and this component increases very rapidly with zone height. Also note that the rays passing through the lens at other than the paraxial and marginal zones show a certain residual aberration known as *zonal spherical aberration.* After a lens has been corrected for the marginal ray, the zonal spherical aberration limits its performance. This zonal aberration, which is nearly always positive with a positive doublet or any positive lens system, has its maximum for a marginally corrected doublet at a zone 0.707 of the distance from the center to the margin. Thus, when a lens has been corrected for $LA'$ at the margin, the residual zonal aberration may be easily determined by tracing a single extra ray through

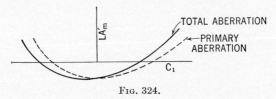

Fig. 324.

the 0.707 zone, and the entire curve of the shape shown in the illustration may then be sketched in.

If we were to take the lens whose $LA'$ is shown in Fig. 323 and try to make it faster by increasing the aperture without changing the focal length, and then correct it for the new marginal ray (*i.e.,* we would try to correct it for point $A$ in the figure), we should find that this would be quite possible, but the zonal aberration would increase tremendously. In practice, we can continue to open up the lens, *i.e.,* increase the aperture ratio, until the zonal aberration has reached the value dictated by the optical tolerance applying to this quantity (see Chap. XXX).

We saw above that the equation relating $LA'$ to zone height was $LA' = aY^2 + bY^4 + \cdots$. The $Y^2$ term is called *primary spherical aberration,* the next *secondary spherical aberration,* and so on. These do not exist independently, but together. In simple lenses the primary is about 90 per cent of the total aberration. In a corrected doublet of small aperture ratio, primary and secondary are equal at the point of correction. In lenses of small aperture ratio the values of $Y$ involved are so small that the higher order terms are negligible, and it is then permissible to perform the preliminary design work by means of the primary spherical aberration. This is important, for, as we shall see later, it is possible to express the primary aberration in terms of data obtained from only a paraxial ray tracing, and such a tracing can be obtained in a very small fraction of the time required for a trigonometrical trace. Furthermore, we shall find that for doublets of considerable aperture ratio, while the primary spherical aberration and the actual spherical aberration curves do not coincide, they will generally run approximately parallel (as shown in Fig. 324). Thus corrections may be made, even after only a single point on the true curve has been determined, by assuming the two curves to have parallel slopes.

It is important to remember that steep curves in any optical system put in a large amount of low-order spherical aberration, which is always accompanied by a large amount of aberration of higher order. To obtain correction, a large amount of low-order aberration (also accompanied by a large amount of higher order) of opposite sign must be added. The higher orders do not cancel out. This results in large zonal residuals when marginal correction is obtained. Thus, to keep the zonal aberration small, *avoid steep curves.*

### REFERENCES

See list at the end of Chap. XXIV.

### PROBLEM

Consider a single refracting surface of radius $r = +5$ in. The medium to the left of the surface is air; to the right is glass of index 1.649. Determine the location of the aplanatic point toward which a ray incident upon the lens from the left would have to be directed to give freedom from spherical aberration. How far from the vertex of this surface would the refracted ray cross the optical axis?

# CHAPTER XXVI

## CHROMATIC ABERRATION

As has been previously indicated, the index of refraction of any piece of glass is a function of wavelength, and the variation of index with wavelength is often specified by the $\nu$-value of the glass. The power of a lens is of course a function of the index of the glass of which the lens is made. It is thus obvious that the power, or focal length, of a lens is a function of wavelength. Thus, if we were to pass beams of light of different wavelength through the lens, we should find different foci for different colors.

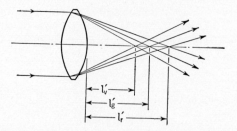

Fig. 325.—Longitudinal chromatic aberration of a single positive lens.

If we were to pass white light through the lens, we should find the different colors comprising this light focused at different points. Figure 325 shows a single positive lens upon which is incident a beam of white light from an infinitely distant axial object point. The violet component would be found to come to a focus at a distance $l'_v$ from the lens, the green component at a distance $l'_g$, and the red at a distance $l'_r$. If we were to place a screen at a distance $l'_v$ from the lens, we should find a sharp violet image of the object surrounded by a colored halo. If the screen were located anywhere between $l'_v$ and $l'_r$, a sharp image would be formed in some color, and this would be surrounded by a colored halo. Thus a good image could not be obtained at any point, and the lens would be said to be afflicted by *longitudinal chromatic aberration*. This aberration is often called *longitudinal color*, or sometimes just *color*. In practice, this aberration is measured in terms of the difference in focus between the red $C$ line and the blue $F$ line of hydrogen. Thus,

$$\text{Longitudinal color} = l'_C - l'_F \tag{136}$$

For a single positive lens this quantity is essentially always positive; so, if $l'_C - l'_F$ is greater than zero, we call the aberration *positive;* if it is negative, we call the aberration *negative.* A lens with positive longitudinal color is termed *chromatically undercorrected;* one with negative color is called *chromatically overcorrected.*

In considering this aberration we shall first consider the aberration that we would find by tracing paraxial rays in the different colors, and we shall designate this *paraxial color.* This of course represents the longitudinal chromatic aberration of rays passing through a lens very close to the axis, *i.e.*, at very small aperture. After merely writing the thin lens equation

$$\frac{1}{f'} = (n - 1) \left( \frac{1}{r_1} - \frac{1}{r_2} \right) \tag{137}$$

for $F$ light, and then writing it again for $C$ light (*i.e.*, for light of the wavelength of the hydrogen $C$ line), the two equations may be combined and solved for the paraxial color of a single thin lens. The result thus obtained for an infinitely distant object is

$$\text{Paraxial color} = l'_C - l'_F = f'_C - f'_F = \frac{f'}{\nu} \tag{138}$$

where $f' = \sqrt{f'_F f'_C}$ and is thus the mean focal length. $\nu$ is of course the reciprocal dispersion of the glass used in the lens and varies from about 60 for crown to 30 for flint. Hence, for a simple thin crown lens, the longitudinal paraxial color is about one-sixtieth of the focal length; for a simple thin flint lens, the paraxial color is about one-thirtieth of the focal length. For objects at finite distances these figures do not hold but must be multiplied by $(l'/f')^2$.

As a single positive lens always gives undercorrection and a single negative lens always gives overcorrection, it is evident that by combining properly chosen positive and negative lenses we can obtain a system free of color. If the two lenses are made of the same glass and are in contact, they will, according to the preceding equations, have to be of the same power to correct color; thus the combination would be of zero power. However, by choosing glasses of different dispersions for the two components, we can get correction for color and still have power left in the system. A doublet freed of color is termed an *achromat* or *achromatic doublet*.

By further applying the thin lens equation given above, it is possible to derive equations stating the focal lengths of the two components of a thin cemented achromatic doublet objective that must be used to obtain a desired focal length for the combination. These equations are

$$f_a' = \frac{f'(\nu_a - \nu_b)}{\nu_a} = \frac{1}{\phi_a} \tag{139}$$

$$f_b' = -\frac{f'(\nu_a - \nu_b)}{\nu_b} = \frac{1}{\phi_b} \tag{140}$$

The subscripts $a$ and $b$ refer, respectively, to the two components, $f'$ is the mean focal length of the combination, and $\nu_a$ and $\nu_b$ are the reciprocal dispersions of the two glasses employed. The wavelength at which $f'$ is expressed is the visually effective one of 589.3 m$\mu$, *i.e.*, this is the mean wavelength of the $D$ lines of sodium, and it is near the peak of the luminosity curve.

From a study of the foregoing equations we immediately see that when two lenses are combined to form an achromatic doublet

1. One lens must be positive and one negative.
2. The positive lens must have the higher $\nu$-value.
3. The two powers depend only on $\nu$-values, not on indices.

Glasses commonly used for such a doublet are 1.51/60 (crown) and 1.61/36 (flint). However it is also possible to use a combination such as 1.61/60 and 1.61/36 but this could not be spherically corrected. We saw in Chap. XXV that it is desirable to keep the curves in a lens system as gentle as possible to avoid high residual aberrations. Thus the focal lengths of these two components should be kept as long as possible for a given $f'$. This may be done by the proper selection of glass. In selecting glass for a doublet, the beginner should try various combinations through using the foregoing simple equations. Until he has learned the other factors that go into the choice of suitable glass, he would do well to select the pair that gives the gentlest curves.[1] This means the selection of a pair having the largest possible difference in $\nu$-values. It is occasionally desirable to compute a system

---

[1] However, see page 397.

having a certain amount of chromatic overcorrection or under-correction in order to compensate for color introduced elsewhere in the system. This can also be done.

Generally speaking, small changes in chromatic aberration require large changes in power, but the aberration is essentially independent of lens shape. A system is usually very sensitive with regard to changes in $LA'$ with a change in bending or power, but a very large change in power is required to give much of a change in color.

Suppose we were to trace paraxial rays of various wavelengths through a doublet that had been *achromatized* (*i.e.*, freed of longitudinal color) by the foregoing equations. We should then get a curve of the type shown in Fig. 326. In this are plotted the

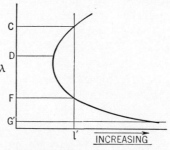

Fig. 326.—Intercept distance vs. wavelength for an achromatic lens combination.

intercept lengths for the various wavelengths. It will be noted that the two wavelengths for which the system was achromatized have the same foci, but all other wavelengths have other foci. A minimum focus exists at a wavelength intermediate between the $C$ and $F$ foci, this being about 555 m$\mu$. Although this does not coincide exactly with the $D$ focus, it is close enough for practical purposes. Of course a lens in the ideal state of achromatization would have the same intercept length for all wavelengths, so the departure from this ideal condition is also an aberration. This aberration, known as *secondary color* or *secondary spectrum*, is measured by the distance between the $D$ focus and the combined $CF$ focus. It of course has meaning only with an achromat. In any positive doublet the $CF$ intercept length will always be longer than the $D$ intercept length. It will be noted that the curve moves away from the $CF$ focus slowly at the long wavelengths and quickly at the short wavelengths (see the $G'$ focus). It will also be noted that for a system achromatized for the $C$ and $F$ lines the minimum intercept length is at the peak of the luminosity curve (555 m$\mu$). This is the reason for the selection of these lines as being of the correct wavelengths for achromatization, for they represent optimum points near the ends of the luminosity curve.[1]  Starting at 555 m$\mu$ there are pairs of wavelengths all the way through the visible spectrum that have equal intercept lengths.   Thus the spectrum has been, in effect, folded back on itself at 555 m$\mu$ by achromatization.   If some other minimum focus wavelength had been selected, the spectrum would have been folded about other than the mid-point and would thus have a longer intercept length region, *i.e.*, there would be increased secondary spectrum.

The effect of secondary spectrum is to surround the image with a violet halo and cover it with a haze.

For common pairs of glasses the secondary spectrum (as just defined) amounts to about 1/2,500 of the focal length of the doublet.   The distance from the *CF* focus to the photographically important *G'* focus is about $\frac{1}{500}$–$\frac{1}{600}$ of the focal length. These data apply to the case of an infinitely distant object point.

Many attempts have been made to develop glasses whose dispersion characteristics were such as to give negligible secondary spectrum, but without success.   The only glasses that offer some promise in this direction are the so-called *crown flints*, having characteristics in the region of 1.523/50.   These can be combined with some crowns to give doublets fairly free of secondary color. However, the differences in $\nu$-values for such combinations are so small that very steep curves are required.   This is of course a major disadvantage, because only small aperture ratios may be used.   Hence these glasses are rarely used in practice.   It may be noted that fluorite can be combined with dense barium crown to give a combination practically free of secondary spectrum. However, fluorite is very rare and is obtainable in optical quality only in very small pieces.   It is used in microscopes to give objectives free of secondary spectrum.   Lithium fluoride and lithium bromide are useful and can be made synthetically.[2] There are no glasses that can be paired with them to eliminate secondary spectrum completely, but by their use secondary spectrum may be greatly reduced.[3]   However, these halides are water soluble and are therefore of limited application.

[1] See, however, Kingslake, *Trans. Opt. Soc.*, Vol. 28, p. 173, 1926–1927.

[2] STOCKBARGER, *J. Optical Soc. Am.*, Vol. 27, p. 416, 1937.

[3] Doublet and triplet objectives using lithium fluoride for the positive component and quartz for the negative component have been computed by Cartwright.   See *J. Optical Soc. Am.*, Vol. 29, pp. 29 and 350. 1939.

So far we have considered the problem of achromatizing a lens system for visual use, bringing the minimum focus to the wavelength of maximum sensitivity of the eye. It is evident that, if a doublet so corrected were to be used with a photographic plate having its maximum sensitivity in the violet, the system would show chromatic aberration as far as the plate was concerned even though it looked perfect to the eye. Thus, when working with a lens system to be used for photographic purposes, we have to select the wavelengths of achromatization accordingly.

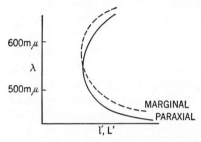

Fig. 327.—Comparison of curves obtained from marginal and paraxial ray-tracing data.

When working with blue-sensitive film, the $D$ and $G'$ lines are brought to a common focus instead of $C$ and $F$. This is known as *photographic* or $DG'$ *achromatism*. The minimum focus is at the $F$ line. If modern orthochromatic or panchromatic plates are to be used, the wavelengths for achromatization should be selected accordingly. It is evident that a lens system can be corrected for only one type of plate and will be only approximately corrected for all others.

Thus far we have considered only the tracing of paraxial rays through our lens systems. We shall now also consider marginal and zonal rays. Figure 327 shows how the curves of marginal and paraxial rays for a corrected doublet will appear. These curves should intersect at about 555 m$\mu$, for this is the wavelength of greatest visibility; it is thus the wavelength at which we wish the highest state of correction.

By tracing rays in $C$ and $F$ light through any zone of a doublet we can bring them to the same focus, *i.e.*, the lens can be achromatized for any zone. The question thus arises as to which zone shall be used to obtain correction, or in other words, in order to obtain the highest degree of achromatization for the whole lens, at what particular zone should the lens be achromatized? A mathematical study of this question shows that achromatization should be obtained for a zone 0.707 of the way from the center of the lens to the edge. When the lens is so adjusted that $C$ and $F$ rays traced through this zone come to the same focus, the marginal rays will be overcorrected, the paraxial rays will be undercorrected, and the marginal overcorrection will approxi-

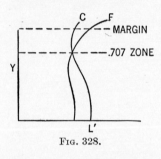

FIG. 328.

mately equal the paraxial undercorrection. Because the area of the lens outside the 0.707 zone equals that inside this zone, equal amounts of light are under- and overcorrected and balance each other. This situation is shown in Fig. 328, in which zone height is plotted against intercept length. Figure 35 should also be consulted. One curve is for $C$ light, the other for $F$ light. These curves show sphero-achromatism, $i.e.$, the chromatic variation of spherical aberration, as well as just showing color. The two curves may be made almost to coincide by use of a special four-element lens system.

We have seen that it is possible to correct a lens for two colors, $C$ and $F$ or $D$ and $G'$, by the use of two glasses; it is similarly possible to correct it for three colors by employing three glasses. This gives greatly reduced secondary spectrum. There are several sets of glasses that may be used for this purpose, but all give very steep curves to the lenses. Thus they are not widely used in practice because the resulting objectives must have small aperture ratios. The advantage of the use of such objectives is that the system may be corrected for both the visual and photographic regions of the spectrum simultaneously, and they are thus known as photo-visual objectives (see Fig. 143). Objectives of this type are necessary in photomicrography where focusing is accomplished visually, and a photographic plate is then exposed. It is obviously necessary to have the visual and photographic foci coincident. Microscope objectives computed for this purpose are termed *apochromats*. Sometimes instead of using three types of glass to get this triple achromatism, a fluorite-glass combination of reduced secondary spectrum is used. These combinations are known as *semi-apochromats*. They are satisfactory for visual use but are not too good for photographic purposes.

It has been pointed out that the intercept length–wavelength curve (Fig. 326) departs from the combined *CF* focus slowly at the long wavelengths. This means that it is possible to perform infra red photography in the near infra red with ordinary *CF* achromatism. Thus, it is possible to use visually corrected lenses for infra red aerial photography when filters are employed.

The equation relating variation in longitudinal color to aperture is

$$\text{Longitudinal color} = a + bY^2 + cY^4 \cdots \qquad (141)$$

The first term $a$ represents paraxial color, which is evidently independent of aperture. It is seen, however, that the total color does vary with the aperture employed. However, the series is rapidly convergent, and the variation with aperture is therefore not great.

When we come to designing telescope objectives, we shall find that we shall employ the foregoing thin-lens equations to achromatize the doublet roughly when it is first laid out. We must then trace rays through this system and use the data from these rays to make the final corrections. It is common practice to do this by tracing a paraxial and marginal ray in $D$ light to evaluate the spherical aberration, and then tracing zonal rays (through the 0.707 zone) in $C$ and $F$ light to evaluate the color. Thus three trigonometrical and one paraxial tracings are involved. We shall now consider a method by which these corrections can be made by tracing only one trigonometrical and one paraxial ray. At present we shall confine our attention purely to the chromatic aberration aspects of this method.

**Achromatization by Conrady's Path Difference Method.**[1]— Consider a ray passing through a piece of glass. In the time it would take this ray to go a distance $S$ in the glass, it will go a distance $nS$ in air, where $n$ is the index of the glass. $nS$ is the equivalent air path. Now suppose we trace a number of rays at different zone heights through an optical system and measure off equal equivalent air paths on all these rays. The locus of all

[1] CONRADY, *Monthly Notices, Roy. Astron. Soc.*, Vol. 64, p. 182, 1904.

"Dictionary of Applied Physics," Vol. IV, p. 224, Macmillan & Company, Ltd., London, 1923.

LEE, *Trans. Optical Soc.*, Vol. 22, p. 227, 1920–21.

these points will represent a wave front at some given instant. This wave front will have different centers of curvature for different zones, and these centers of curvature are the foci for the different zones. If two wave fronts, formed from different color rays, have the same radii of curvature after passing through a given zone, they will both have the same focus for that zone; thus that zone is the zone of achromatization. Furthermore, it can be demonstrated that if two wave fronts formed in different colors intersect at the marginal zone, they will be *parallel* at the 0.707 zone, *i.e.*, they will have equal radii of curvature. Thus the lens will be achromatized at the 0.707 zone, which we found to be the best state of correction. Therefore this method of achromatization depends on our making the equivalent air paths equal along the marginal rays so that the two colors will be brought to the same focus. This is the general theory of the method. The mechanics of the technique will now be briefly outlined. Assume that we have a system tentatively calculated.

1. For each component of the system, calculate the index of refraction ($n_{555}$) for the "brightest light," *i.e.*, the most visually active light, by using

$$n_{555} = n_D + 0.188(n_F - n_C) \qquad (142)$$

where $(n_F - n_C) = (n_D - 1)/\nu$.
(The constant should be 0.187 for dense flints and 0.189 for light crowns.)

2. Trace a marginal and a paraxial ray in this color. Note that the difference between the final intercepts gives the spherical aberration.

3. Calculate the height of incidence of the marginal ray at each surface from

$$Y = r \sin (U + I) = r \sin (U' + I') \qquad (143)$$

4. Then for each *glass* lens (not air space) compute

$$D = \frac{Y_1 - Y_2}{\sin U'_1} \qquad (144)$$

Here the subscript 1 refers to data from the first surface of each lens; subscript 2 refers to data from the second surface. The value of $D$ obtained here is the actual length of the path of the ray traveling through the lens (see Fig. 329).

5. Now calculate the difference of the equivalent air paths (making the $C$ and $F$ wave fronts coincide on the axis) for $C$ and $F$ light from

$$PD = \Sigma(t - D)(n_F - n_C) \tag{145}$$

where $t$ is the axial thickness of each glass component and PD is the path difference. Thus this value, which applies to the marginal ray, is obtained for each glass component, and all are added together. If the lens system has been properly achromatized, the sum will be zero. The largest permissible value for this sum is 0.000025 cm or 0.00001 in. For a really good system, the sum should not be more than one-half this tolerance.

Now suppose that the sum actually came out different than zero, indicating the presence of color. It can be brought to zero by one of two methods. The value of $(n_F - n_C)$ at any lens can be changed by a change of glass; thus by changing the glass the system is easily achromatized. However, this implies that the designer can find in the catalogues a glass that has just the necessary value of $(n_F - n_C)$ to bring the sum to zero, and this glass must have the same index as the original glass to keep the spherical aberration from changing. As this is not usually possible, another method of achromatization is necessary. Therefore color is corrected by changing the last radius. The steps to be followed are as follows:

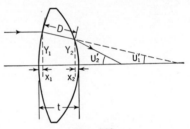

Fig. 329.

1. Calculate $PD_0 = \Sigma_0(t - D)(n_F - n_C)$. This sum is taken for all lenses *except the last.*

2. Compute the required value of $D$ for the *last* lens from

$$D = t + \frac{PD_0}{n_F - n_C} \tag{146}$$

$PD_0$ is the value obtained in 1.

3. Calculate the new $Y_2$ for the *last* lens from

$$Y_2 = Y_1 - D \sin U_1' \tag{147}$$

4. Calculate the new $X_1$ for the last lens from

$$X_1 = 2r_1 \sin^2 \left( \frac{U_1 + I_1}{2} \right) \tag{148}$$

5. Next compute the new $X_2$ for the last surface from

$$X_2 = X_1 - t + D \cos U_1' \tag{149}$$

6. Calculate the new radius $r_2$ of the last surface from

$$r_2 = \frac{Y_2^2}{2X_2} + \frac{X_2}{2} \tag{150}$$

Note that all these calculations are performed with data from the last lens only. These calculations are all perfectly straightforward and are very simple. Once the new value of the last radius has been determined, the marginal and paraxial rays are traced through this surface, and the path difference sum is recalculated. It should now be zero, showing that the lens has been achromatized.

The various quantities employed in these equations are shown in Fig. 329.

Although this path difference method is very fast, it does not always give exactly correct results. Thus, when it is used in any design work, the state of achromatization of the final system should be finally checked by trigonometrical tracing of rays in $C$ and $F$ light through the 0.707 zone before the results of the computations are sent to the shop. If some residual color is found in the system, it is best to eliminate it by adjusting the power of the last element through varying the last surface. Thus, if $L_C$ and $L_F$ are the intercept distances of the rays in $C$ and $F$ light *incident on* the last surface, and $n_C$ and $n_F$ are the indices of the last element for $C$ and $F$ light, respectively, the radius of the last surface that will eliminate color may be computed from

$$\frac{1}{r} = \frac{(L_C - L_F)n_C}{L_F L_C (n_F - n_C)} + \frac{1}{L_F} \tag{151}$$

It will be noted that no information concerning the last surface is required to apply this equation. Therefore it is possible to trace rays in $C$ and $F$ light (through the 0.707 zone) up *to* the last surface, and then use this equation to achieve achromatization. When the lens system has been achromatized by the path difference method and otherwise corrected, and then the final tracing shows some residual color, the color may be eliminated by using this equation. In this case some spherical aberration or coma (or other aberration) may get back into the system because of this change of the last surface and must then be eliminated by a further slight bending. If the use of this last equation does not completely achromatize the system, the color may be evaluated for several values of the last radius, and then the value of this radius that will eliminate color may be easily determined by interpolation.

## REFERENCES

See list at the end of Chap. XXIV.

## PROBLEMS

**1.** Derive Eq. (138).

**2.** Given borosilicate crown glass of these characteristics: 1.5164/64.9 and extra dense flint of these: 1.6495/33.7, calculate the powers and focal lengths of the two components of an achromatic doublet of 10 cm focal length. Do the same with the glasses 1.5164/64.9 and 1.6215/53.6. Note the effect of the $\nu$-value on the powers of the components. Which pair of glasses would you choose, and why? Estimate the amount of secondary spectrum to be expected with both combinations (infinitely distant object).

**3.** In an ordinary doublet, achromatization is accomplished by bringing the $C$ and $F$ rays to the same focus. Secondary spectrum is the residual aberration and is measured by the distance between the $D$ and the combined $CF$ focus. This secondary spectrum is given (for the case of an infinitely distant object) by

$$f'_D - f'_{CF} = \frac{f'}{\nu - \nu'}\left(\frac{n_F - n_D}{n_F - n_C} - \frac{n'_F - n'_D}{n'_F - n'_C}\right) \tag{152}$$

where $f'$ is the focal length of the doublet, the unprimed letters refer to the first component of the doublet, and the primed letters to the second. The index of refraction of a glass (as a function of wavelength) can be represented to a fairly close approximation by this form of Cauchy's equation:

$$n = n_o + \frac{A}{\lambda^2} + \frac{B}{\lambda^4} \tag{153}$$

where $n_o$, $A$, and $B$ are constants for the glass. If one were to plot the values of $A$ against $B$ for all available glasses, how would he choose from this graph a pair of glasses to use in an achromat with zero (or as little as possible) secondary spectrum?

# CHAPTER XXVII

## COMA

Coma is the aberration that must be given consideration in the design of a doublet after spherical and chromatic aberrations have been accounted for. Since it is an aberration that affects

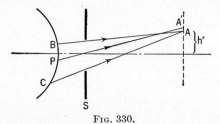

Fig. 330.

only image points off the axis, it is not of importance with systems that cover only very small fields. As the field becomes appreciable in extent, say above 2 or 3°, this aberration begins to play a very important part in the quality of the image; for systems

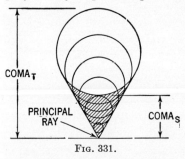

Fig. 331.

with sizable fields it is of great importance that this image defect be corrected. The theoretical considerations involved in a study of coma are rather extensive in character and find no place in a work of this sort. Consequently the factors of importance in a study of this aberration will be mentioned but briefly. The character of coma is shown in Fig. 330 in which is represented the last surface of a lens system. $A$ is an extra-axial image point. The rays $BA$ and $CA$ are the extreme marginal rays passing through the edge of the aperture stop $S$. The ray $PA'$ passing through the middle of this stop is by definition the principal ray. It will be noted that this ray does not strike the focus $A$ but rather intersects the image plane at $A'$. The fact

414

that $A$ and $A'$ do not coincide means that the image point, instead of being sharp, will be spread out laterally.

The image of an extra-axial point object formed by a system afflicted with pure coma is shown in Fig. 331. The circles represent the loci of the images formed by rays through various zones of the lens system. The tip of the inverted triangle is the location of the principal ray. The type of coma shown, in which the two tangent lines intersect at 60°, is the type commonly encountered and is known as 60° coma. It is a type of coma formed by third-order aberration. The length of the aberration figure is proportional to the distance $h$ of the image point from the axis. Fifth-order aberration gives another form of 60° coma proportional to $h^3$, and the higher orders give yet other forms of coma: 83° coma, etc. The equations we shall give later on will deal solely with third-order coma, *i.e.*, primary coma, for the equations for the higher orders are too complicated to be of much practical value.

Coma formed by the tangential rays (rays through a principal section containing the axis of the optical system) is known as *tangential coma*, or *coma$_T$*, while the coma formed by the sagittal rays, which are skew rays, is known as *sagittal coma* or *coma$_S$*. The relationship of these is indicated in Fig. 331, tangential coma being three times as great as sagittal coma (third-order). The third-order equations that we shall use in preliminary layout work for an optical system give sagittal coma. The coma we can find by ordinary ray tracing is tangential coma.

The distribution of energy throughout the comatic image is not uniform, and the parts shaded in the illustration receive the major contribution. Thus the comatic image often has an arrow-like appearance (Fig. 25).

As has been indicated, primary coma varies directly with $h$. It is also important to remember that the size of the primary comatic image at any point in the field varies directly with the square of the clear aperture of the system.

Coma is a function of the bending of a lens and is commonly controlled by proper shaping of the element. Fortunately, coma varies linearly with bending (as measured, for example, by $c_1 = 1/r_1$ for a given lens) and is thus handled reasonably easily.

After a system has been tentatively calculated, the various aberrations are evaluated by means of ray tracing. Coma could be evaluated by tracing the rays $BA$, $CA$, and $PA'$ in Fig. 330, but this would be a tedious process. Luckily we have available a theorem, known as *Abbe's sine theorem*,[1] which enables us to calculate coma for reasonably small fields and apertures from ordinary marginal ray-tracing data. Lower-order coma, by use of this theorem, is commonly evaluated in terms of a quantity known as the *offense against the sine condition*, or $OSC'$. This quantity $OSC'$ is, by definition, equal to coma$_s/h'$. The size of the primary comatic image varies throughout the field with $h'$, and thus the ratio coma$_s/h'$ is *constant* throughout the field. For this reason, this ratio is often used instead of the varying size of the comatic image as a measure of coma. It is evident that with a knowledge of the value of $OSC'$ for a given system we can easily calculate the value of coma at any point in the field. The equation giving $OSC'$ in terms of easily determined quantities is

$$OSC' = 1 - \left(\frac{\sin U_1}{u_1}\right)\left(\frac{u'_k}{\sin U'_k}\right)\left(\frac{l'_k - l'_{pr_k}}{L'_k - l'_{pr_k}}\right) \qquad (154)$$

In this equation the quantities with the subscript $pr$ refer to the principal ray from the edge of the field. For a telescope objective the aperture stop can be considered as coinciding with the last surface, and thus $l'_{pr_k}$ can be taken as zero. The letters with subscript 1 refer to data associated with the first surface of the system, and those with the subscript $k$ refer to data from the *last* surface of the system. A paraxial and a marginal ray for an axial object point are all that must be traced to evaluate $OSC'$ for a telescope objective. These same two rays also serve to evaluate spherical and longitudinal chromatic aberrations. In tracing these rays it is customary to choose arbitrarily $u_1 = U_1$, i.e., the marginal and paraxial rays are traced with the same initial slope angle. This enables the quantity in the first parentheses in Eq. 154 to become unity. It is thus obvious that this equation can be greatly simplified for use with telescope objectives. For the case of an

[1] According to this theorem, if $U_1$ is the slope angle of a ray incident on an optical system and $U'_k$ is the slope angle of the corresponding refracted ray, the system will be free of coma if the ratio $\sin U'_k/\sin U_1$ is constant for all zone heights. This applies only to third-order aberration and holds only for a system corrected for spherical aberration. If the object is infinitely distant (i.e., $U_1 = 0$), the ratio $y_1/\sin U'_k$ must be constant for all zone heights $y_1$ for the system to be coma free. This, too, applies only to third-order aberration and holds only for a system having no spherical aberration.

infinitely distant object, $u_1 = U_1 = O$. In this case the quantity in the first parentheses becomes $0/0$, or indeterminate, and is replaced by $Y_1/y_1$, these being the heights of incidence of the marginal and paraxial rays, respectively. Normally we choose $y_1 = Y_1$. This simplifies the computation. Thus for telescope objectives $OSC' = 1 - \left(\dfrac{u'_k}{\sin U'_k}\right)\left(\dfrac{l'_k}{L'_k}\right)$.

Equation (154) states that if spherical aberration is present the coma may be controlled by varying the position of the stop. We shall use this method of controlling coma in the design of eyepieces. If the spherical aberration is zero, as with a corrected telescope objective, coma cannot be eliminated by a shift of the stop; it must be removed by bending.

In order to consider at greater length the character of coma, let us return for a moment to the consideration of what is meant by focal length. This was defined, for a thick lens and paraxial rays, as the distance from the second principal point to the second focal point. It may be determined by tracing a paraxial ray, at any desired fictitious height, from an infinitely distant axial object point through the lens. If the initial height of the ray was $y_1$ and the ray arrived at the focal point with the final slope angle $u'_k$, the equivalent focal length is given by

$$f' = \frac{y_1}{u'_k} \tag{155}$$

This is the standard method of computing focal length and may be used for a single lens or a system of lenses.

The image height for rays passing through a given zone will depend on the focal length of that zone (see Fig. 93). The focal lengths of different zones can be determined by trigonometrically tracing rays through those zones. Thus for a zone located a distance $Y_1$ from the axis, the equivalent focal length is determined by tracing through the system a ray incident parallel to the axis and dividing $Y_1$ by the sine of the final slope angle, or

$$f'_z = \frac{Y_1}{\sin U'_k} \tag{156}$$

This, too, can be applied either to a single lens or to a system of lenses. The method of applying it to a system is shown in Fig. 332. The focal length is seen to be measured along the ray, not parallel to the axis. If the different zones have different focal lengths, they will have different image heights, and this will result in coma. If they have the same focal length, there will be no coma, provided there is no spherical aberration. In this case the second principal surface $P'$ will be a sphere with its center at the focal point (see Fig. 333). Thus we can determine

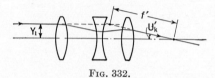

FIG. 332.

the presence of coma by plotting the value of $f'_z$, as computed by Eq. (156), against zone height $Y_1$. For a perfect lens this would give a straight line, indicating a spherical principal surface; in practice, a curve similar to that of spherical aberration is obtained. The departure of this curve from a straight line is a valid measure

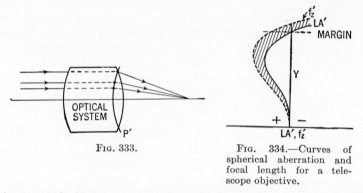

FIG. 333.

FIG. 334.—Curves of spherical aberration and focal length for a telescope objective.

of coma only if there is no spherical aberration. The curves of $f'_z$ and spherical aberration $(LA')$ for an actual lens are shown in Fig. 334. We have seen that there is a connection between spherical aberration and coma, and this connection manifests itself in such a way that the shaded area between these curves is normally a measure of the effective coma. If the two curves coincide, there will be no coma. In a well-corrected lens the curves will fall very close together. This condition is contained in the following equation

$$OSC' = \frac{1}{f'}\left[(F' - f') - (L'_k - l'_k)\left(\frac{F'}{L'_k - l'_{pr_k}}\right)\right] \quad (157)$$

To evaluate this quantity for a given zone, a paraxial ray and a trigonometrical ray through the zone, both from an infinitely distant axial object point (*i.e.*, parallel to the axis), are traced. $F'$ and $f'$ are the respective equivalent focal lengths of the zonal and paraxial regions, and $L'_k$ and $l'_k$ are the back focal lengths. $l'_{pr_k}$ gives the location of the exit pupil referred to the last vertex (Why?), and for a telescope objective may be taken as zero. Normally this quantity is brought to zero (*i.e.*, corrected) for the marginal zone (Why?).

For telescope objectives, $OSC'$ should not be greater than $\pm 0.0025$.

### REFERENCES

See list at the end of Chap. XXIV.

### PROBLEMS

1. What is the focal ratio of the fastest system that can be corrected for coma in the absence of spherical aberration? *Hint:* Consider the shape of the principal surface.

2. Derive Eq. (156).

## CHAPTER XXVIII
## DESIGN OF APLANATIC OBJECTIVES

An aplanatic objective is defined as one that has been freed of spherical aberration and coma. The spherical aberration and coma are both corrected for the marginal zone. As a matter of course, such a doublet is also corrected for chromatic aberration. It is thus necessary to have at least three variables to control these three aberrations. There are various methods of controlling these aberrations:

1. Use of two separated elements, individually bent. These have as degrees of freedom:
    a. Relative power of crown and flint
    b. Bending of the crown
    c. Bending of the flint
2. Use of two separated elements, with variable airspace. The degrees of freedom are
    a. Relative power of crown and flint
    b. Bending of the lens as a whole
    c. Variation of the airspace
3. Use of a cemented doublet made of specially chosen glasses. The degrees of freedom that exist are
    a. Relative power of crown and flint (depends on $\nu$-values)
    b. Ratio of indices of the two components
    c. Bending of lens as a whole
 This is the sort of objective used in gun sights, etc. A barium crown (1.57/57) and a medium flint (1.615/36.7) are often used. However, a borosilicate crown (1.517/64.5) and an extra dense flint 1.649/33.8 may be used with success.
4. Use of a triplet objective. This sort of objective consists of a positive crown lens with a negative flint element cemented to each face or two positive lenses cemented to a negative element (Figs. 335, 336). The degrees of freedom are
    a. Relative total powers of crown and flint
    b. Amount of flint in front of crown
    c. Bending of the lens as a whole

420

**Design Considerations.**—The first step in the design of an aplanatic objective is to select proper glasses. A few general rules have been given previously, and as one's experience broadens he learns of new factors that assist him in making a decision.

The glasses having been chosen, the designer writes the equations fixing the various conditions that he is planning to satisfy and solves these simultaneously to obtain a tentative solution.

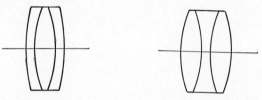

FIG. 335.               FIG. 336.
FIGS. 335 and 336.—Cemented-triplet telescope objectives.

To achromatize the system, Eqs. (139) and (140) may be used or one may prefer the following relationship which expresses the condition for removal of longitudinal color:

$$\sum \frac{y^2\phi}{\nu} = 0 \tag{158}$$

In this equation $y$ is the height at which the ray strikes a given lens, $\phi$ is the power of the given lens $(=1/f)$, and $\nu$ is the reciprocal dispersion of the glass used in the lens. One of these terms is written down for each lens, and they are all summed up and equated to zero. It is customary to assume the lens to be infinitely thin in making this preliminary solution, for this enables the designer to make some useful simplifications in his equations. If we are considering the design of a cemented doublet and if we have two infinitely thin components, the rays strike both components at the same height. The $y$ term is thus constant for both elements and may be canceled out. Thus, for a cemented doublet Eq. (158) takes the very simple form

$$\frac{\phi_A}{\nu_A} + \frac{\phi_B}{\nu_B} = 0 \tag{159}$$

The subscript $A$ refers to data from the first lens, the subscript $B$ refers to those of the second. It is desirable to work with powers rather than focal lengths. However, if one wished to use focal lengths, the above equation would of course take the form

$$f'_A \nu_A + f'_B \nu_B = 0 \tag{160}$$

This equation gives the ratio of the powers of the two elements to achromatize the lens. However it does not specify the total power $S$ of the system. This must be expressed by another equation:

$$S = \Sigma y \phi \tag{161}$$

Of course for a thin cemented doublet this would reduce to the form

$$S = \phi_A + \phi_B \tag{162}$$

Thus in setting up a system, Eqs. (158) and (161), or their various simplifications, are solved simultaneously to evaluate $\phi_A$ and $\phi_B$ to give an achromatic lens of the required focal length. The use of Eqs. (139) and (140), which are equivalent to the above, is quicker but they may be used only with a thin cemented system.

Now, with a knowledge of $\phi_A$ and $\phi_B$, a paraxial ray, incident upon the first lens at a fictitious height $y_A$, corresponding to full aperture, is traced through the system lens by lens by using

$$\frac{1}{l'} = \frac{1}{l} + \phi \tag{163}$$

The height at which this ray strikes each successive lens is calculated by use of

$$y_B = y_A \left( \frac{l_B}{l'_A} \right), \text{ etc.} \tag{164}$$

In the computation of telescope objectives, the heights of incidence on all elements are the same, for the components are assumed to be infinitely thin and in contact. Sufficient data have now been accumulated to determine the conditions for the elimination of spherical aberration and coma.

The expression covering the elimination of primary spherical aberration from a system of thin lenses is

$$\Sigma y^4 (G_1 c^3 - G_2 c^2 c_1 + G_3 c^2 v_1 + G_4 cc_1^2 - G_5 cc_1 v_1 + G_6 cv_1^2) = 0 \tag{165}$$

This expression is of course evaluated for each lens and then summed up. $y$ is the height of incidence at each lens; $c$ is the total curvature of each individual lens, being equal to $c_1 - c_2$, where these two terms are the curvatures of the first and second surfaces, respectively; $v$ is the reciprocal of the object distance for each lens, thus $v = 1/l$ and $v' = 1/l'$. The $G$'s are functions of the index of refraction, and are defined as follows:

$$G_1 = \frac{n^2(n - 1)}{2} \tag{166}$$

$$G_2 = \frac{(2n + 1)(n - 1)}{2} \tag{167}$$

$$G_3 = \frac{(3n + 1)(n - 1)}{2} \tag{168}$$

$$G_4 = \frac{(n + 2)(n - 1)}{2n} \tag{169}$$

$$G_5 = \frac{2(n^2 - 1)}{n} \tag{170}$$

$$G_6 = \frac{(3n + 2)(n - 1)}{2n} \tag{171}$$

If a cemented doublet is being designed, everything will be known in Eq. (165) but the shape factors of the two lenses. As the doublet is cemented, the shape of one lens will of course be determined by that of the other, *i.e.*, the whole doublet is bent as a unit, and this bending represents only a single degree of freedom. In other words, $c_2$ of the first element (surface 2, Fig. 337) equals $c_1$ of the second (surface 3, Fig. 337). Thus it is evident that, if the term in Eq. (165) that referred to the first lens had $c_2$ for a variable and if the term referring to the second lens had $c_1$ for an unknown, the two unknowns would be equal and the whole expression would have only one unknown: the common contact radius. Thus we desire a method of expressing Eq. (165) in terms of $c_2$ instead of $c_1$ as the variable quantity. We can use for this purpose an alternate form of Eq. (165) in which the term in parentheses in that equation is replaced by

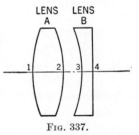

LENS   LENS
  A      B

Fig. 337.

$$(G_1c^3 + G_2c^2c_2 - G_3c^2v_2' + G_4cc_2^2 - G_5cc_2v_2' + G_6cv_2'^2) \tag{172}$$

This may be used interchangably with the expression in brackets in Eq. (165). The $G$'s are defined as before. It should be remembered that the subscripts of the $G$'s do not refer to specific lenses. The subscripts of the $c$'s and the $v$'s refer to the particular side of the lens being considered. $c_1$ is the curvature of the first surface of a lens of total curvature $c$; $v_2'$ equals $1/l_2'$ for the lens under consideration, where $l_2'$ is the image distance for the second surface.

If a cemented doublet were being designed, Eq. (165) would be solved merely for the single variable: the curvature of the contact surface. Thus one surface of each of the two elements would be defined. As the powers of these two components have already been determined, it is then a simple matter to compute the other surfaces by use of $\phi = 1/f' = (n - 1)(c_1 - c_2)$.

If an aplanat were being designed, however, we should have to provide for the elimination of coma. To do this, we use the following equation, which is valid for a system of lenses very close to each other or in contact:

$$\Sigma(\tfrac{1}{4}G_5cc_1 - G_7cv_1 - G_8c^2) = 0 \tag{173}$$

It might at times be desirable to express the term in parentheses in terms of data from the second surface for the same reason that this was done with spherical aberration, and in this case the term in parentheses may be replaced by

$$(\tfrac{1}{4}G_5cc_2 - G_7cv_2' + G_8c^2) \tag{174}$$

This will be seen to be identical with the $G$-sum in Eq. (173), except for the sign of the last term. The various letters in this expression have the same significance that they possessed in the spherical aberration equations. The $G$'s are defined by

$$G_5 = \frac{2(n^2 - 1)}{n} \tag{175}$$

$$G_7 = \frac{(2n + 1)(n - 1)}{2n} \tag{176}$$

$$G_8 = \frac{n(n - 1)}{2} \tag{177}$$

Thus far we have considered only the equations governing spherical and chromatic aberrations and coma. This is all we need to consider in the design of telescope objectives, for, with such objectives, in the usual case of the stop being at the objective itself, distortion and lateral chromatic aberration are essentially zero. The astigmatism is fixed and has the large value $h_k'^2/2f'$, where $h_k'$ is the height of the final image formed by the objective, measured from the axis; $f'$ is the focal length of the objective. The only way compensation may be obtained for this astigmatism is by proper design of the eyepiece. The curvature of field is also fixed, and it too must be controlled by manipulation of the eyepiece. Thus the three aberrations already considered are all with which we shall deal in considering the technique of objective design.

As has already been pointed out, in designing an aplanatic objective the first step is to determine the powers of the two elements by application of Eqs. (158) to (162). Now suppose we are designing an objective of the first type mentioned at the beginning of this chapter: one with two uncemented elements that will be separately bent (Fig. 337). The equations governing the condition for removal of spherical aberration and coma for the system are now written down. Each expression will have two unknowns: the shape factors of the first and second components. These equations are solved simultaneously for the two shape factors. Thus all the radii of the components have been determined. However, these equations have dealt with only primary aberration; furthermore, the lenses have been assumed to be infinitely thin, so the system will actually be far from satisfactory in performance at this stage. Next the system is drawn to scale, and appropriate thicknesses for the elements are determined from this drawing. As the two elements have been bent separately, it is not possible to cement the system. The two elements are normally mounted as close together as possible without touching. A very small gap may be left between the adjacent edges of the two elements, and an appropriate axial spacing to produce this gap is chosen. Now the system is tested trigonometrically. Single marginal and paraxial rays are traced through the system in "brightest light" as described in Chap. XXVI, and the system is achromatized by the path difference method also described in that chapter. The marginal and paraxial rays are now traced through the newly determined last surface (chosen to achromatize the system), and from them $LA'$ is instantly determined. By computation from these rays of $OSC'$ the state of correction for coma is also determined. It is now necessary to determine trigonometrically what bendings will be necessary to eliminate the $LA'$ and $OSC'$ that are always left because of the various approximations used in obtaining the preliminary solution. If the system is adjudged nearly correct, it is permissible to bend arbitrarily the first lens a small amount $\Delta c_A$ and again trace rays through the system to determine what changes in $LA'$ and $OSC'$ have occurred. This is repeated with the second lens with a bending $\Delta c_B$. Suppose that the changes in $LA'$ and $OSC'$ that result from the bending of the first lens are $\Delta LA'_A$ and $\Delta OSC'_A$. Then, if the selected bending of the first lens was $\Delta c_A$, we can evaluate the differential coefficients

$$P = \frac{\Delta LA'_A}{\Delta c_A} \tag{178}$$

$$Q = \frac{\Delta OSC'_A}{\Delta c_A} \tag{179}$$

Similarly for the second lens we can evaluate

$$R = \frac{\Delta LA'_B}{\Delta c_B} \tag{180}$$

$$S = \frac{\Delta OSC'_B}{\Delta c_B} \tag{181}$$

If the original curvatures of the two surfaces of the first lens were $c_1$ and $c_2$, the new curvatures after the bending would be $c_1 + \Delta c_A$ and $c_2 + \Delta c_A$. Thus the *same* curvature change is applied to both surfaces to hold the power constant. Similarly, when lens B is bent, each of its two curvatures is changed by the amount $\Delta c_B$.

On the basis of the differential coefficients evaluated above, it is now possible to determine what changes in shape will be required to eliminate $LA'$ and $OSC'$. Thus we now decide what change in $LA'$ and $OSC'$ we must have to perfect the system. These desired changes will of course be the negative of the amount of these aberrations actually present, *i.e.*, if $LA' = +0.0073$ cm and $OSC' = -0.0046$, then the required change in $LA'$ is $-0.0073$ cm; the required change in $OSC'$ is $+0.0046$. We now apply the equations

Desired change in $LA' = P\Delta c_A + R\Delta c_B$ $\qquad$ (182)
Desired change in $OSC' = Q\Delta c_A + S\Delta c_B$ $\qquad$ (183)

These equations are solved simultaneously for $\Delta c_A$ and $\Delta c_B$.

The lenses are bent the amount given by these equations, marginal and paraxial rays are again traced, the system is again achromatized, and $LA'$ and $OSC'$ are again evaluated. It is possible that another application of the same treatment will be necessary to complete the design work, for $LA'$ and $OSC'$ may be found to have been reduced insufficiently. It is very important to note that this differential method of correction is based on the assumption that both $LA'$ and $OSC'$ vary linearly with bending. This of course is not generally true, particularly for $LA'$. Thus this method can be successfully applied only when the corrections to be computed are so small that the small section of the shape vs. aberration curve involved is essentially linear.

If the first trigonometrical analysis shows that the system is too far from being correct for the differential method to be employed, a procedure that may be inferred from the following is used.

For a system of thin lenses mounted close together the coma contribution (designated $CC'$) may be determined from

$$CC' = h'_k y^2 \Sigma \text{ (coma } G\text{-sums of individual lenses)} \qquad (184)$$

The coma contribution is a very useful measure of coma. $h'_k$ is the height of the final image and $y$ is the height of the fictitious paraxial ray passing through the edge of the objective. The coma $G$-sum is the term in brackets in Eqs. (173) and (174). Similarly we can use as a measure of $LA'$ in this type of lens system the spherical contribution $SC'$ given by

$$SC' = l'^2_k y^2 \Sigma \text{ (spherical } G\text{-sums of individual lenses)} \qquad (185)$$

Here $l'_k$ is the final intercept length (or image distance) and $y$ is the height at which the marginal paraxial ray passes through the objective, *i.e.*, it is half the total aperture. This holds only for a system in air and does not apply to a system immersed in any other medium.

These aberration contributions are direct measures of the aberrations themselves and may be used to determine approximately the aberrations.

In order to compute an aplanatic objective, the coma contributions and spherical contributions of the two individual components (Fig. 337) may be plotted as shown in Fig. 338. It will be understood that to plot these curves the two individual elements should be bent several times, and the aberration contributions calculated for each bending by the $G$-sum equations. These values are plotted on the chart and connected with a smooth curve. In this graph the two contribution curves for the negative lens are plotted with reversed sign so that they fall on the same side of the axis as the contributions of the positive lens. Thus any straight horizontal line intersecting the two $SC'$ curves will give a doublet without $LA'$, for the two values of $SC'$ will be equal and opposite. Similarly, any straight horizontal line intersecting the $CC'$ curves will give a doublet corrected for coma. Inasmuch as a straight horizontal line intersecting the

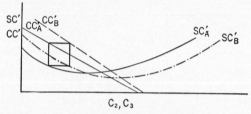

Fig. 338.—Curves of spherical and coma contributions of the objective of Fig. 337. The numbered subscripts refer to the surfaces of that objective, the lettered subscripts to the individual lenses.

$CC'$ curves gives a doublet free of coma, and one intersecting the $SC'$ curves gives a doublet free of $LA'$, in order to get an aplanatic doublet we must satisfy both conditions at once. This is accomplished by locating a square that touches all four curves (see Fig. 338). The two horizontal lines show that this combination is free of $LA'$ and coma; the two vertical lines show that the same bendings simultaneously accomplish both these corrections. Note that the shape of the first lens is given in terms of $c_2$, its second radius, while that of the second lens is given in terms of $c_3$, its first radius. In some cases the two vertical lines can be made to coincide. This means that at the point of correction $c_2 = c_3$, i.e., the lens may be cemented. This does not often happen. If the curves were projected off to the left of the illustration another solution would be found. This would, however, involve extreme shapes and would not be useful. It will be appreciated that again this method of attack involves only primary aberrations and infinitely thin lenses, and the solution obtained is therefore only very approximate. After the system has been achromatized and the residual $LA'$ and $OSC'$ determined by ray tracing, the contribution equations can be differentiated to determine in what direction the lens should be bent to come nearer to a correct solution. As the region of the final solution is approached, the differential method outlined above is used for the final corrections.

Once the final solution has been obtained, it is wise to check the chromatic correction by tracing rays in $C$ and $F$ light through the 0.707 zone (see conclusion of Chap. XXVI).

Now let us consider briefly the design of the second type of aplanatic objective: that with a variable airspace. This is much easier to design than the first type because, as the air gap changes, $LA'$ changes greatly while $OSC'$ remains nearly constant. Thus the air gap may be used to vary $LA'$ independently of $OSC'$.

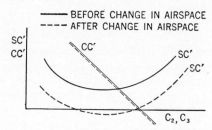

Fig. 339.—The numbered subscripts refer to the surfaces of the objective of Fig. 337.

The characteristics of this system are shown in Fig. 339 in which the curves of the two aberrations are plotted before and after a change of airspace. It will be seen that coma ($CC'$) remains practically fixed. The aberrations have thus been separated, and a double solution of the type discussed above is no longer necessary.

After the powers of the two elements have been selected by the achromatization condition the curves shown in Fig. 339 are computed by means of the contribution equations, rays are traced to determine the residual aberrations and achromatize the system, and corrections are made on this solution by using the curves. The final correction may be made with the differential method.

Next we shall consider the third type of aplanatic objective: that consisting of a cemented doublet fabricated of specially selected glasses. Generally speaking, the differences in $\nu$-values of the glasses used in common doublets is about 24. A smaller difference than this gives too steep curves. Thus suppose we arbitrarily select this difference for our doublet and locate in the catalogues the various pairs of glasses that give this difference. We take a given pair and, with these glasses, determine the ratio of powers necessary for achromatization. Using the contribution equations, we calculate the spherical and coma contributions for the doublet, bending it several times as a whole. These we plot, getting the usual parabola in plotting $SC'$ vs. $c_1$, and a straight line in plotting $CC'$ against $c_1$. In order to get an aplanat it is necessary that both these curves cross the axis (*i.e.*, give zero aberration) for the same value of $c_1$, showing that this shape will correct both aberrations simultaneously. If we do not get this sort of solution for the glasses chosen, another pair is taken and the whole procedure is tried again. This is continued until a solution is found, or the available glass pairs are exhausted. As has been previously suggested, the glasses 1.57/57 and 1.615/36.7 can be used for this purpose. The pair 1.517/64.5 and 1.649/33.8 have recently come into favor. It is pointed out that in the design of these doublets the cemented surface should be left well over-corrected as it is the only dispersive surface in the system. The final trigonometrical adjustment is performed as outlined previously.

Another good method of designing this type of aplanatic doublet is to adopt fixed values of the indices, letting the $\nu$-values go. Roughly correct radii are selected for the lens arbitrarily on the basis of experience. Now the second radius is varied and its effects on the aberrations noted. The same procedure is followed with the last radius. The differential method is used to obtain a double solution for the radii that will eliminate $LA'$ and $OSC'$ simultaneously. The lens will now be aplanatic but not achromatic. The various values of $n_F - n_C$ for glasses having the desired indices are obtained from glass catalogues; these are multiplied by the $(t - D)$ values for the two lenses to determine which will satisfy the condition for achromatization by the path difference method. Of course, when equal and opposite values of $(n_F - n_C)(t - D)$ are obtained for the two elements, the lens will be achromatized. If a solution is not obtained, the indices are changed and the whole procedure is repeated.

Aplanatic objectives of the cemented doublet type are widely used in prism binoculars and gun sights.

Finally, we shall give some consideration to the design of the fourth type of aplanatic objective: the cemented triplet. The first step is the computation of the total power of flint and crown that will be required to give achromatization. Here we assume that we have only a single flint element. Later we shall break this up into two, keeping the total power of the flint components correct to obtain achromatization. Now we have as variables for the control of $LA'$ and coma the bending of the objective as a whole and the distribution of the amount of flint in front of, and behind, the crown. Although a preliminary solution can be obtained by application of the primary aberration equations, it is customary to select a system arbitrarily and trace rays. The various parameters are now systematically varied to determine the rate of variation of the aberrations with the quantities used for their control. Then a differential solution is obtained. The design of this type of objective has been outlined only sketchily, for the procedure followed in any given case will depend on a number of variables, such as glasses available, and experience of the designer. An attempt has been made to give merely the general approach; the details may be worked out by the designer. A few suggestions will be given, however. A good first guess for the external shape of the whole triplet is the plano-convex form with the convex surface facing the incident light. This plano-convex form is of course rather well corrected for spherical aberration with parallel incident light. The designer can start with half of the flint before the crown and the rest behind. The inexperienced designer is warned against the possibility of finding that a large change in bending produces a small or zero change in $LA'$. If this occurs, he is working at the bottom of the spherical aberration parabola and should govern his actions accordingly.

These triple aplanatic objectives have several advantages over the various other types of aplanats. In the first place, they are cemented and thus require no spacing rings. The relationship of the various components is firmly established. Second, any glass may be used; special glasses are not required. This is sometimes of considerable importance. Lenses of this type are used in some telescope objectives and are occasionally used even in low-power (32- and 45-mm) microscope objectives.

This brief outline of the technique used in the design of aplanatic telescope objectives should serve to give the reader a very rough idea of the general procedure followed in lens design.

The design of more highly corrected systems, such as microscope or photographic objectives, is of course vastly more complex and is a laborious process indeed.

### REFERENCES

See list at the end of Chap. XXIV.

### PROBLEMS

**1.** Show that, for an infinitely distant object, it is not possible to eliminate the spherical aberration of a single thin lens made of any available glass. What would the index have to be in order to eliminate spherical aberration?

**2.** In computing a certain air-spaced doublet objective you obtain the following aberration coefficients: $P = +0.0015$, $Q = -0.0023$, $R = -0.0037$, $S = +0.0102$. This system has the following aberration characteristics: $LA' = -0.00033$, $OSC' = -0.00047$. Determine the changes in the shapes of the two components that would be required to effect correction.

# CHAPTER XXIX

## EYEPIECE DESIGN

This brief discussion of eyepiece design will assume a certain knowledge concerning eyepieces on the part of the reader. It is suggested that the section on Eyepieces (pages 190–195) be thoroughly mastered before consideration is given to these more advanced details.

One of the most important aberrations to consider in the design of eyepieces is lateral chromatic aberration, more familiarly known as lateral color. This aberration may be regarded as a difference in magnification with wavelength. Conrady has developed a very elaborate formula stating the conditions to be satisfied for the elimination of this aberration in two-component eyepieces. In practice it will be found feasible to use a much simpler formula, for this formula is used only to lay out the system roughly, and the final corrections are performed on the basis of ray tracing, as with an objective. The simple expression stating the condition for the elimination of lateral color in two-component eyepieces is

$$d = \frac{f'_a + f'_b}{2} \tag{186}$$

where $d$ is the spacing between the two elements, which may be assumed thin in the preliminary work; $f'_a$ is the focal length of the eye lens; and $f'_b$ is the focal length of the field lens. Both must be of the same glass.

**Huygenian Eyepiece.**—The first type of eyepiece we shall consider will be the Huygenian (Fig. 340). $AB$ represents a marginal ray, from an infinitely distant axial object point, and $CD$ is a principal ray from an object at the extreme edge of the field. A real image is of course formed at $F$, at which point the field stop is located.

As has been pointed out in Chap. XII, page 191, the shapes of the lenses shown there have been found to give good correction for astigmatism, so we shall not assume shape to be a variable. The only variables we have are the spacing $d$ between the two elements, the focal length of the objective with which the eyepiece is used, and the ratio of the powers of the eyepiece elements. The total power of the eyepiece is of course determined by considerations of magnification, for the magnification is the ratio of the focal lengths of objective and eyepiece. The spacing $d$ will be fixed to give correction for lateral color in accordance with Eq. (186).

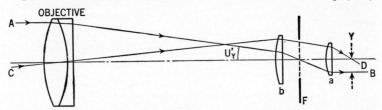

FIG. 340.—Telescope with Huygenian eyepiece. The eye lens is $a$; the field lens is $b$.

Once the focal length of the eyepiece is determined from the required magnification, we can use the equation

$$f'_e = \frac{f'_a f'_b}{f'_a + f'_b - d} \tag{187}$$

where $f'_e$ is the focal length of the eyepiece. In this equation and (186) there are three unknowns, $f'_a$, $f'_b$, and $d$, and we thus need one more equation in order to determine all three. The third equation gives the ratio of the powers of the field lens and the eye lens. It is

$$k = \frac{f'_b}{f'_a} = \frac{\phi_a}{\phi_b} \tag{188}$$

We can use this last degree of freedom, $i.e.$, the choice of $k$, for any of several purposes. It can be mathematically demonstrated that the best over-all state of correction will be attained if it is used to free the eyepiece of coma; we shall accordingly use it for that purpose. In the discussion on coma (page 417), mention was made of the fact that in a system afflicted with spherical aberration, correction for coma could be obtained by shifting the position of the stop. As the Huygenian eyepiece consists of two single positive elements, it must always be undercorrected for spherical aberration; therefore the stop-shift method of removing coma is applicable. Since the principal ray of an astronomical or terrestrial telescope passes through the center of the objective, the objective acts as the aperture stop and entrance pupil for the eyepiece. Hence by moving the objective closer to or farther from the eyepiece we are in effect shifting the stop. The only way in which we can move the objective, and keep the real image in the plane of $F$ in Fig. 340, is to change its focal length. A change in the focal length of the objective (with $f'_e$ kept constant) of course means a change in the magnification. Experience has demonstrated that if, for a desired magnification, we start with the correct value of $k$ [Eq. (188)] the eyepiece will turn out corrected for coma when used with an objective of the desired focal length. Table V gives the values of $k$ that are approximately correct for various magnifications.

TABLE V

| Magnification | $k$ |
|---|---|
| Infinite | 2.3 |
| 20 | 2.0 |
| 10 | 1.7 |
| 5 | 1.4 |
| 4 | 1.35 |
| 3 | 1.3 |

This table applies to telescopes. It will be noted that $k$, as well as being the ratio of the focal lengths of the two eyepiece components, is also the ratio of the radii of the convex surfaces of the two components provided that they are plano-convex. Although the values given in Table V are intended for use with telescopes, they may also be used in designing microscope eyepieces. In this case the magnification is defined as the ratio of the tube length to the focal length of the eyepiece. Generally speaking, for a telescope a value of $k$ of about 2 is good; for a microscope, 1.4.

Thus in designing an eyepiece we select the focal length $f'_e$ from magnification considerations, and choose an appropriate value of $k$ from Table V. These values are inserted in Eqs. (186) to (188), and the equations are solved simultaneously for $f'_a$, $f'_b$, and $d$. This is of course only a preliminary design and must now be adjusted trigonometrically.

In Chap. XXVII it was pointed out that coma could be measured by a quantity known as $OSC'$ and, further, that this quantity could be computed from certain marginal and paraxial ray-tracing data. In order to apply this concept to eyepiece design it is necessary to trace a marginal and a paraxial ray through the eyepiece. These rays are traced from right to left, for we know that they must leave the eyepiece parallel to the axis. Thus we trace the two rays (parallel to the axis) into the eyepiece from the right, both being at the same height $y$, which is the radius of the desired exit pupil. These will strike the axis of the system to the left of the field lens, the paraxial ray at a distance $l'_y$ from $b$ (Fig. 340), and the marginal ray at a distance $L'_y$. In practice this system can be set up with the objective at the right and the eyepiece at the left; the parallel rays may then be traced in the usual left-to-right fashion. With the results of this tracing available, we can calculate the focal length of the objective that should be used with this eyepiece by means of the following equation which was derived from the $OSC'$ equation given in Chap. XXVII.

$$f'_o = \frac{(l'_y - L'_y)(1 - OSC')}{\dfrac{u'_y}{\sin U'_y} - (1 - OSC')} \tag{189}$$

In this equation $(l'_y - L'_y)$ is a measure of the spherical aberration present in the eyepiece, $OSC'$ is the amount of lower order coma that will be introduced by the eyepiece, and $f'_o$ is the focal length of the objective that will cause the eyepiece to introduce an amount of lower order coma equal to $OSC'$. $U'_y$ is shown in Fig. 340.

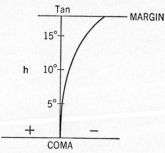

Fig. 341.—Variation of coma (all orders) with image height with an eyepiece having $OSC' = 0$.

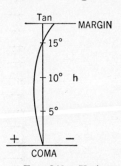

Fig. 342.—Variation of coma (all orders) with an eyepiece having a small positive amount of $OSC'$.

It might be thought that the amount of $OSC'$ it is desired to have the eyepiece introduce would be zero. This is actually not the case because the variation of coma (all orders) with field angle is as shown in Fig. 341. Note that coma first goes up linearly with the field ($h'$) and then increases more rapidly (with $h'^3$). The $h'^3$ component is always negative, and compensation should be made for it by the introduction of positive $OSC'$. If we make $OSC'$ zero we get the curve shown in the illustration. This is very good at the center of the field, but poor at the margin because of higher orders. However, if we introduce sufficient positive $OSC'$, we get the curve shown in Fig. 342. Conrady determined empirically that for this reason it is desirable to introduce a positive amount of $OSC'$ equal to $+0.2 \sin^2 U'_y$ for a

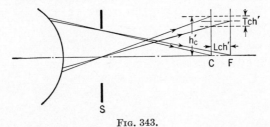

FIG. 343.

$30°$ (total) apparent field, and equal to $+0.3 \sin^2 U'_y$ for a $40°$ apparent field. Most eyepieces are not particularly critical with respect to the focal length of the objective with which they are used being of the value determined by Eq. (189), and variations of 50 or 100 per cent from this value may be tolerated.

Having now determined the focal length of the objective with which the eyepiece must be used to correct coma, we can consider chromatic aberration. It has already been indicated that with eyepieces we are not greatly concerned over longitudinal color but are quite interested in lateral color. In order to evaluate this quantity from ray trace data, we must obtain a new equation. The quantities involved are shown in Fig. 343, in which is represented the last surface of an optical system with a stop $S$. Principal rays in $C$ and $F$ light, from the edge of the field, form images at the points shown. The quantity labeled $Lch'$ is the longitudinal chromatic aberration. That labeled $Tch'$ is the transverse chromatic aberration, or lateral color. We shall measure this aberration in terms of a quantity defined very similarly to $OSC'$ and shall call it *chromatic difference of magnification, or CDM'*. This will be defined by

$$CDM' = \frac{Tch'}{h'_c} = \frac{\text{lateral color}}{h'_c} \qquad (190)$$

where $h'_c$ is the image height in $C$ light. It is a useful quantity for the same reasons that $OSC'$ is useful. Fortunately it can be computed in terms of paraxial rays in $C$ and $F$ light, and it is thus very easily calculated. Thus another general expression for this quantity is

$$CDM' = 1 - \frac{u'_C}{u'_F} \frac{(l'_C - l'_{pr})}{(l'_F - l'_{pr})} \tag{191}$$

Here $l'_c$ and $l'_F$ are the final intercept lengths of the paraxial rays traced in $C$ and $F$ light, and $l'_{pr}$ is the final intercept of a *paraxial principal* ray (*i.e.*, a principal ray traced with the paraxial tracing equations). In checking an eyepiece, the ray tracing can be simplified by tracing rays in $D$ and $G'$ light instead of $C$ and $F$ (this eliminates the tracing of one ray) and by writing the equation in the following form, which eliminates the need of tracing a principal ray:

$$CDM' = \left(\frac{u'_D}{u'_{G'}} - 1\right) + \left(\frac{u'_D}{u'_{G'}}\right)\left(\frac{l'_D - l'_{G'}}{f'_o + l'_D - l'_{G'}}\right) \tag{192}$$

$CDM'$ should not be zero but should be about $+0.001$ because of higher order aberration effects similar to those discussed for coma. If the $CDM'$ is between about $+0.0035$ and $-0.0015$, the eyepiece will be acceptable. These figures are modified somewhat if the chromatic aberration of the eye is taken into account.

In designing an eyepiece we set it up tentatively with the equations as outlined and then trace from the eye end only a marginal and paraxial ray in $D$ or brightest light, and a paraxial ray in $G'$ light. From these may be calculated $OSC'$, $LA'$, and $CDM'$. If brightest light has been used, longitudinal color may also be evaluated by the path difference method. If the aperture ratio of the eyepiece is not higher than about $f/7$, the $LA'$ will not be found excessive. For high aperture ratios, when large amounts of $LA'$ are encountered, it is necessary to overcorrect the objective for this aberration to get a system that functions well. If the $CDM'$ is found to be excessive, it will be necessary to compute several more eyepieces with the same value of $k$ but different airspaces (these must be chosen arbitrarily). A curve of $CDM'$ vs. airspace can then be plotted and an appropriate solution extracted. If the value of $f'_o$ that will correct coma differs too widely from the focal length desired, several more eyepieces with different values of $k$ should be computed, and a graph may be plotted. A change in airspace will be found to change the coma correction as well as $CDM'$; similarly a change in $k$ will affect $CDM'$ as well as coma. Thus a double solution of some sort should be made. This can be done by the evaluation of coefficients as described in Chap. XXVIII.

After this is done, to insure the best possible performance, it is desirable to check by trigonometrical or third-order methods astigmatism, distortion, and curvature of field. The methods of doing this are, however, beyond the scope of the present text.

Generally speaking, as the focal length of the objective decreases, the field lens must be strengthened. In some cases it will assume quite large powers, and this may require the bending of both components to obtain the best performance. In doing this it is necessary to be careful to avoid the introduction of excessive distortion, which is usually about 2 or 3 per cent at the edge of the field. The Huygenian eyepiece has insufficient negative astigmatism to balance the positive curvature of field of the objective.

**Ramsden Eyepiece.**—One of the most important features of the Ramsden is that the focal plane is outside the eyepiece; thus a reticle may be used. In order to obtain this condition, it is necessary to make the spacing between the elements less than that given by Eq. (186). Thus correction for lateral color is sacrificed. In order to satisfy the condition expressed by Eq. (186) as closely as possible and still have an accessible focal plane, we could place the reticle just outside the field lens and locate the focal plane at this point. This would make it possible almost to satisfy Eq. (186). Such an arrangement would work satisfactorily for observers with normal vision, but myopic individuals who attempted to focus the eyepiece would find that it would bump into the reticle. Thus it is necessary to locate the reticle some distance from the field lens. In order to accomplish this, Conrady recommends that the spacing between the elements be fixed by

$$d = 0.7f'_a \qquad (193)$$

The values of $k$ to be used with a Ramsden are more restricted in range than those used with the Huygenian. Limits of about 1 and 1.4 must be imposed, with a value of about 1.1 holding for a magnification of 20. In practice, several values of $k$ will be arbitrarily chosen, and an eyepiece designed with each with the aid of Eqs. (193) and (187).   Several other spacings can be tried, and a graphical solution may then be made.

This type of eyepiece has nice correction for curvature of field and distortion and is afflicted with less spherical aberration than the Huygens form.   If correction for lateral color must be obtained, as in binoculars, the eye lens is split into a doublet, giving an achromatized Ramsden, or Kellner, eyepiece.

**Kellner Eyepiece.**—If we were to study the conditions that must be satisfied to free a Ramsden eyepiece completely of lateral color, we should find that it would be necessary to overcorrect the eye lens with regard to longitudinal color.   This would call for such steep curves that the other aberrations would be adversely affected.   Thus we generally bring the longitudinal color in the eye lens only about to zero and do not make it negative.   This means that we leave a residual of lateral color.   This residual is reduced in prism binoculars by the aberration characteristics of the prisms.

The secret of success in designing a Kellner eyepiece lies in the proper choice of glass.   As the index difference existing between the two components of the eye lens increases, the field is given a rapidly increasing negative curvature through the introduction of negative astigmatism.   A small amount of negative curvature is desirable in order to compensate for the positive curvature of objective (and field lenses and erectors if they are used); thus a small difference in index is usually employed.   A useful pair of glasses for many purposes is 1.574/58 and 1.604/38.   If an instrument covering a wide field is being designed, the eye lens will have to be made quite large; thus the curvatures of the surfaces must be moderate to avoid excessive thickness.   In this case it is sometimes necessary to use a very small index difference.

In setting up a Kellner eyepiece, the powers of the eye and field lenses are determined as described under Ramsden Eyepiece. Then the eye lens is broken into two components and achromatized by the thin lens equations given in Chap. XXVI.   The system is finally corrected trigonometrically in the usual fashion. The index difference between the components of the eye lens and the bending of that lens may be used to flatten the field and eliminate distortion.

**Doublet Eyepiece.**—In designing all the preceding eyepieces it should be borne in mind that the eye relief should not be permitted to drop below 8 mm. It is sometimes difficult to fill this condition with long focal length objectives; in this case, it is sometimes possible to use a simple achromatic doublet for an eyepiece. The degrees of freedom are the second radius (*i.e.*, ratio of powers) and the bending of the whole doublet. The second radius is varied until lateral color is corrected, and the doublet is bent as a whole to correct either field curvature or coma. If the lens is corrected for field curvature, there will usually be coma left. Now the dispersions of the glasses are held constant and the index difference may be adjusted to eliminate coma. A quite satisfactory design may thus be evolved if sufficient glasses are available.

**General Remarks.**—Eyepieces work at speeds up to $f/4$ and cover apparent fields up to 40 to 75°.

They must be of short focus, and the stop (objective) must be a long way outside to give the proper eye position. As the stop approaches the eyepiece, the eye point moves back, increasing the eye relief. This is desirable in some cases and undesirable in others. The stop position can be controlled to some extent by the field lens as explained in Chap. XV.

The considerations dealt with in this chapter have assumed that the telescope was of the astronomical type, without erectors. When an erecting telescope is considered, it should be remembered that the entrance pupil for the eyepiece is the image of the stop formed by the field lens and the erectors, and it is the distance to this image rather than to the objective itself that is measured and used for $f'_o$ when coma is being corrected and Eq. (189) is applied. Also, in determining $k$, the distance from the focal plane of the eyepiece to this image is divided by the focal length of the eyepiece when a magnification is being selected for use in applying Table V.

It is evident from Fig. 149 that as the apparent field and eye relief increase, the diameter of the eye lens must increase. In gun-sighting telescopes moderate fields must be covered, and large eye reliefs are necessary. They, therefore, require rather large eye lenses. Because of the steep curves of the Kellner eye lens, it cannot be opened up sufficiently for this application, and a symmetrical eyepiece (Fig. 149) must therefore be used instead, in spite of its greater cost. It is possible to get quite a large aperture with a symmetrical eyepiece because larger index differences between the components of the doublets may be used than with a Kellner, and thus less sharp curves may be obtained.

The design of the more complicated forms of eyepieces commonly found in military instruments is considerably more complex than the procedure outlined herein. However, the methods involved are not dissimilar. The design is carried out largely by the use of third-order equations of the various aberrations. The variables available to the designer are each altered several times in turn, and the various aberrations are determined by third-order equations. These are plotted on graphs, and by a study of these graphs a reasonably good compromise solution is selected. The possibilities open to the designer are endless and probably never will be fully explored.

## REFERENCES

See list at the end of Chap. XXIV.

## PROBLEMS

**1.** You are designing an astronomical telescope of 20 power and are using an objective of 500-mm focal length. Perform the preliminary design work on a Huygenian eyepiece for use in this telescope, using crown glass of index 1.512. Determine the powers and spacing of the components and make a scale drawing of the eyepiece.

**2.** Compute a Ramsden eyepiece for the foregoing telescope and make a scale drawing of it. Compare it with the Huygens mentioned in Prob. 1.

**3.** Perform the preliminary design work on a Kellner eyepiece for this telescope, using the same glass as before for the field lens, and the glasses 1.574/58 and 1.604/38 for the eye lens. Make a scale drawing of the eyepiece and compare it with those computed in Probs. 1 and 2.

**4.** Why is $h'_C - h'_F$ not a satisfactory measure of lateral color (see Fig. 343)? (*Hint:* consider the case of $h'_C - h'_F = 0$; $Lch' \neq 0$).

# CHAPTER XXX

## OPTICAL TOLERANCES

In designing a mechanical system, the mechanical engineer must know exactly the tolerances he may expect in the various components, *i.e.*, he must know how much these components will deviate from the desired dimensions. With this knowledge he can decide how satisfactory the device will be in over-all performance.

In the design of an optical system, the optical designer is faced with the problem of deciding how much aberration can be tolerated under a given set of circumstances. Thus, in computing a system, it is often not possible to bring all the aberrations to zero. It is therefore necessary to know how much aberration of each type may be left in the system without causing deterioration of the image. Again, it is often necessary to have some criterion to ascertain the effect on the image quality of the normal variations of radii, lens thicknesses, and airspaces that occur during manufacture.

To aid in the solution of these problems the lens designer has at his disposal certain optical tolerances. The basis of our present concept of these tolerances was laid by Lord Rayleigh in 1878 after he had interested himself in a study of the paths of light through optical systems. Aberrations result from a difference in the path length of different rays traced through the system. Rayleigh was interested in determining the actual difference in path that would lead to a noticeable deterioration of the image. On the basis of a few mathematical studies he postulated the theorem that the performance of an optical system would not fall far short of perfection if the difference between the optical paths leading to a selected focus did not exceed one quarter of a wavelength. This theorem has stood the test of time. It has been reduced to various formulas that give tolerances that may be directly applied to any specific aberration.

Rayleigh stated that a path difference as large as the quarter-wave limit, known as the *Rayleigh limit*, would lead to a slight deterioration of the image, but he did not state exactly what the nature of this deterioration would be.

This point has been more recently investigated. It will be remembered that even with a perfect optical system the image of a true point source will be a bright disk surrounded by alternate light and dark rings, 84 per cent of the light being in the central bright disk and the remaining 16 per cent being distributed throughout the ring system. Up to the Rayleigh limit, and actually up to nearly twice the limit, the central bright disk does not increase in diameter; in some cases it actually becomes smaller. This means that the resolving power of the system does not decrease up to the Rayleigh limit. However, the central disk does become less bright and the light removed from it appears in the surrounding rings and is distributed over the entire ring system. The bright parts of the image thus lose light, the dark ones acquire it, and contrast suffers. At the Rayleigh limit the original 84 per cent of the light in the central disk has dropped to 68 per cent. The resultant fogginess and loss of contrast are appreciable and can affect the visibility of very fine detail. However, there is no loss of resolving power for the well-illuminated parts of the image. It is thus seen that aberrations should be kept well within the limits of the tolerances and should be allowed to reach these limits only when some definite advantage is gained.

If an image defect comes up to only *one quarter* of the Rayleigh limit, the loss of light from the central disk is only 1 per cent. Thus defects of this magnitude may be accepted without qualm. In fact, the ordinary computing error due to five-place calculations will give aberrations of about this magnitude. This is one reason for the extensive use of five-place calculations for optical work.

If a decided advantage in other aberrations will result, it is permissible to draw upon one-half the Rayleigh limit for a given aberration. The use of the entire limit is justified only when great advantage is to be obtained. In extreme cases even twice the limit may be used.

A manufacturer may be developing an instrument to compete with one already on the marke . He may find that in order to keep within the Rayleigh limit it is necessary to use either a smaller aperture or a smaller field than the competing instrument offers. Even though he could get better imagery than the competitor by sticking to the tolerance, he would probably not be able to market his instrument successfully. He would have to exceed the tolerance to get aperture and field at least equal to that of the competitive instrument to give his product any chance of success.

In order to apply the Rayleigh limit, it is necessary to trace a ray from an axial object point, through the margin of the aperture stop, to its final intercept in the image on the axis. This ray will make an angle $U'_m$ with the axis at the image. The value of $U'_m$ plays an important part in the calculation of tolerances.

A perfectly corrected lens system will have a certain range, known as *depth of focus*,[1] throughout which the image plane may be located without having an optical path difference exceeding the Rayleigh limit. This depth of focus may be applied in either direction from the true focus and is given by

$$\text{Depth of focus} = \pm \frac{\lambda}{n' \sin^2 U'_m} \tag{194}$$

$U'_m$ has the significance given above, and $n'$ is the index of refraction of the medium in which the image is located. For a system operating in air $n'$ is of course 1. $\lambda$ is the wavelength of the light used. The value selected for this depends on the spectral quality of light and the spectral sensitivity of the receptor. For an instrument to be used visually with white light, $\lambda$ may be taken as 0.00055 mm or 0.000022 in. For a sound-recording system to be used with blue light and blue sensitive film, a wavelength of 0.00040 mm would be appropriate.

If a system is not perfectly corrected for spherical aberration for the marginal ray (of course, a properly corrected system has the spherical aberration for the marginal ray zero), the amount of aberration corresponding to the Rayleigh limit is

$$\text{Permissible marginal spherical aberration} = \frac{4\lambda}{n' \sin^2 U'_m} \tag{195}$$

[1] For photographic purposes, *depth of focus* is defined as the distance along the optical axis that the film may be moved without producing deterioration of the image. The criterion of definition is arbitrarily selected. *Depth of field* is defined as the distance over which an object may be moved along the optical axis without causing its image to move out of focus by more than some arbitrary amount. Depth of field and depth of focus are obviously closely related, being manifestations of the same phenomenon.

This equation should be used only when the spherical aberration is largely primary[1] (see page 400).

If the system is corrected for spherical aberration at the margin, the quantity that will limit the performance of the system, as far as this aberration is concerned, is the residual zonal spherical aberration. The Rayleigh limit gives for this case:

$$\text{Permissible zonal spherical aberration} = \frac{6\lambda}{n' \sin^2 U'_m} \quad (196)$$

When considering coma, the tolerance corresponding to the Rayleigh limit for sagittal coma (designated coma$_s$) is

$$\text{Permissible coma}_s = \frac{\lambda}{2n' \sin U'_m} \quad (197)$$

The tolerance for tangential coma is thrice that for sagittal coma.

Coma is often measured by the offense against the sine condition. The Rayleigh limit gives this tolerance for it

$$\text{Permissible } OSC' = \frac{\lambda}{2n'h'_k \sin U'_m} \quad (198)$$

where $h'_k$ is the height, measured from the axis, of the image point farthest removed from the axis, *i.e.*, the point in the image corresponding to the edge of the field. The reason that these equations use the first power of the sine instead of the second power, as in the case of spherical aberration, is that coma is a lateral, or transverse, aberration, while spherical aberration is measured longitudinally.

Inasmuch as coma is a transverse aberration, it is often possible to neglect the Rayleigh tolerance and consider the angle that the aberration pattern will actually subtend at the eye, or the blur it will make on a photographic plate. This is particularly desirable because the tolerances based on the Rayleigh limit are unnecessarily severe. Another important factor is that the energy in the comatic image is not uniformly distributed but is concentrated at one end and the image thus looks smaller than it actually is. Taking these data plus the resolving power of the eye into account, Conrady has found that for ordinary telescopes,

---

[1] See, however, Wang, *Proc. Physical Soc.*, Vol. 53, p. 157, 1941.

microscopes, and photographic objectives the admissible $OSC'$ is $\pm 0.0025$ and the highest admissible value of coma$_s$ is $\pm 0.0025 h'_k$. Where the actual linear size of the comatic image is to be considered, he gives the following tolerances for

Admissible coma$_s$

$$\left. \begin{array}{l} = 0.001 \text{ in. for extremely sharp definition} \\ = 0.004 \text{ in. for good definition} \\ = 0.010 \text{ in. for decidedly soft definition} \end{array} \right\} \quad (199)$$

$$\text{Admissible } OSC' = \frac{\text{admissible coma}_s}{h'_k} \quad (200)$$

Chromatic aberration is generally measured as the distance between two foci, normally $C$ and $F$. The Rayleigh limit gives

Permissible longitudinal chromatic aberration

$$= \frac{\lambda}{n' \sin^2 U'_m} \quad (201)$$

The wavelength to be used in this equation is selected as before.

Lateral chromatic aberration is often measured by the chromatic difference of magnification. The tolerance for $CDM'$ is $+.0025$. It is similar to the $OSC'$ tolerance.

When astigmatism and curvature of field are considered, the Rayleight limit is found to give an extremely small tolerance, which appears to be unnecessarily severe. Conrady has proposed as a satisfactory substitute:

Extreme difference of focus $\times \tan U'_m$ may be

$$\left. \begin{array}{l} = 0.001 \text{ in. for extremely sharp definition} \\ = 0.004 \text{ in. for good definition} \\ = 0.010 \text{ in. for decidedly soft definition} \end{array} \right\} \quad (202)$$

In practice, $\sin U'_m$ may be used instead of $\tan U'_m$, for they are nearly equal at the angles encountered in most optical work.

The tolerance for distortion varies greatly, depending upon the use to which the optical system in question will be put.

### REFERENCES

BUXTON: *Monthly Notices, Roy. Astron. Soc.*, Vol. 81, p. 547, 1921.
CONRADY: "Applied Optics and Optical Design," Oxford University Press, New York, 1929.
CONRADY: *Monthly Notices, Roy. Astron. Soc.*, Vol. 79, p. 575, 1919.
CONRADY: *Proc. Optical Conv.*, Part 2, p. 830, 1926.

"Dictionary of Applied Physics," Vol. IV, p. 215, Macmillan & Company, Ltd., London, 1923.

MARTIN: "An Introduction to Applied Optics," Vol. I and II, Sir Isaac Pitman & Sons, Ltd., London, 1930 and 1932.

MARTIN: *Trans. Optical Soc.*, Vol. 27, p. 249, 1926.

## PROBLEMS

**1.** In computing an $f/7$ telescope objective of 1-meter focal length a designer finds the marginal spherical aberration to be 0.000079 meters. Is this an acceptable value?

**2.** The designer brings the marginal spherical aberration in the foregoing objective to zero. He finds that the objective then has residual zonal spherical aberration (at the 0.707 zone) of 0.000104 meter. Can he use this objective?

**3.** In a certain instrument a single thin lens of 8-in. focal length and 3-in. clear aperture is used. It is made of the following glass: 1517/64.5. Approximately how much longitudinal chromatic aberration will this lens have? Will this exceed the Rayleigh limit?

**4.** A certain $f/3.5$ photographic objective of 5-in. focal length forms an image in which, at the edge of the field, the distance between the sagittal and tangential image planes is 0.018 in. What sort of definition will this lens give at that point in the field?

# Name Index

## A

Abbe, E., 91, 277
Adie, 250
Ahrens, W., 325
American Standards Association, 82n.
Atkinson, Campbell, Palmer, and Winch, 377n.

## B

Baker, J. G., 142n.
Baker, T. Y., 399
Barnard, G. P., 377
Bell, L., 109
Berek, M., 143
Bertele, L., 138
Blodgett, K., 119, 121
Bodine Electric Co., 364
Boston, O., 311
Bremiker, K., 384n.
Buchmüller and König, 377n.
Burghardt, H. D., 312
Buxton, A., 447

## C

Campbell and Frieth, 377n.
Campbell and Ritchie, 377
Cartwright, C. H., 119, 125, 406n.
Chase, H., 312
Chrétien, H., 384, 389
Cobb, P. W., 74n., 186
Conrady, A. E., 389, 409, 437, 439, 446, 447
Czapski and Eppenstein, 165, 231, 389

## D

Dallmeyer, J. H., 130, 131
Danjon and Couder, 202

Davies, H. J., 312
Delmonte, J., 109
Drude, P., 69, 117

## E

Eastman Kodak Co., 82n., 135, 136, 338
Edser, E., 28
Emerson and Martin, 186

## F

Faires, V. M., 340
Försterling, K., 117
French, J. W., 86n.

## G

Galileo, 169
Gardner, I. C., 165, 248, 280
Gifford, J. W., 199n., 248
Gleichen, A., 143, 165, 220, 231, 248, 273, 280
Goldberg, E., 127
Grousilliers, de, H., 250
Gudden, B., 377
Guild, J., 84

## H

Hardy, A. C., 68n., 69
Hardy and Perrin, 28, 69, 71n., 90, 97n., 110, 117, 203, 389
Harting, H., 137
Hartridge, H., 74n.
Hayes, T. J., 248
Hecht, Peskin, and Patt, 79n.
Helmholtz, H., 90
Hendrix and Christie, 142n.
Higbie, H. H., 69

# Subject Index

## A

Abbe's infinity adjuster, 277, 278
 König's modification of, 278
Abbe's number, 92
Abbe's sine theorem, 12, 416
Aberration, 27, 28, 30*ff.*
 (*See also* Lens aberrations)
 detection of, in telescopes, 39, 40
 variation of, with aperture, 30, 46
  chromatic, 42
  with field angle, 46
  with image height, 46
  with image position, 45–46
Aberration parabola, 397
Accommodation, 71, 83, 85–86
Accuracy of computations, 14, 384
Accuracy limitations in rangefinders, 271–273
Achromatic doublet objective, 404
 409–413
 design of, 420–432
 (*See also* Telescope objectives)
Achromatic prisms, 152
Achromatization, 405–413
 conditions for, 404
 equations for, 404
 by interpolation, 413
 by path-difference method, 409–413
 photographic, 407–408
 selection of wavelengths for, 405–
  407
 at three wavelengths, 408
 tolerance for, 447
 by trigonometrical adjustment,
  412–413
 visual, 405–408
 zone of, selection of, 407–408
Achromatized Ramsden eyepiece,
  193, 194
 design of, 440

Achromats, 91, 404
 new, 91
 old, 91
Acid process at coating lenses, 122–
  125
 increase in transmission caused by,
  125
Action, line of, 327
Acuity, stereoscopic, 88–89, 253, 256
 comparison with vernier acuity,
  89, 256
 in rangefinders, 272
 vernier, 86–88, 256
 comparison with stereoscopic
  acuity, 89, 256
 effect of astigmatism on, 88
 of magnification on, 88
 in rangefinders, 256, 272
 visual, 75
 (*See also* Resolving power of
  the eye)
Adaptation, 79, 82, 83
Addendum, 326–327
Adjuster, infinity, Abbe's, 277, 278
 König's modification of, 278
 Barr and Stroud, 278
 lath, 275–277
Adjustments, infinity, 275–279
 method of making, 276–277
Aerial photography, resolving power
  for, 177, 178
Aerotar objective, 133
After-images, 80–81
Aiming point, 244
Air bells, 94
 detection of, 97
Air path, equivalent, 409
Air-spaced doublet objective, 189
Aircraft enclosures, plastics for, 105,
  106

453